Hydraulics for Civil Engineers

Hydraulics for Civil Engineers

Peter Wynn
formerly senior lecturer in civil engineering, Anglia Ruskin University

Published by ICE Publishing, One Great George Street, Westminster,
London SW1P 3AA.

Full details of ICE Publishing sales representatives and distributors can be found at:
www.icevirtuallibrary.com/info/printbooksales

Other titles by ICE Publishing:
ICE Textbook Series
Core Principles of Soil Mechanics.
Sanjay Kumar Shukla. ISBN 978-0-7277-5847-7

Related titles
Water Distribution Systems
C Binnie and M Kimber. ISBN 978-0-7277-5816-3
Basic Water Treatment, 5th Edition
D A Savic and J K Banyard. ISBN 978-0-7277-4112-7
Tables for the Hydraulic Design of Pipes, Sewers and Channels: 8th edition
HR Wallingford, DIH Barr. ISBN 978-0-7277-3355-9
Pressure Transients in Water Engineering: A Guide to Analysis and Interpretation of Behaviour
J Ellis. ISBN978-0-7277-3592-8

www.icevirtuallibrary.com

A catalogue record for this book is available from the British Library

ISBN 978-0-7277-5845-3

© Thomas Telford Limited 2014

ICE Publishing is a division of Thomas Telford Ltd, a wholly-owned subsidiary of the Institution of Civil Engineers (ICE).

All rights, including translation, reserved. Except as permitted by the Copyright, Designs and Patents Act 1988, no part of this publication may be reproduced, stored in a retrieval system or transmitted in any form or by any means, electronic, mechanical, photocopying or otherwise, without the prior written permission of the Publisher, ICE Publishing, One Great George Street, Westminster, London SW1P 3AA.

This book is published on the understanding that the author is solely responsible for the statements made and opinions expressed in it and that its publication does not necessarily imply that such statements and/or opinions are or reflect the views or opinions of the publishers. Whilst every effort has been made to ensure that the statements made and the opinions expressed in this publication provide a safe and accurate guide, no liability or responsibility can be accepted in this respect by the author or publishers.

Whilst every reasonable effort has been undertaken by the author and the publisher to acknowledge copyright on material reproduced, if there has been an oversight please contact the publisher and we will endeavour to correct this upon a reprint.

Commissioning Editor: Jo Squires
Production Editor: Vikarn Chowdhary
Market Development Executive: Catherine de Gatacre

Typeset by Academic + Technical, Bristol
Index created by Pauline Davies
Printed and bound by CPI Group (UK) Ltd, Croydon CR0 4YY

Contents

	Preface	vii
	List of symbols	ix
01	**Pressure in liquids: its effects and measurement**	**1**
	1.1. Introduction	1
	1.2. Density and pressure within a liquid	1
	1.3. Measurement of pressure	3
	1.4. Forces on immersed surfaces	5
	1.5. Buoyancy and flotation	12
	References	17
02	**Conservation equations applied to flow of liquid in pipes**	**19**
	2.1. Introduction	19
	2.2. Continuity equation	20
	2.3. Momentum equation	21
	2.4. Bernoulli (or Energy) equation	26
	Reference	34
03	**Real flow in pipes**	**35**
	3.1. Introduction	35
	3.2. Viscosity of fluids	35
	3.3. Laminar and turbulent flow	37
	3.4. Modification of Bernoulli equation for head loss due to friction	39
	3.5. Boundary layers in turbulent flow	44
	3.6. Derivation of λ values and use in design charts	44
	References	50
	Further reading	51
04	**Turbines and pumps**	**53**
	4.1. Introduction	53
	4.2. Turbines	53
	4.3. Pumps	59
	4.4. Cavitation in turbines and pumps	63
	References	63
	Further reading	64
05	**Steady uniform flow in open channels**	**65**
	5.1. Introduction	65
	5.2. Sustainable design of river channels	65
	5.3. Basic definitions	67
	5.4. Discharge equations	70
	5.5. Velocity variation over channel cross-section	74
	5.6. Most economically efficient section	74
	5.7. Specific energy	76
	References	81
	Further reading	82
06	**Open channel flow with varying conditions**	**83**
	6.1. Changes to flow regime	83
	6.2. Examples of flow changes	87
	6.3. Flow rate measurement based on changes in section	96
	6.4. Gradually varied flow	99
	References	103

07	**Hydrology of river flow**	**105**
	7.1. Introduction	105
	7.2. Return period approach	105
	7.3. Hydrograph approach	111
	References	116
08	**Hydrology of surface water drainage**	**119**
	8.1. Introduction	119
	8.2. Short duration rainfall intensity	119
	8.3. Hydraulic design of surface water sewers	121
	8.4. Sustainable drainage systems	128
	8.5. Difference between greenfield and development runoff	131
	References	133
	Further reading	133
09	**Coastal hydraulics**	**135**
	9.1. Introduction	135
	9.2. Sea level records	135
	9.3. Mean sea level	136
	9.4. Astronomical tides	136
	9.5. Meteorological effects, including surges	138
	9.6. Waves	141
	References	152
	Further reading	152
10	**Dimensional analysis**	**153**
	10.1. Introduction	153
	10.2. Dimensions	153
	10.3. Dimensional equations	154
	10.4. Dimensional analysis	156
	10.5. Similarity	159
	10.6. Use of dimensionless numbers in model scaling	160
	References	164
	Further reading	164
11	**Two-dimensional ideal flow**	**165**
	11.1. Introduction	165
	11.2. Theoretical basis	165
	11.3. Uniform straight line flow	176
	11.4. Sources	177
	11.5. Sinks	179
	11.6. Free vortex	179
	11.7. Forced vortex	183
	11.8. Combination of flow	185
	References	188
	Index	**189**

Preface

I have entitled this volume 'Hydraulics' rather than 'Fluid Mechanics' because the latter implies the treatment of gases as well as liquids. Previous textbook authors have not always made the distinction.

My teaching experience has shown me that students are often put off hydraulics by the mathematics contained within the subject rather than the subject itself. Rather than attempting to avoid the mathematics by saying things like 'it is easy to show that ...' I have shown full workings wherever possible.

In a subject that is largely based on simplifying theory, it is tempting to end up with a simple design with little regard to the aesthetics or environmental impact. Hence hydraulic engineers have often produced (for example) inappropriate concrete-lined river channels of rectangular cross-section, and specific comment on this is contained in Chapter 5. The traditional hydraulic engineers' desire for piped solutions is also challenged by moves towards the sustainable drainage systems included in Chapter 8.

Teachers in universities and colleges are becoming alarmed at the failure of students to give proper attribution to work they use. Not all authors of textbooks have been innocent in this regard, however. For this reason I have attempted to identify the original publications on which much current practice is based. Hence many of the references quoted go back to the nineteenth century. In turn I apologise if I have not properly attributed material myself and would be grateful to learn of any such transgressions on my part.

List of symbols

		Used in chapters
		1 2 3 4 5 6 7 8 9 10 11
A	Area	× × × × × × ×
a	Amplitude of wave	×
a	Acceleration	×
B	Width	× × × ×
b	Expression of slope angle (1 in b)	×
BFI	Baseflow index	×
C	Wave celerity	×
C	Coefficient of discharge	×
C	Chezy coefficient	×
C_0	Deep water celerity	×
C_d	Coefficient of discharge	×
C_p	Pressure coefficient	×
C_R	Routing coefficient	×
C_V	Volumetric runoff coefficient	×
CWI	Catchment wetness index	×
D	Diameter	× × × ×
d	Still water depth	×
$DPRCWI$	Dynamic runoff component	×
$DPRRAIN$	Dynamic runoff component	×
E	Energy transferred in turbine	×
E	Specific energy	× ×
E	Wave energy	×
ς	Specific energy of wave	×
Eu	Euler number	×
F	Force	× × × ×
f	Friction factor (North America)	× ×
Fr	Froude number	× ×
g	Acceleration due to gravity	× × × × × × × × × ×
h	Depth; height; head	× ×
H	Water depth	× × ×
H	Waveheight	×
H_0	Deep water waveheight	×
H_c	Critical depth	× ×
h_f	Head loss due to friction	× ×
h_G	Depth to centroid	×
h_L	Head loss at change of section	×
$H_{\max}$	Highest wave in a storm	×
h_p	Depth to centre of pressure	×
h_p	Sudden change in bed level	×
H_{rms}	Root mean square waveheight	×
H_s	Significant waveheight	×
i	Rainfall intensity	× ×
IF	Effective impervious area factor	×
IG	Second moment of area	×
k	Surface roughness	× × ×
K	Coefficient of roughness (channel bed)	×
k	Wave number	×
K_s	Sluice coefficient	×
K_s	Shoaling coefficient	×

		Used in chapters
		1 2 3 4 5 6 7 8 9 10 11
L	Length	× × × × × ×
L	Wavelength	×
L_0	Deep water wavelength	×
M	Mass	× ×
m	Hydraulic mean depth	× ×
N	Runner speed of turbine or pump	×
n	Mannings roughness coefficient	× ×
N	Periods of record	×
n	Ratio of wave group to individual wave velocities	×
N	Number of waves in a storm	×
$NAPI$	30 day antecedent precipitation index	×
N_s	Specific speed of turbine or pump	×
P	(Intensity of) pressure	× × × × ×
P	Wetted perimeter	× ×
P	Probability	× ×
P	Wave power	×
PF	Moisture depth parameter	×
$PIMP$	Percentage impermeable area	×
PR	Percentage runoff	× ×
Q	Volume rate of discharge	× × × × × × × × ×
q	Volume flow rate per unit width	× ×
q	Strength of a source	×
$QMED$	Median annual maximum flood	×
QP	Peak runoff	×
R	Hydraulic radius	× ×
r	Rank order	×
R	Wave runup	×
r	Radial distance	×
RD	Rainfall depth	×
Re	Reynolds number	× ×
S	Hydraulic gradient	× ×
s	Length of section of a streamtube	×
$SAAR$	Standard average annual rainfall	×
SF	Friction gradient	×
S_o	Bed slope	× ×
$SOIL$	Index of water holding capacity	×
SPR	Standard percentage runoff	×
t	Time	×
T	Return period	× ×
T	Wave period	×
t_C	Time of concentration	×
t_E	Time of entry	×
t_F	Time of flow	×
T_P	Time to peak	×
$UCWI$	Urban catchment wetness index	×
U_p	Unit hydrograph peak flowrate	×
$URBEXT$	Extent of urbanisation	×
V	Velocity	× × × × × × × ×

		Used in chapters
		1 2 3 4 5 6 7 8 9 10 11
V_c	Critical velocity	×
Vol	Volume	×
$VolXS$	Excess runoff volume caused by development	×
W	Weight	× ×
w	Weight density	× ×
w	Weighting factor	×
We	Weber number	×
Y	Plate separation	×
z	Height above datum, elevation head	× × × ×
α	Velocity distribution coeficient	×
α	Proportion of paved area draining to network or watercourse	×
α	Angle of wave approach	×
α	Proportion of pervious area draining to network or watercourse	×
α	Slope angle of beach	×
Γ	Strength of a vortex	×
η	Percentage of velocity maintained; efficiency	×
κ	Circulation	×
λ	Friction factor	× ×
μ	Dynamic viscosity	× ×
ν	Kinematic viscosity	× ×
ρ	Mass density	× × × × × × × × ×
σ	Angular frequency of waves	×
τ	Shear stress	×
τ	Shear stress on bed	×
χ	Surf similarity parameter	×
χ	Vorticity	×
ϕ	Velocity potential	×
ψ	Stream function	×

Hydraulics for Civil Engineers
ISBN 978-0-7277-5845-3

ICE Publishing: All rights reserved
http://dx.doi.org/10.1680/hce.58453.001

1

Pressure in liquids: its effects and measurement

 **Learning aims**

After studying this chapter you should be able to

- recall the relationships between density, mass and weight of a liquid and the units and symbols used for these
- calculate pressures at any depth in a liquid
- express pressures in terms of 'head' of different liquids
- describe common methods of measuring pressure within liquids
- calculate forces on horizontal, vertical and inclined plane immersed surfaces in a liquid and establish the depth to the centre of pressure
- calculate horizontal and vertical components of force on curved immersed surfaces and from these find the resultant force and its direction
- appreciate the relationship between centre of buoyancy, centre of gravity and metacentre and its role in establishing the stability of a floating body.

1.1. Introduction

Forces acting on bodies are of major interest to the engineer. This chapter shows how the value and location of forces acting on immersed bodies can be determined from a knowledge of the liquid properties and the geometry of the surfaces into which the liquid comes into contact. Methods of pressure measurement are introduced. Towards the end of the chapter, these techniques are used to determine the stability of floating bodies. Whilst the emphasis within this chapter is on liquids at rest (hydrostatics), the methods of determining pressures and forces will be applicable to the consideration of liquids in motion (hydrodynamics) considered in the rest of the book.

1.2. Density and pressure within a liquid
1.2.1 Mass density
Mass density is denoted by ρ (the Greek letter rho). It is the mass of a substance divided by the volume it occupies.

$$\rho = \frac{M}{Vol} \qquad (1.1)$$

In the SI system of units M is measured in kg and Vol in m^3 leading to ρ being in kg/m^3.

The mass density of fresh water is generally taken as 1000 kg/m³ although there is slight variation with temperature. The maximum mass density of water occurs at 4°C. Salt water has a slightly higher mass density.

When the word 'density' is used without further qualification, it is usually taken to indicate 'mass density'.

1.2.2 Weight density
Weight is the force exerted on a mass in a gravitational field.

$$W = Mg \tag{1.2}$$

If M is in kg and g in m/s² then W will be in newtons (N), a special name for kg·m/s².

In this book g is taken as 9.81 m/s², although it needs to be recognised that this value is only approximate and varies from place to place. Because of this approximation, it is not sensible to quote answers to questions in which g is a factor to more than three significant figures.

The weight density w is given by

$$w = \rho g \tag{1.3}$$

This is also sometimes called the 'unit weight' or 'specific weight' of the liquid and its SI unit is N/m³.

1.2.3 Hydraulic pressure
The intensity of pressure at a depth h in a liquid of density ρ is given by

$$P = \rho g h \tag{1.4}$$

In common use the words 'intensity of' are often omitted. It is important to appreciate that *hydraulic pressure is exerted equally in all directions*. We will usually express pressure relative to atmospheric pressure. Strictly speaking we should refer to this relative pressure as gauge pressure, though this is often not done.

The SI unit of pressure has the unit of pascal Pa (a special name for N/m²), although in civil engineering hydraulics applications to avoid large numbers it is usually convenient to convert final answers to kPa.

Example 1.1
Seawater in a tank 4 m deep has a density of 1025 kg/m³. What pressure does this exert on the base of the tank?

$$P = \rho g h = 1025 \times 9.81 \times 4 = 40\,221\,\text{Pa} \tag{1.5}$$

Taking account of the approximate value of g used, this should be rounded to 40 200 Pa or 40.2 kPa.

1.2.4 Pressure head

Pressures are sometimes expressed in terms of 'head' h

$$h = P/\rho g \qquad (1.6)$$

This is the height of a column of a named liquid (often water or mercury) that would cause an equal pressure to that being measured.

Example 1.2

In Example 1.1 on seawater in a tank what is the pressure head on the base of the tank

(a) in terms of metres of freshwater?
(b) in terms of metres of mercury, if the density of mercury is 13 600 kg/m^3?

$$(a) \quad h = \frac{40\,221}{1000 \times 9.81} = 4.10\,\text{m head of fresh water} \qquad (1.7)$$

$$(b) \quad h = \frac{40\,221}{13\,600 \times 9.81} = 0.301\,\text{m head of mercury} \qquad (1.8)$$

As can be seen from this example, because of its high density, values expressed in metres head of mercury are usually very small. For this reason they will often be quoted as millimetres head instead.

Revision points

- The density of a liquid can be expressed as mass density or weight density. The word 'density' is often used by itself to indicate the former of these.
- The intensity of hydraulic pressure in a liquid is the unit weight of the liquid times the depth of liquid above the level at which the pressure is calculated.
- The words 'intensity of' are generally omitted.
- Hydraulic pressure acts equally in all directions.
- It is common to express pressure in terms of the height of a column of liquid, especially water or mercury, that would cause the same pressure as that being measured.

1.3. Measurement of pressure
1.3.1 Piezometers

These are a simple means of measuring the pressure in a pipe. A small diameter tube is connected into the pipe and the height to which the liquid rises in the pipe gives the pressure head at the tapping point as shown in Figure 1.1(a).

Sometimes it is the difference in pressure between two points that is of interest and two piezometers connected as illustrated in Figure 1.1(b) can be used even if the actual pressure head extends beyond the height of the piezometer. This is achieved by applying air pressure to the top of the linking tubing.

Figure 1.1 Piezometers and manometers

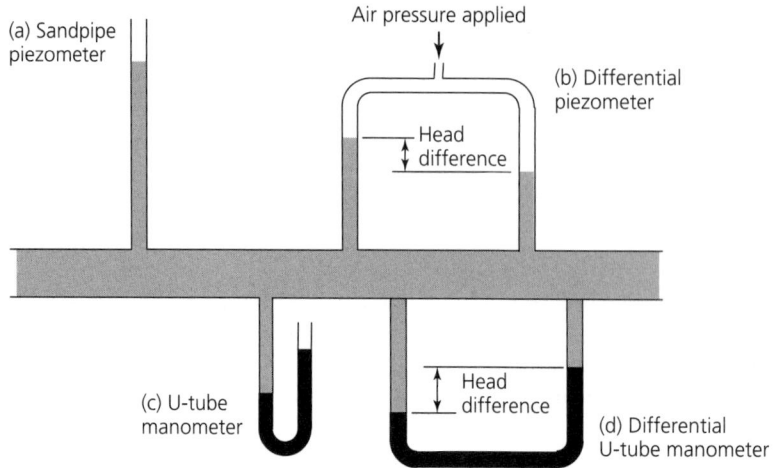

This will depress the liquid surface in the two tubes by an equal amount. The recorded head difference is therefore not affected by the application of the air pressure.

1.3.2 U-tube manometers

Pressure over the liquid in one limb of the manometer is balanced by a head of liquid in the other limb as in Figure 1.1(c). Most commonly the liquid in the second limb is mercury. The U-tube mercury manometer was invented by Poiseuille (1828). Because of mercury's high density the height of tube needed is relatively small.

As long as the manometer liquid is designed appropriately so that the liquid is not forced round the bottom of the U, these manometers can be used in two circumstances in which the piezometer cannot: the measurement of pressures in gases and pressures below atmospheric.

Pressure differences along a pipeline can be measured with a differential U-tube manometer shown in Figure 1.1(d).

1.3.3 Mechanical pressure gauges

The most common of these is the Bourdon gauge. This consists essentially of a bent metal tube. When pressure is applied to the inside of the tube, it tends to straighten. The movement is transferred to an indicator needle on the face of the gauge.

1.3.4 Transducers

These work on the basis that a change in pressure stretches a wire with a resulting change in electrical resistance that can be monitored electronically.

> **Revision point**
>
> - Pressures can be measured using piezometers, mechanical gauges or transducers.

1.4. Forces on immersed surfaces
1.4.1 Introduction
'The hydrostatic force F acting on the surface is the average intensity of pressure P times the surface area A over which it acts.

$$F = PA \tag{1.9}$$

1.4.2 Force acting on a horizontal immersed surface
Since all parts of the surface will be the same depth below the top of the liquid, the pressure will have a uniform value of $\rho g h$ across the surface and the force *which acts perpendicularly to the surface* will be obtained from the application of the previous equation.

Example 1.3
The tank holding the seawater in Examples 1.1 and 1.2 has a rectangular base 4 m wide and 5 m long. What is the force acting on the base?

$$F = 40\,221 \times 4 \times 5 = 804\,420\,\text{N} \tag{1.10}$$

Again the basic SI unit has a high numerical value and would probably be better expressed in kilonewtons. Hence to three significant figures the force acting on the base of the tank is 804 kN.

1.4.3 Force acting on a vertical immersed surface
For a surface of height h whose top is coincident with the top of the liquid, the pressure diagram will be triangular and the force will be given by

$$F = 0.5\rho g h A \tag{1.11}$$

For surfaces whose top is not coincident with the top of the liquid the pressure diagram will be trapezoidal and the force will be given by

$$F = \rho g \left(\frac{h_1 + h_2}{2}\right) A \tag{1.12}$$

where h_1 and h_2 are the depths of liquid above the top and base of the submerged surface.

Example 1.4
A 2-m-wide rectangular screen is placed vertically within the tank of seawater previously considered. The top of the screen is situated 1 m below the water surface and the bottom of the screen is 3.5 m below the water surface. What is the hydrostatic force acting on one face of the screen?

$$F = \rho g \left(\frac{h_1 + h_2}{2}\right) A = 1025 \times 9.81 \times \left(\frac{1 + 3.5}{2}\right) \times (2 \times 2.5) = 113\,122\,\text{N}$$

$$= 113\,\text{kN}\,(3\,\text{sig. figs.}) \tag{1.13}$$

For reasons that will become apparent to the reader later in this chapter, although it is a lengthier process, it is often useful to derive the force in the following way.

The pressure at the top of the screen

$$P_1 = 1025 \times 9.81 \times 1 = 10\,055.3\,\text{Pa} \tag{1.14}$$

and the pressure at the bottom of the screen

$$P_2 = 1025 \times 9.81 \times 3.5 = 35\,193.4\,\text{Pa} \tag{1.15}$$

These values are shown in Figure 1.2 as a sketch of pressure against depth. It can be seen that the pressure diagram can be split into rectangular and triangular sections.

Figure 1.2 Pressure distribution on submerged vertical surface

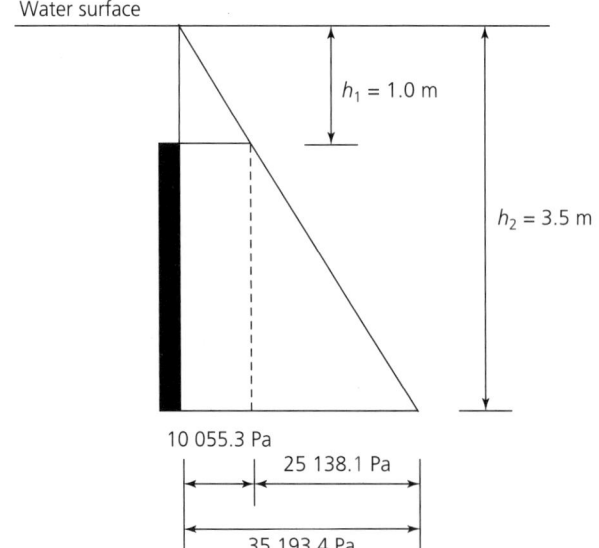

Applying

$$F = PA \tag{1.16}$$

to each section, the contributing elements of force are

rectangular section $\quad F_R = 10\,055.3 \times (2 \times 2.5) = 50\,277\,\text{N} \tag{1.17}$

triangular section $\quad F_T = 0.5 \times 25\,138.1 \times (2 \times 2.5) = 62\,845\,\text{N} \tag{1.18}$

The sum of these is 113 122 N, the same as previously found.

For a rectangular immersed surface $(h_1 + h_2)/2$ is the depth h_G to the centroid so that the expression for force can be rewritten as

$$F = \rho g h_G A \qquad (1.19)$$

In this form the equation may be applied to surfaces of any shape provided that h_G is known.

1.4.4 Location of resultant force acting on vertical immersed rectangular surface

The point through which the resultant hydrostatic force on an immersed surface acts is called the *centre of pressure*. As the pressure increases with depth, the centre of pressure will always be below the centre of gravity of the immersed rectangular surface.

For a rectangular surface the centre of pressure may be found by taking moments of the elements of the pressure diagram as in the following example.

Example 1.5

Determine the depth below the water surface of the centre of pressure for the submerged screen introduced in Example 1.4.

It was determined earlier in this chapter that the force may be considered as made up of two elements, F_R and F_T.

F_R can be taken to act at the centre of the screen and F_T at two thirds of the height of the screen below its top.

If the centre of pressure lies at depth h_P below the water surface, we can take moments about this surface as shown in Figure 1.3, to obtain

$$113\,122 h_P = 50\,277\left(1 + \frac{2.5}{2}\right) + 62\,845\left(1 + \frac{2 \times 2.5}{3}\right)$$

$$h_P = 280\,710/113\,122 = 2.48 \text{ m (3 sig. figs)} \qquad (1.20)$$

Figure 1.3 Force elements and overall force on submerged vertical surface

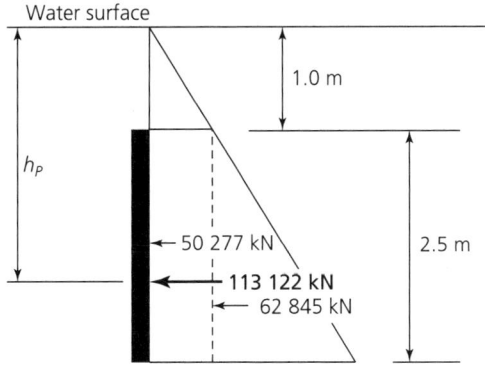

Table 1.1 Second moment of area of selected shapes about an axis through their centroid

Shape	I_G
Rectangle of width B and height D	$BD^3/12$
Triangle of base width B and height D	$BD^3/36$
Circle of radius R	$\pi R^4/4$

1.4.5 Location of resultant force acting on vertical immersed surface of any shape

In general the width of the shape, as well as the pressure, varies with depth. For the general case of vertical surfaces the depth h_P to the centre of pressure can be found using

$$h_P = h_G + \frac{I_G}{Ah_G} \tag{1.21}$$

where I_G is the second moment of area of the surface about an axis through its centroid. Values of I_G for some common shapes are given in Table 1.1. Derivations of these are contained in most engineering mathematics textbooks such as Stroud and Booth (2007).

Example 1.6

Verify that the same value for h_P for the submerged rectangular screen of Example 1.5 is obtained if the general formula is used.

$$h_P = h_G + \frac{I_G}{Ah_G} = 2.25 + \frac{(2 \times 2.5^3)/12}{(2 \times 2.5) \times 2.25} = 2.25 + 0.231 = 2.48 \text{ m (3 sig. figs)} \tag{1.22}$$

1.4.6 Force acting on an inclined immersed surface

For this case in particular it is important to remember that the *force acts at right angles to the surface* but its value is derived from a pressure distribution that depends on the vertical height of the liquid above the surface.

Example 1.7

A 4 m length of formwork sloping at an angle of 60° to the horizontal is to support a 3-m-high pour of concrete as shown in Figure 1.4. Assuming the concrete acts as a liquid with a density 2550 kg/m³, calculate the force exerted on the formwork.

$$F = \rho g h_G A = 2550 \times 9.81 \times 1.5 \times \left(4 \times \frac{3}{\sin 60°}\right) = 519\,937 \text{ N} = 520 \text{ kN (3 sig. figs)} \tag{1.23}$$

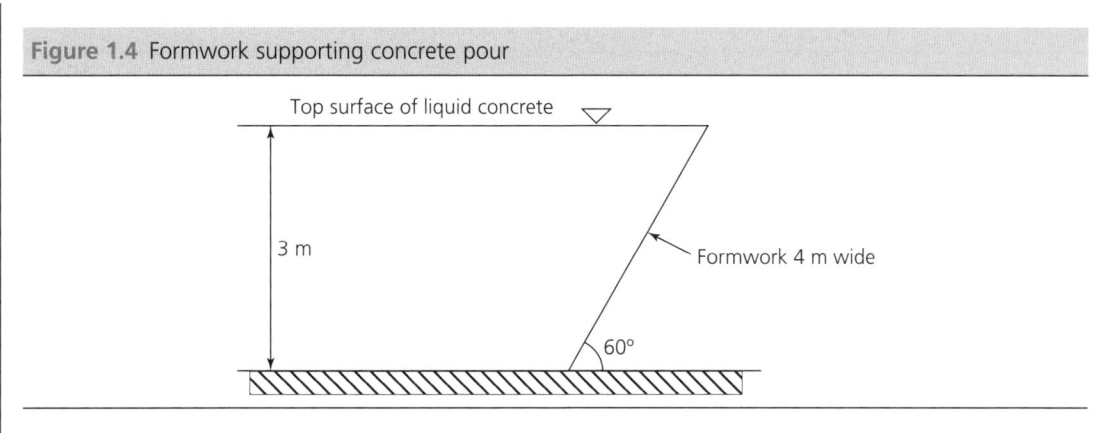

Figure 1.4 Formwork supporting concrete pour

1.4.7 Location of resultant force acting on an inclined immersed surface

The vertical depth of the centre of pressure below the surface of the liquid is given by

$$h_P = h_G + \frac{I_G \sin^2 \theta}{A h_G} \qquad (1.24)$$

where θ is the angle of inclination of the surface to the horizontal.

Example 1.8

At what depth below the top of the concrete can the force exerted on the formwork of Example 1.7 be taken to act?

The second moment of area

$$I_G = \frac{\left(4 \times \left(\frac{3}{\sin 60}\right)^3\right)}{12} = 13.856 \text{ m}^4 \qquad (1.25)$$

The depth to the centre of pressure

$$h_p = h_G + \frac{I_G \sin^2 \theta}{A h_G} = 1.5 + \frac{13.856 \times \sin^2 60}{\left(4 \times \frac{3}{\sin 60}\right) \times 1.5} = 1.5 + 0.5 = 2.00 \text{ m (3 sig. figs)} \qquad (1.26)$$

1.4.8 Forces on curved immersed surfaces

Consider the surface AB curved in one plane subject to a hydrostatic force F shown on Figure 1.5. AC and BC are horizontal and vertical projections of AB. By considering the equilibrium of the liquid contained in the volume defined by ABC, it can be established that the horizontal component of force F,

Hydraulics for Civil Engineers

Figure 1.5 Components of hydrostatic force on curved immersed surface

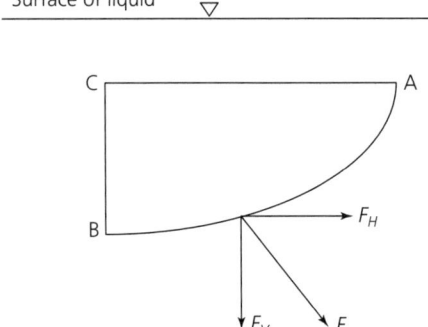

F_H is equal to hydrostatic force acting on surface AC
F_V is equal to weight of liquid in volume ABC plus weight of liquid above AC
F is found by vector addition of F_H and F_V

which is F_H, is equal to the same force as would be acting on a vertical surface BC and that the vertical component of force F, which is F_V, is the weight of liquid vertically above the surface AB.

Vector addition of the horizontal and vertical components enables the magnitude and direction of F to be determined.

If the surface AB forms an arc of a circle, then the resultant force acts through the centre of curvature. For curved surfaces of non-circular section, it would be necessary to take moments about point C to establish the position at which F acts.

A similar approach can be used if the contact with the liquid is on the underside of a surface. In this case F_V acts upwards and is numerically equivalent to the hypothetical weight of liquid that would exist above the surface if the surface was removed.

Marriott (2009, pp.14–15) presents a more rigorous derivation of the hydrostatic force on a curved surface.

 Example 1.9

A 5 m-wide sluice gate holds back water as shown in Figure 1.6. The surface of the gate in contact with the water can be taken as part of a cylinder of radius 4 m. Determine the magnitude and direction of the hydrostatic force on the gate.

The horizontal component is obtained using the equation for the force on a vertical submerged rectangular surface.

$$F_H = \rho g \left(\frac{h_1 + h_2}{2}\right) A = 1000 \times 9.81 \times \left(\frac{1+3}{2}\right) \times (2 \times 5) = 196\,200 \text{ N} \quad (1.27)$$

Figure 1.6 Cross-section through cylindrical sluice gate

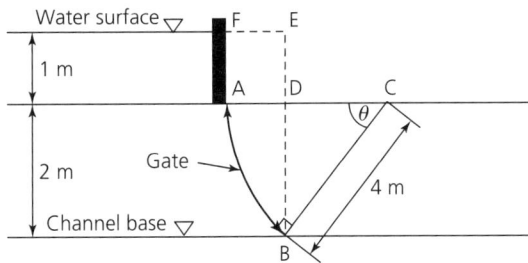

The vertical component is obtained from the weight of water that would occupy the space above the sluice up to the level of the retained water. This requires some calculations of lengths and areas. Firstly obtain the angle subtended by the closed gate.

$$\theta = \sin^{-1}\frac{BD}{BC} = \sin^{-1}\frac{2}{4} = 30° \tag{1.28}$$

This allows us to get the area of the sector

$$ABC = \frac{30}{360} \times \pi \times 4^2 = 4.188\,79\,\text{m}^2 \tag{1.29}$$

The length $CD = BC\cos\theta = 4 \times \cos 30° = 3.464\,10\,\text{m}$ (1.30)

Area of triangle $BCD = \frac{1}{2}BD \times CD = \frac{1}{2} \times 2 \times 3.464\,10 = 3.464\,10\,\text{m}^2$ (1.31)

$\therefore$ area $ABD = 4.188\,79 - 3.464\,10 = 0.724\,69\,\text{m}^2$ (1.32)

Area DEFA above $AD = (4 - 3.464\,10) \times 1 = 0.535\,90\,\text{m}^2$ (1.33)

Volume of water above $AB = 5 \times (0.724\,69 + 0.535\,90) = 6.302\,595\,\text{m}^3$ (1.34)

$F_V = 1000 \times 9.81 \times 6.302\,95 = 61\,832\,\text{N}$ (1.35)

The resultant force is

$$F = \sqrt{196\,200^2 + 61\,832^2} = 205\,712.5\,\text{N} = 206\,\text{kN}\ (3\ \text{sig. figs}) \tag{1.36}$$

This acts at an angle

$$= \tan^{-1}\frac{61\,832}{196\,200} = 17.5°\ \text{to the horizontal} \tag{1.37}$$

Revision points

- The force acting on a submerged surface is equal to the average pressure times the area of the surface, and acts at right angles to the surface.
- Because pressure increases with depth, for non-horizontal surfaces the centroid and the centre of pressure are not co-incidental.
- The resultant hydrostatic force acting on a curved submerged surface is found by vector addition of the horizontal and vertical components.

1.5. Buoyancy and flotation

Examples of civil engineering applications include oil rigs, immersed tube tunnelling, pontoons and transport of components by water.

1.5.1 Buoyancy force

Figure 1.7 shows the vertical hydrostatic forces acting on the top and bottom of a closed body of constant cross-sectional area A and volume V submerged in a liquid of density ρ.

The net upward force

$$F = F_2 - F_1 = \rho g h_2 A - \rho g h_1 A = \rho g(h_2 - h_1)A = \rho g Vol \tag{1.38}$$

is the same as the weight of the liquid displaced by the body. It is called the buoyancy force.

This demonstrates Archimedes' principle, which states that the upthrust acting on an object in a liquid is equal to the weight of liquid displaced by the object.

1.5.2 Centre of buoyancy

This is the centre of gravity of the liquid displaced by the object. A submerged body will orientate itself such that its own centre of gravity is located vertically above its centre of buoyancy.

Figure 1.7 Vertical hydrostatic forces on top and bottom of closed body of constant cross-sectional area

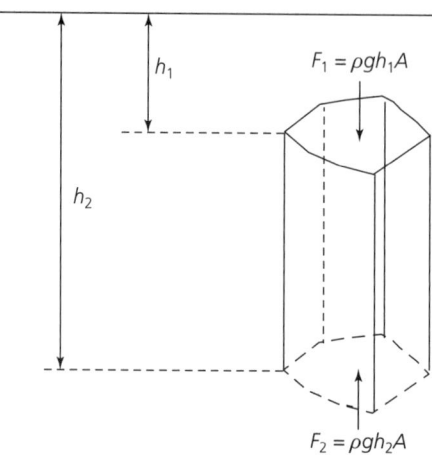

Pressure in liquids: its effects and measurement

Figure 1.8 Distribution of hydrostatic pressure on undisplaced floating body

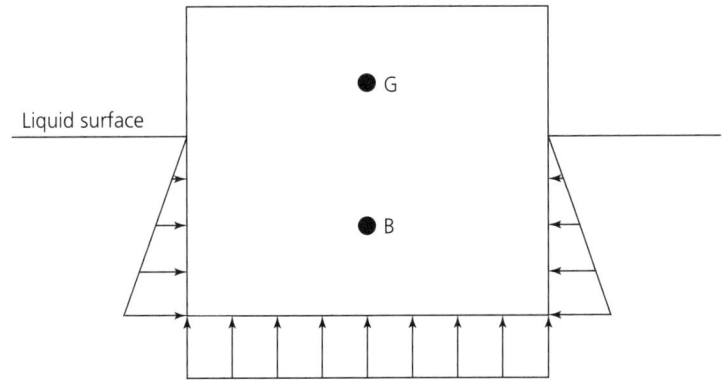

The buoyancy force can be taken to act through the centre of buoyancy.

1.5.3 Immersion depth of a floating body

The immersion depth of a floating body, such as a barge, depends upon its weight and shape. Figure 1.8 shows the hydrostatic pressure distribution on a rectangular body floating in an upright position. The centre of buoyancy is indicated by B and the centre of gravity of the floating body by G.

It can be seen that the effects of hydrostatic pressure on the sides of the body are self-cancelling. The resulting force from the hydrostatic pressure on the base acts through the centre of buoyancy which is vertically below the centre of gravity, and that is balanced by the weight of the body also acting through the centre of gravity.

1.5.4 Metacentre

If the body is now tilted, perhaps as a result of being hit by a wave, the pressure diagram changes to that shown in Figure 1.9.

The centre of buoyancy has moved to a new temporary position B*. The upward buoyancy force acting through B* together with the weight acting vertically downwards through G form a couple that tends to return the body to its normal position. The *metacentre* is defined as the point where a vertical line through B* intersects a vertical line passing through B and G when the body has returned to its original position.

When, as in the figure, the metacentre is above the centre of gravity of the body, the body is stable. If M is below G, as could happen if the body was, say, a floating crane, then a situation of instability may arise. It is therefore important to know the position of the metacentre. Its distance from the centre of buoyancy can be found using

$$\text{BM} = \frac{I}{Vol} \tag{1.39}$$

where I is the second moment of area of the body at the water level about its longitudinal axis.

Hydraulics for Civil Engineers

Figure 1.9 Distribution of hydrostatic pressure on rotated floating body

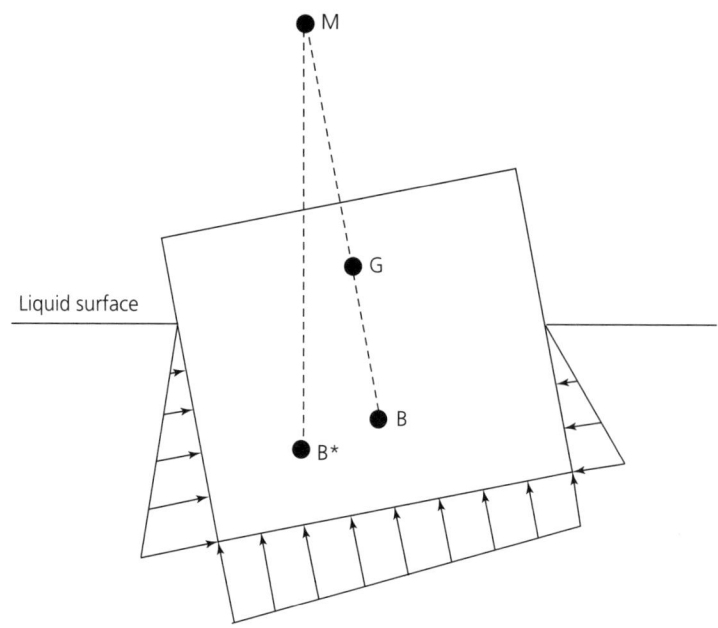

Example 1.10

A rectangular pontoon is to be used to transport an engineering component by canal to a coastal location.

The pontoon is 8 m long by 5 m wide with sides 1.8 m high and has a mass when empty of 15 t and the mass of the component to be carried is 25 t. The top of the component will be 2.5 m above the base of the pontoon. The combined centre of gravity of the pontoon and the load lies 1.9 m above the pontoon base.

(a) At one point along the canal the pontoon will have to pass under a bridge whose underside is 2.0 m above the water surface. If the water in the canal has a density of 1000 kg/m^3, what will be the vertical clearance between the top of the component and the bridge?
(b) Assuming that the sea water has a density of 1025 kg/m^3, determine whether the pontoon will be stable in the marine situation.

Part (a) is illustrated in Figure 1.10. The clearance will depend on the immersion depth of the pontoon which we can find by applying Archimedes' principle.

The mass of water displaced M is equal to the combined mass of the pontoon and the component.

$$M = 1000(15 + 25) = 40\,000 \text{ kg} \tag{1.40}$$

14

Pressure in liquids: its effects and measurement

Figure 1.10 Clearance of component under bridge

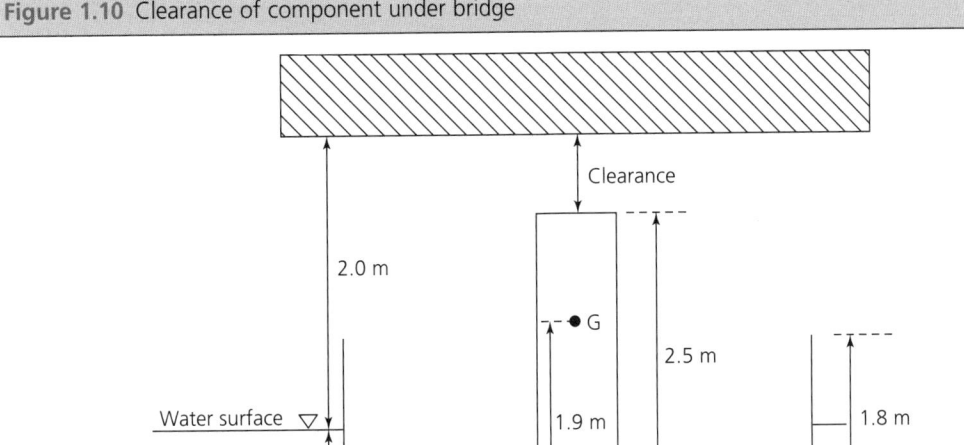

The volume of water displaced

$$Vol = \frac{M}{\rho} = \frac{40\,000}{1000} = 40\,\text{m}^3 \tag{1.41}$$

Hence the depth of immersion of the barge

$$= \frac{40}{(5 \times 8)} = 1.0\,\text{m} \tag{1.42}$$

and

$$\text{clearance} = 1.0 + 2.0 - 2.5 = 0.5\,\text{m} \tag{1.43}$$

Now consider the marine situation, illustrated in Figure 1.11.

Volume of seawater displaced is

$$Vol = \frac{M}{\rho} = \frac{40\,000}{1025} = 39.024\,\text{m}^3 \tag{1.44}$$

Depth of immersion $= 39.024/(8 \times 5) = 0.9756\,\text{m}$ \hfill (1.45)

Height of centre of buoyancy above the pontoon base is $OB = 0.9756/2 = 0.4878\,\text{m}$ \hfill (1.46)

The height of the centre of gravity above the pontoon base is $OG = 1.9\,\text{m}$ \hfill (1.47)

$BG = 1.9 - 0.4878\,\text{m} = 1.4122\,\text{m}$ \hfill (1.48)

15

Figure 1.11 Pontoon in the marine situation

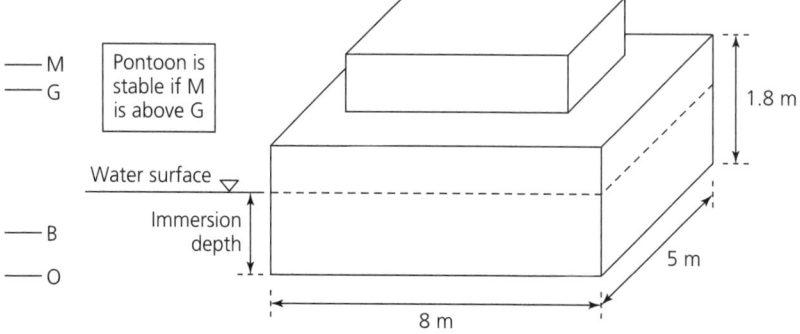

For this situation for a submerged body of rectangular section

$$I = \frac{LB^3}{12} \tag{1.49}$$

where L and B are the plan length and width of the body.

Hence

$$I = \frac{8 \times 5^3}{12} = 83.333 \, \text{m}^4 \tag{1.50}$$

The distance of the metacentre above the centre of buoyancy is given by

$$\text{BM} = \frac{I}{\text{Vol}} = \frac{83.333}{39.024} = 2.135 \, \text{m} \tag{1.51}$$

As we have shown that BM is greater than BG, the pontoon is stable in the marine situation.

Revision points

- The buoyancy force acting on a floating body is equal to the weight of liquid it displaces.
- The buoyancy force acts through the centre of buoyancy which is the centre of gravity of the displaced liquid.
- The immersion depth of a floating body is such as to provide a balance between its weight and the hydrostatic force acting on its base.
- The metacentre is the intersection of a vertical line through the centre of buoyancy of a tilted floating body with a line passing through the centre of gravity and original centre of buoyancy in its untilted state.
- If the metacentre lies above the centre of gravity, the body is stable.

✓ Chapter summary

- Hydraulic pressure acts equally in all directions and is the product of the unit weight of the liquid times the depth of liquid above the level at which the pressure is being calculated.
- 'Head' is the height of a column of a stated liquid that would cause the same pressure as that being measured.
- The hydraulic force acting on a plane submerged surface is equal to the average pressure on the surface times the area of the surface and acts at right angles to the surface.
- The buoyancy force acting on a floating body is equal to the weight of liquid it displaces.
- The stability of a floating body can be established from the relative positions of its metacentre and its centre of gravity.

Questions for practice

(a) A rectangular tank 4.5 m long by 1.5 m wide, contains water to a depth of 2 m. Find the intensity of pressure on the base of the tank and the total force on one end.

(b) A circular plate 1.65 m in diameter is immersed vertically in water with its horizontal centreline 1.50 m below the surface. Find the total force on one face and the depth of the centre of pressure.

(c) A canal company wishes to establish whether a dragline can be fitted into an existing pontoon. The pontoon is rectangular in plan, 15 m long and 6.5 m wide. The height of its sides is 4.5 m. The estimated 'weight' of the pontoon is 43 tonne and of the dragline (including accessories and effects of loads) is 155 tonne. The combined centre of gravity of the pontoon and dragline is 3.190 m above the pontoon base.
Find the freeboard with the dragline aboard and determine whether the pontoon/dragline combination is stable.

REFERENCES

Marriott M (2009) *Nalluri and Featherstone's Civil Engineering Hydraulics*, 5th edn. Wiley-Blackwell, Oxford, UK.

Poiseuille JLM (1828) *Recherches Sur la Force du Cur Aortique*. Doctoral thesis. Ecole Polytechnique, Paris, France (in French).

Stroud KA and Booth DJ (2007) *Engineering Mathematics*, 6th edn. Palgrave Macmillan, Basingstoke, UK, http://link.springer.com/book/10.1007%2F978-1-4615-9653-0.

Hydraulics for Civil Engineers
ISBN 978-0-7277-5845-3

ICE Publishing: All rights reserved
http://dx.doi.org/10.1680/hce.58453.019

2
Conservation equations applied to flow of liquid in pipes

 **Learning aims**

After studying this chapter you should be able to

- appreciate the difference between steady and unsteady flow
- appreciate the difference between uniform and non-uniform flow
- apply the continuity equation to problems where there are changes of pipe cross-section
- understand the concept of a 'control volume' and apply the continuity and momentum equations to problems to establish resultant forces on bends in pipework
- appreciate how the Bernoulli equation is related to the principle of conservation of energy
- use the Bernoulli equation *inter alia* to establish values of pressure at various locations within a pipe system
- understand how pressure measurements within a Venturi meter may be used to establish flow rates.

2.1. Introduction

The general concepts of the laws of conservation of mass, momentum and energy lead to a corresponding set of three equations that may be used to solve problems of pipe flow.

In the application of these equations it is assumed that the liquid under consideration is not compressible. For the time being frictional effects are not considered.

Velocity is a vector having both magnitude and direction. When we talk about velocity of flow within a pipe we usually mean the average velocity. In reality the flow velocity will vary across the cross-section of the pipe and generally the liquid will not move in a straight line.

In steady flow the discharge, or volume flow rate, is constant over time. In uniform flow the cross-sectional area of the pipe is constant. This chapter will consider steady, but not necessarily uniform, flow.

2.2. Continuity equation

This stems from the *law of conservation of mass*. For an incompressible fluid flowing between two sections of a pipe of varying cross-sectional area

$$Q = A_1 V_1 = A_2 V_2 \tag{2.1}$$

where Q is the volume rate of discharge (m³/s), A is the cross-sectional area (m²), and V is the velocity of flow (m/s). The suffixes 1 and 2 relate to the two cross-sections.

Some simple problems may be solved just by application of this equation. In other problems it is likely to be the first equation used.

Example 2.1

A domestic hose pipe 12 mm diameter passes 400 l/hr. It has a 3 mm-dia. nozzle. What is the average velocity in the hose and the nozzle?

Although this appears a simple question, there are a number of potential traps, principally in terms of the units used. We need to convert these to preferred ones of m³/s and m at an early stage. A common elementary error in pipe flow questions is to confuse radius and diameter.

Converting the flow rate we obtain

$$Q = \frac{400 \times 0.001}{60 \times 60} = 0.000\,111\,1 \text{ m}^3/\text{s} \tag{2.2}$$

Cross-sectional area of the hose

$$A_1 = \pi \left(\frac{6}{1000}\right)^2 = 0.000\,113\,1 \text{ m}^2 \tag{2.3}$$

Velocity in hose

$$V_1 = \frac{Q}{A_1} = \frac{0.000\,111\,1}{0.000\,113\,1} = 0.98 \text{ m/s} \tag{2.4}$$

Cross-sectional area of the nozzle

$$A_2 = \pi \left(\frac{1.5}{1000}\right)^2 = 0.000\,007\,069 \text{ m}^2 \tag{2.5}$$

Velocity in nozzle

$$V_2 = \frac{Q}{A_2} = \frac{0.000\,111\,1}{0.000\,007\,069} = 15.7 \text{ m/s} \tag{2.6}$$

Revision points

- Velocity of flow is a vector quantity, having direction as well as magnitude.
- Discharge is the velocity of flow times the cross-sectional area of the pipe through which flow is taking place.
- In steady flow discharge is constant with time.
- In uniform flow the cross-sectional area of the pipe is constant.
- Problems involving changes of pipe cross-sectional area only may be solved using the continuity equation.

2.3. Momentum equation

Force is required to change the velocity of a body, in either magnitude or direction. This is expressed as force = rate of change of momentum.

As momentum = mass × velocity, a change in momentum can be brought about by

- a change in mass
- a change in velocity direction or magnitude (acceleration)
- a change in both mass and velocity.

Traditionally in solid mechanics the momentum, or impulse equation, has been applied to discrete bodies where changes in momentum usually only result from changes in velocity. In pipe flow, however, a continuous flow is involved, in which it is assumed that the stream is infinite. We therefore need to develop an approach for this situation and to consider the rate of change of momentum within a 'control volume'.

As in the solid mechanics case, considering just changes in velocity, we can state

$$\text{Force } F = M\left(\frac{V_2 - V_1}{t}\right) \tag{2.7}$$

where M is the mass flowing between sections 1 and 2 in time t and V_2 and V_1 are the velocities at these sections. A subtle rearrangement of the equation gives

$$F = \frac{M}{t}(V_2 - V_1) \tag{2.8}$$

where M/t can be called the mass flow rate.

However, from the definition of density, we can establish that the mass flow rate is equal to the density of the liquid times its volume rate of discharge, hence

$$\frac{M}{t} = \rho Q \tag{2.9}$$

Hence

$$F = \rho Q(V_2 - V_1) \tag{2.10}$$

The force *F* will be made up of a number of elements, typically including external pressure forces and reactions from pipework. To reflect this, the equation may be re-expressed as

$$\Sigma F = \rho Q(V_2 - V_1) \tag{2.11}$$

Velocity is a vector quantity, having both magnitude and direction, so the momentum equation has to be applied in a specified direction.

In general, problems in this area are likely to involve three steps in succession to the control volume

(a) the application of the continuity equation
(b) the application in one or more directions of the momentum equation, ensuring that all relevant external forces acting on the fluid within the control volume are considered
(c) if necessary vector addition to determine the magnitude and direction of the resultant force.

A particular point to watch is that the change in momentum may be small relative to some of the elements of forces involved. This may result in numbers of very different magnitude being added or subtracted from each other. To maintain consistent accuracy, it is advisable to work to a higher than usual precision in the calculation of the pressure forces.

Especially where a change in direction of flow is involved, it is advisable to draw a sketch of the control volume, clearly showing these flows and the external forces related to a defined co-ordinate system.

2.3.1 Pipe bends
From the following two examples it will become apparent why thrust blocks, or other means of restraint, are provided at bends in pipelines.

Example 2.2

A horizontal pipe of 500 mm internal diameter has a 90° bend. The discharge of water through the pipe is 0.15 m³/s and the upstream pressure head is 28 m. Calculate the magnitude and direction of the resulting force on the pipe bend.

Figure 2.1 shows the control volume with the co-ordinate system, flows and external forces on the water within the control volume. It does not include the weight force which is not relevant to this example as it has no horizontal component. Nor does it include friction, which for this short length of pipe can be considered negligible. The reaction of the bend on the water F_R can be resolved into components F_{RX} and F_{RY}.

The average velocity of water entering the bend is given by

$$V_1 = \frac{Q}{A} = \frac{0.15}{\pi \times 0.25^2} = 0.76394 \text{ m/s} \tag{2.12}$$

This velocity is entirely in the x direction. The velocity of water V_2 leaving the pipe has the same numerical value but is now in the y direction.

Conservation equations applied to flow of liquid in pipes

Figure 2.1 90° horizontal pipe bend: forces and flows

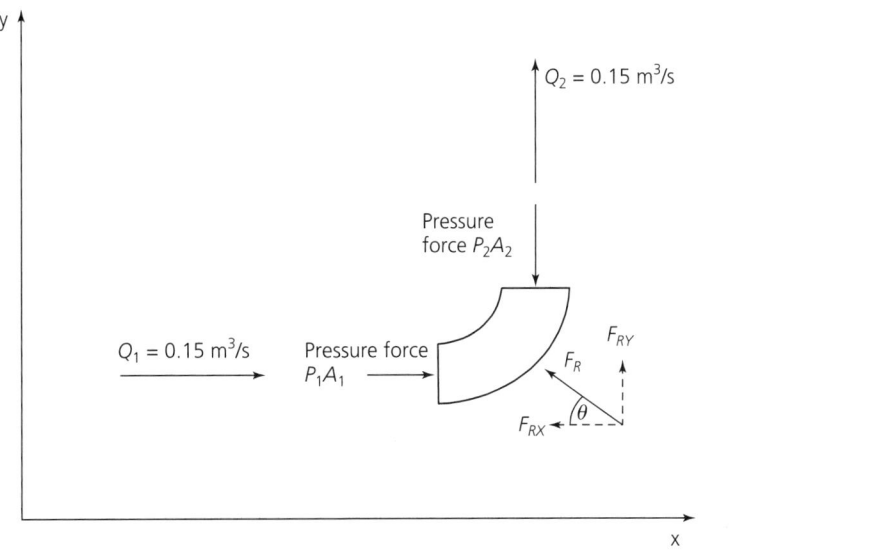

The upstream pressure is given as a head value. This needs to be converted to Pa.

$$P_1 = \rho g h = 1000 \times 9.81 \times 28 = 274\,680 \text{ Pa} \qquad (2.13)$$

Considering the x direction

$$\Sigma F_X = P_1 A_1 - F_{RX} \qquad (2.14)$$

Placing this in the momentum equation gives

$$P_1 A_1 - F_{RX} = \rho Q(V_{2X} - V_{1X}) \qquad (2.15)$$

leading to

$$F_{RX} = P_1 A_1 - \rho Q(V_{2X} - V_{1X}) \qquad (2.16)$$

Substituting the numerical values

$$F_{RX} = 274\,680 \times \pi \times 0.25^2 - 1000 \times 0.15 \times (0 - 0.763\,94) = 54\,047.88 \text{ N} \qquad (2.17)$$

Considering the y direction

$$\Sigma F_Y = F_{RY} - P_2 A_2 \qquad (2.18)$$

and substituting in the momentum equation

$$F_{RY} = P_2 A_2 - \rho Q(V_{2Y} - V_{1Y}) \qquad (2.19)$$

23

leading to

$$F_{RY} = P_2 A_2 + \rho Q(V_{2Y} - V_{1Y}) \qquad (2.20)$$

Assuming there is no pressure loss between the start and end of the control volume

$$F_{RY} = 274\,680 \times \pi \times 0.25^2 - 1000 \times 0.15 \times (0 - 0.763\,94) = 54\,047.88\text{ N} \qquad (2.21)$$

Note the importance of observing the signs of the velocity and pressure force values in applying the momentum equation. It may help you to get the latter right if you remember that it is the external pressure values acting on the control volume that are required.

We can now find the numerical resultant force of the bend on the water in the control volume using Pythagoras' theorem

$$F_R = \sqrt{F_{RX}^2 + F_{RY}^2} = \sqrt{54\,047.88^2 + 54\,047.88^2} = 76\,435\text{ N} \qquad (2.22)$$

This value can now be rounded to 76.4 kN (three significant figures).

The direction of the force can be found using

$$\theta = \tan^{-1}\left(\frac{54\,047.88}{54\,047.88}\right) = 45° \qquad (2.23)$$

The question asked for the force acting on the pipe bend. This will be equal in value and opposite in direction to the force we have just calculated acting on the water within the control volume.

 Example 2.3

Repeat Example 2.2 but for a pipe bend of 30°.

Figure 2.2 shows the arrangement for the bend. The calculations for this example are slightly more complex than those for previous examples, because the velocity V_2 in the outlet from the control volume and the external pressure force at the outlet have components in both the x and y directions.

As in the previous example, the velocity along the pipe axis entering and leaving the control volume is 0.763 94 m/s and the external pressure at each end of the control volume is taken as 274 680 Pa leading to a force of 53 933.29 N.

Substituting the forces in the momentum equation in the x direction and re-arranging gives

$$F_{RX} = P_1 A_1 - P_2 A_2 \cos\beta - \rho Q(V_2 \cos\beta - V_1)$$
$$= 274\,680 \times \pi \times 0.25^2 - 274\,680 \times \pi \times 0.25^2 \cos 30 - 1000 \times 0.15$$
$$\times (0.763\,94 \cos 30 - 0.763\,94) = 7241.04\text{ N} \qquad (2.24)$$

Figure 2.2 30° horizontal pipe bend: forces and flows

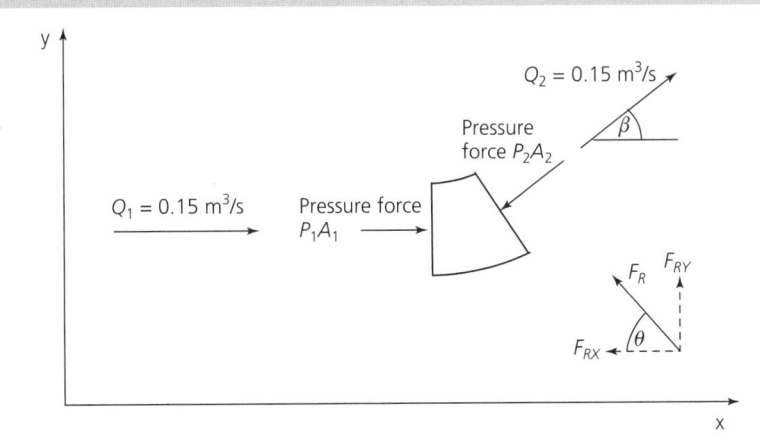

Similarly in the y direction

$$F_{RY} = P_2 A_2 \sin \beta + \rho Q(V_2 \sin \beta - 0)$$
$$= 53\,933.29 \sin 30 + 1000 \times 0.15 \times (0.763\,94 \sin 30 - 0) = 27\,023.94 \text{ N} \quad (2.25)$$

The numerical value of the resultant force is given by

$$F_R = \sqrt{F_{RX}^2 + F_{RY}^2} = \sqrt{7241.04^2 + 27\,023.94^2} = 27\,977.72 \text{ N} \quad (2.26)$$

This can be rounded to 28.0 kN (three significant figures).

The direction of the force can be found using

$$\theta = \tan^{-1}\left(\frac{27\,023.94}{7241.04}\right) = 75° \quad (2.27)$$

As in the previous example, the force on the bend will be equal in value and opposite in direction to the force we have just calculated acting on the water within the control volume.

Revision points

- Since velocity is a vector, a change in direction of flow, such as at a bend in a pipe, implies that the liquid is subject to a force.
- Calculations involving the momentum equation are based on changes within a control volume of the liquid in the pipe.
- Where a change in direction of flow occurs, the momentum equation is applied separately in two mutually perpendicular directions and the overall magnitude and direction of the resultant force acting on the liquid is obtained by vector addition.
- It is usually the force acting on the pipe that is of interest. This is equal and acts in the opposite direction to that acting on the control volume of fluid.

2.4. Bernoulli (or Energy) equation
2.4.1 Conservation of energy

Energy cannot be destroyed, only converted from one form to another. You may recall from solid dynamics that as a body falls, its potential energy gets converted into kinetic energy. In the context of hydraulics we are concerned with three forms of energy

$$\text{Potential energy} = Mgz \tag{2.28}$$

where z is the height above the datum level

$$\text{Kinetic energy} = \tfrac{1}{2}MV^2 \tag{2.29}$$

where V is the velocity

$$\text{Pressure energy} = PAL \tag{2.30}$$

Although these may look different to each other, each have the same unit, the joule (J) which is also the unit used for work. This reflects the fact that energy is the capacity to do work. You may recall that work is derived from force × distance and joule is the special name given to the Nm.

While potential energy and kinetic energy may be relatively easy to visualise, pressure energy is probably a more difficult concept. It can be regarded as an intermediate form of energy. Unlike an independent solid body that is free to increase its velocity as it moves downhill, an incompressible liquid in a pipe of uniform cross-section flowing downhill cannot do so. Instead of being converted into kinetic energy, it changes to pressure energy. The alternative name of 'flow work' may help you to visualise it. If a pressure force PA is applied to the liquid, then the work done when the liquid moves through a distance L is PAL.

$$\text{The total energy} = Mgz + \tfrac{1}{2}MV^2 + PAL \tag{2.31}$$

Usually we want to work in terms of the energy per unit weight of the liquid.

Replacing Mg by the weight W gives

$$\text{Total energy} = Wz + \frac{1}{2}\frac{WV^2}{g} + \frac{PW}{\rho g} \tag{2.32}$$

From this

$$\text{the energy per unit weight of the fluid} = z + \frac{V^2}{2g} + \frac{P}{\rho g} \tag{2.33}$$

Note that all three terms in the equation have units of metres. We refer to the three terms as follows.

z is called the elevation head (or datum head or position head)

$V^2/2g$ is called the velocity head

$P/\rho g$ is called the pressure head (sometimes also shown as h or y)

and their sum is called the total head.

Strictly speaking, Bernoulli's equation refers to the constancy of the total head between two points on a streamline, provided that there is no loss through friction.

$$\frac{V_1^2}{2g} + \frac{P_1}{\rho g} + z_1 = \frac{V_2^2}{2g} + \frac{P_2}{\rho g} + z_2 \tag{2.34}$$

In practice the equation is applied beyond the streamline basis used in its derivation.

The three elements of head all have the units of metres. It is therefore possible to represent the equation diagrammatically as sketched in Figure 2.3 for a situation where all three types of head are relevant. Such a diagram gives a visual interpretation of what is going on and is a very useful tool for understanding the flow. The total energy at different points along the pipe axis are shown in Table 2.1.

Some simple applications may involve only Bernoulli's equation. However often it is necessary to use all three equations (continuity, momentum and Bernoulli) to solve a problem.

Figure 2.3 Conversion of energy within a flow system

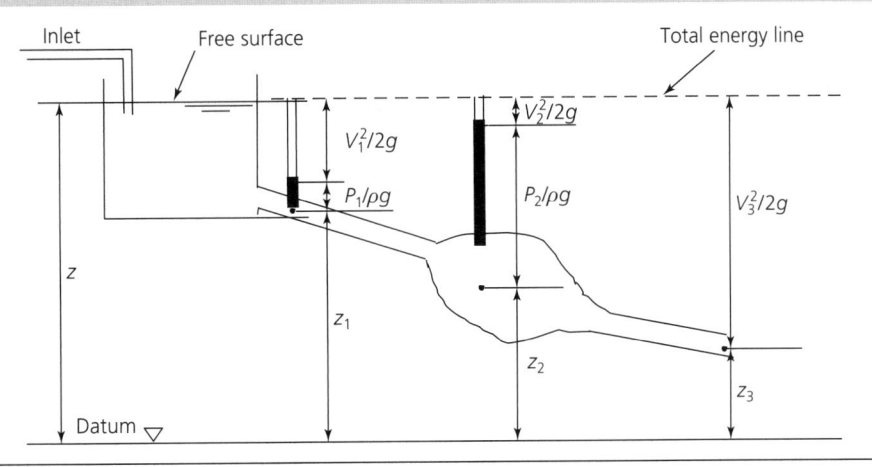

Table 2.1 Elements of head along pipe of Figure 2.3

Location	Elevation head: m	Pressure head: m	Velocity head: m
Free surface	z	Zero	Zero
1	z_1	$P_1/\rho g$	$V_1^2/2g$
2	z_2	$P_2/\rho g$	$V_2^2/2g$
3	z_3	Zero	$V_3^2/2g$

Example 2.4

Figure 2.4 shows a large tank containing a liquid with a density of 1010 kg/m³. The internal diameter of the siphon pipe is 75 mm. Determine the volume discharge rate and the gauge pressure at the top of the siphon.

Because the tank is stated to be large, we can assume that the level of liquid will not change in the period under consideration.

The discharge rate can be obtained by applying the Bernoulli equation between the surface of the liquid in the tank (denoted by suffix 1) and the outlet of the siphon (suffix 2).

$$\frac{V_1^2}{2g} + \frac{P_1}{\rho g} + z_1 = \frac{V_2^2}{2g} + \frac{P_2}{\rho g} + z_2 \tag{2.35}$$

As is common in the application of the equation, a number of values of parameters are either zero or can be assumed to be. In this case at both the liquid surface and the siphon outlet there is atmospheric pressure only (i.e. $P_1 = P_2 = 0$). It is reasonable to assume that there is minimal velocity at the liquid surface (i.e. $V_1 \approx 0$).

Bernoulli's equation therefore simplifies to

$$z_1 = \frac{V_2^2}{2g} + z_2 \tag{2.36}$$

This can be rearranged to give

$$V_2 = \sqrt{2g(z_1 - z_2)} \tag{2.37}$$

$(z_1 - z_2)$ is the difference in elevation between the liquid surface and the outlet from the siphon.

Figure 2.4 Siphon for withdrawing liquid from a large tank

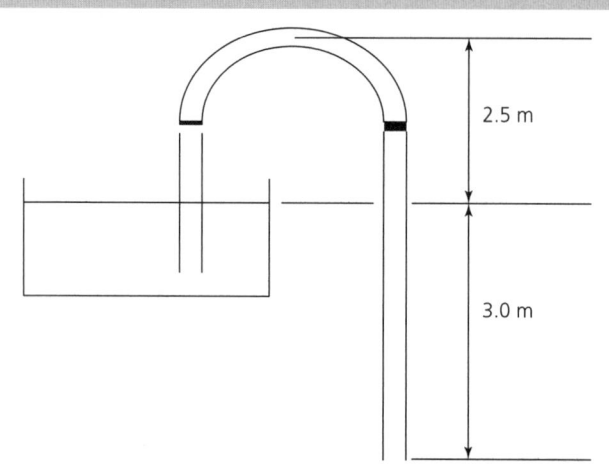

Hence

$$V_2 = \sqrt{2 \times 9.81 \times 3} = 7.672 \, \text{m/s} \, (7.67 \, \text{m/s to 3 sig. figs}) \quad (2.38)$$

The discharge can be found by substituting this value into

$$Q = V_2 A_2 = 7.672 \times \left(\pi \times \left(\frac{0.075}{2}\right)^2\right) = 0.033\,89 \, \text{m}^3/\text{s)} \quad (2.39)$$

Using the suffix 3 to denote values of parameters at the top of the siphon, we can again apply Bernoulli's equation to determine the pressure head P_3.

$$\frac{V_1^2}{2g} + \frac{P_1}{\rho g} + z_1 = \frac{V_3^2}{2g} + \frac{P_3}{\rho g} + z_3 \quad (2.40)$$

As noted previously $V_1 \approx 0$ and $P_1 = 0$. Also from the continuity equation, since there is no change in diameter of the siphon tube

$$V_3 = V_2 = 7.672 \, \text{m/s} \quad (2.41)$$

The difference in elevation heads $(z_3 - z_1) = 2.5 \, \text{m}$ \quad (2.42)

Hence the Bernoulli equation can be expressed as

$$0 = \frac{7.672^2}{2 \times 9.81} + \frac{P_3}{1010 \times 9.81} + 2.5 \quad (2.43)$$

from which

$$P_3 = -544\,94 \, \text{Pa} \, (-55.0 \, \text{kPa to 3 sig. figs}) \quad (2.44)$$

The minus sign indicates that the pressure at the top of the siphon is below atmospheric pressure.

Example 2.5

Figure 2.5 shows the plan of a horizontal 180° reducing bend in a pipe network. Water enters the bend with an average velocity of 2 m/s. The head at the entry to the bend is 3.5 m. Determine the magnitude and direction of the force exerted on the bend.

The approach used is to apply, in order, the continuity equation to find the volume flow rate at the entrance and exit from the bend together with the velocity at the exit, then the Bernoulli equation to obtain the pressure at the exit from the bend, and finally the momentum equation to determine the resultant force. Suffixes 1 and 2 denote conditions at the entrance and exit to the bend.

Cross-sectional area of pipe at bend entrance

$$A_1 = \pi \times 0.4^2 = 0.5027 \, \text{m}^2 \quad (2.45)$$

Figure 2.5 180° Horizontal pipe bend

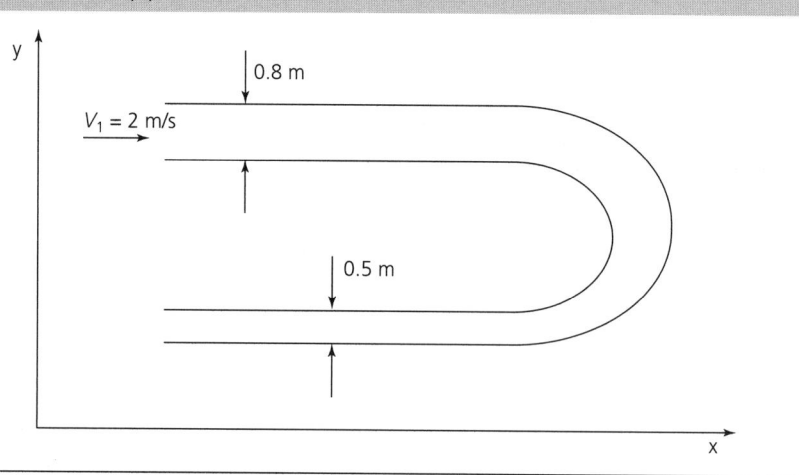

Cross-sectional area of pipe at bend exit

$$A_2 = \pi \times 0.25^2 = 0.1963 \text{ m}^2 \tag{2.46}$$

Volume flow rate

$$Q_1 = 2 \times 0.5027 = 1.0054 \text{ m}^3/\text{s} \tag{2.47}$$

From the continuity equation

$$Q_2 = 1.0054 \text{ m}^3/\text{s} \tag{2.48}$$

The velocity at the exit

$$V_2 = Q/A_2 = 1.0054/0.1963 = 5.1218 \text{ m/s} \tag{2.49}$$

Assuming no energy loss, Bernoulli's equation gives

$$\frac{P_1}{\rho g} + \frac{V_1^2}{2g} = \frac{P_2}{\rho g} + \frac{V_2^2}{2g} \tag{2.50}$$

Note that in this case there is no need to include the position head, since the pipework is horizontal.

$$\frac{1000 \times 9.81 \times 3.5}{1000 \times 9.81} + \frac{2^2}{2 \times 9.81} = \frac{P_2}{1000 \times 9.81} + \frac{5.1218^2}{2 \times 9.81}$$

$$3.5 + 0.2039 = \frac{P_2}{9810} + 1.337$$

$$P_2 = 2.3669 \times 9810 = 23\,219 \text{ Pa} \tag{2.51}$$

There is no component of velocity in the y direction at either the entrance or the exit to the bend. Therefore we only need to apply the momentum equation in the x direction thus

$$P_1 A_1 + P_2 A_2 - F_{RX} = \rho Q (V_2 - V_1) \tag{2.52}$$

where F_{RX} is the force applied to the water by the pipe.

Hence

$$F_{RX} = P_1 A_1 + P_2 A_2 - \rho Q (V_2 - V_1) \tag{2.53}$$

Substituting the numerical values

$$\begin{aligned} F_{RX} &= (1000 \times 9.81 \times 3.5) \times 0.5027 + 23\,219 \times 0.1963 - 1000 \times 1.0054 \times (5.1218 - 2) \\ &= 18\,679\,\text{N} = 187\,\text{kN}\,(3\text{ sig. figs}) \end{aligned} \tag{2.54}$$

The force on the pipe bend is equal in magnitude, but acts in the opposite direction.

2.4.2 The Venturi meter

This equipment, depicted in Figure 2.6, takes advantage of the continuity and Bernoulli equations to establish flow rates of a liquid. The internal cross-sectional area decreases between locations 1 and 2, the latter position being called the throat of the meter. From the continuity equation, as the pipe cross-sectional area decreases, the velocity of the fluid must increase. Thus V_2, the velocity at location 2, will be greater than V_1.

If the meter is horizontal, the Bernoulli equation between these points is

$$\frac{V_1^2}{2g} + \frac{P_1}{\rho g} = \frac{V_2^2}{2g} + \frac{P_2}{\rho g} \tag{2.55}$$

Figure 2.6 Long section through a Venturi meter

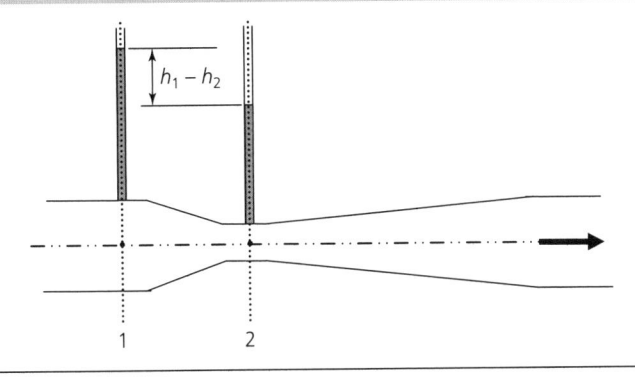

The increase in velocity therefore leads to a decrease in pressure between locations 1 and 2 as indicated by the heads in the piezometers shown in Figure 2.6. Remembering that head

$$h = \frac{P}{\rho g} \tag{2.56}$$

allows the equation to be rewritten as

$$\frac{(V_2^2 - V_1^2)}{2g} = (h_1 - h_2) \tag{2.57}$$

and from the continuity equation

$$V_1 = \frac{V_2 A_2}{A_1} \tag{2.58}$$

allowing further rewriting of the equation as

$$V_2^2 - \frac{V_2^2 A_2^2}{A_1^2} = 2g(h_1 - h_2) \tag{2.59}$$

from which

$$V_2 = A_1 \sqrt{\frac{2g(h_1 - h_2)}{(A_1^2 - A_2^2)}} \tag{2.60}$$

Hence the volume flow rate

$$Q = A_2 V_2 = A_1 A_2 \sqrt{\frac{2g(h_1 - h_2)}{(A_1^2 - A_2^2)}} \tag{2.61}$$

In practice, because there is some energy loss between locations 1 and 2, this equation slightly overestimates the value of Q. It is therefore necessary to correct the flow rate by a coefficient of discharge C_d

$$Q = C_d A_1 A_2 \sqrt{\frac{2g(h_1 - h_2)}{(A_1^2 - A_2^2)}} \tag{2.62}$$

The value of C_d is typically around 0.97 to 0.98.

Franzini and Finnemore (1997, pp. 535–540) discuss the optimal design of Venturi meters in terms of entrance/throat diameter ratios, angles of convergence and divergence from the throat section and position within the pipe system.

Example 2.6

The data in Table 2.2 were obtained during the calibration of a horizontally installed laboratory Venturi meter having an inlet diameter of 50 mm and throat diameter 25 mm.

Table 2.2

Head difference h_1-h_2: mm	10	20	30	40	50	60	70	80	90	100
Measured flow rate: l/min	13.1	18.7	23.0	26.2	29.6	32.1	34.8	37.2	39.8	41.5

Establish the discharge coefficient for the meter.

Note that the units used are not the usually preferred ones of m for dimensions, including head values, and m^3/s for flow rate. This is to avoid very small numbers. 'Because of the repetitive nature of the calculations, this example can be conveniently solved using a spreadsheet to give the flow rates shown in Table 2.3.

Table 2.3

h_1-h_2: mm	10	20	30	40	50	60	70	80	90	100
Derived flow rate: l/min	13.5	19.1	23.3	26.9	30.1	33.0	35.6	38.1	40.4	42.6

From Figure 2.7, a discharge coefficient of 0.98 is obtained.

Figure 2.7 Actual and theoretical flow rates for a Venturi meter

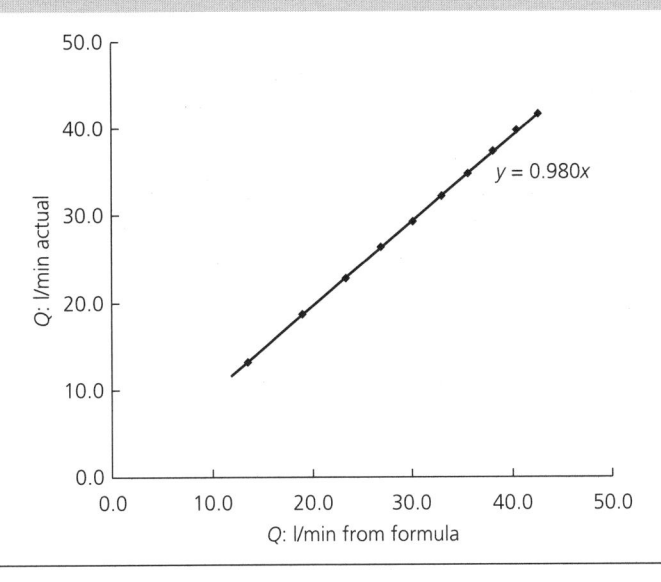

$y = 0.980x$

Q: l/min actual vs Q: l/min from formula

Hydraulics for Civil Engineers

> ✏️ **Revision points**
>
> - The principle of conservation of energy means that energy cannot be destroyed; it can only be converted from one form to another.
> - In hydraulic engineering systems we are generally concerned with changes between potential, kinetic and pressure energy.
> - The Bernoulli equation expresses the principle of conservation of these forms of energy in terms of the energy contained per unit weight of the liquid.
> - Conveniently the energy per unit weight of fluid can be directly expressed as head.
> - The Venturi meter makes use of the continuity and Bernoulli equations to enable the discharge to be determined based on the difference in head measured at sections of the meter having different cross-sectional areas.

> ✓ **Chapter summary**
>
> - Discharge in steady flow is constant with time.
> - For uniform flow, the cross-sectional area of the pipe is constant.
> - The continuity equation can be used to solve problems that only involve changes in pipe cross-sectional area.
> - Changes in flow direction imply that a force acts on the liquid.
> - Application of the continuity and momentum equations allow the resultant force on the 'control volume' to be determined.
> - The force on a pipe bend is equal in size and acts in the opposite direction to that on the control volume.
> - The Bernoulli equation expresses the principle of conservation of energy in terms of the energy contained per unit weight of the liquid: this can be directly expressed as head of the liquid.

Questions for practice

(a) A jet of water, 50 mm in diameter, impinges normally onto a fixed plate, and has a velocity of 30 m/s. Find the normal force on the plate.

(b) Water flows through a 60° reducing elbow, at a rate of 0.30 m^3/s. The diameter at the inlet is 300 mm and at the outlet is 150 mm. The pressure at the inlet to the elbow is 175 kPa. Find the pressure at the outlet from the elbow and the resultant force on the elbow, assuming the bend to be on a horizontal plane.

REFERENCE

Franzini JB and Finnemore EJ (1997) *Fluid Mechanics with Engineering Applications*, 9th edn. McGraw-Hill, New York, NY, USA.

Hydraulics for Civil Engineers
ISBN 978-0-7277-5845-3

ICE Publishing: All rights reserved
http://dx.doi.org/10.1680/hce.58453.035

3
Real flow in pipes

Learning aims

After studying this chapter you should be able to

- relate viscosity to shear stress within a moving liquid
- distinguish between dynamic viscosity and kinematic viscosity
- appreciate the significance of Reynolds number
- describe the characteristics of laminar and turbulent flow
- calculate head losses due to friction and changes in pipe section
- use Wallingford charts for calculation of discharge and velocity
- analyse simple pipe networks using the Hardy–Cross method.

3.1. Introduction

Pipe velocities in Chapter 2 were based on average conditions within the pipe. As stated there, in practice velocity varies across the pipe section, being greatest at the centre of the section. One reason for this is friction between the liquid and the pipe surface and within the liquid itself. The friction arises from a property of the fluid known as viscosity.

3.2. Viscosity of fluids

In essence, dynamic viscosity (μ) is a measure of the shear force per unit area needed to drag one layer of the liquid with unit velocity past another layer of it, unit distance away. Its SI unit is the newton-second per square metre. As the pascal is an alternative name for a newton per square metre, the unit for dynamic viscosity is also called the pascal second (Pa s).

Figure 3.1 shows a liquid between a fixed and a moving plate distance Y apart. Adjacent to the fixed plate the velocity of the liquid is zero. As a result of shear stress between the moving plate and the liquid, the liquid immediately adjacent to the plate moves at the same velocity V_p as the plate. The shear stress exerted by the moving plate on the liquid is given by

$$\tau = \mu \frac{V_p}{Y} \qquad (3.1)$$

where μ is the dynamic viscosity of the liquid.

Figure 3.1 Velocity profile for a liquid between a fixed and a moving plate

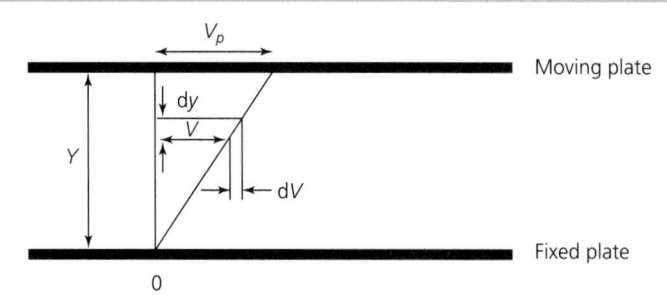

For a Newtonian liquid, such as water, the relationship between distance from the fixed plate and the velocity is uniform. Assuming that the liquid behaves as if it were a series of thin layers each moving relative to each other, calculus allows the shear stress within the liquid to be written as

$$\tau = \mu \frac{dV}{dy} \tag{3.2}$$

Viscosity can also be expressed as kinematic viscosity (v). Kinematics is the study of motion without reference to masses. The kinematic viscosity is the ratio of a liquid's dynamic viscosity to its density.

$$v = \frac{\mu}{\rho} \tag{3.3}$$

Kinematic viscosity has the unit square metre per second, satisfying the need to avoid inclusion of mass.

Example 3.1

Verify that kinematic viscosity has the unit of square metre per second.

$$\text{Unit of } \mu = \text{newton-second per square metre} \tag{3.4}$$

The newton is the SI unit of force and is derived from a mass of 1 kg being accelerated at 1 m/s².

Thus in terms of fundamental units, we can write

$$\text{units of } \mu = \text{kg} \times \frac{m}{s^2} \times \frac{s}{m^2} = \frac{kg}{m\,s} \tag{3.5}$$

and from definition

$$\text{units of } \rho = \frac{kg}{m^3} \tag{3.6}$$

$$\text{Hence units of } \frac{\mu}{\rho} = \frac{kg}{m\,s} \div \frac{kg}{m^3} = \frac{kg}{m\,s} \times \frac{m^3}{kg} = \frac{m^2}{s} \tag{3.7}$$

> **Revision points**
> - Viscosity is a measure of the internal resistance of a liquid to flow.
> - Dynamic viscosity is a direct expression of this resistance.
> - Kinematic viscosity is the dynamic viscosity of a liquid divided by its density.

3.3. Laminar and turbulent flow
3.3.1 Distinction between the two types of flow

The discussion of the effect of viscosity on velocity of flow assumed that flow was taking place parallel to the pipe sides. This is called laminar flow. However in many circumstances flow is turbulent, with motion taking the form of eddies. The distinction between the two types of flow was recognised by Hagen (1839) and Poiseuille (1840a, 1840b and 1841). Stokes (1845) established that under certain circumstances a very small disturbance could cause an established steady (laminar) flow to become sinuous (turbulent) and the change was studied experimentally by Reynolds (1883 and 1884). In the latter's experiments a small container attached to a reservoir injected a streak of dye into the flow of water entering a pipe as in Figure 3.2.

When the flow velocity was low, the streak passed through the glass tube intact in a laminar fashion (Figure 3.2(a)). Provided that the specific gravity of the dye and liquid was the same, the streak did not move transversely across the tube, irrespective of how close or how far the streak was from the edge of the tube initially.

As the velocity was gradually increased Reynolds found that suddenly mixing occurred and the tube became full of coloured water (Figure 3.2(b)). More detailed examination showed that this mixing was the result of eddy formation as indicated in Figure 3.2(c). Reynolds noted that the more viscous the liquid, the less prone it is to eddying. In particular he observed that eddies were more likely to

Figure 3.2 Reynolds's experiments on laminar and turbulent flow (from Reynolds (1883))

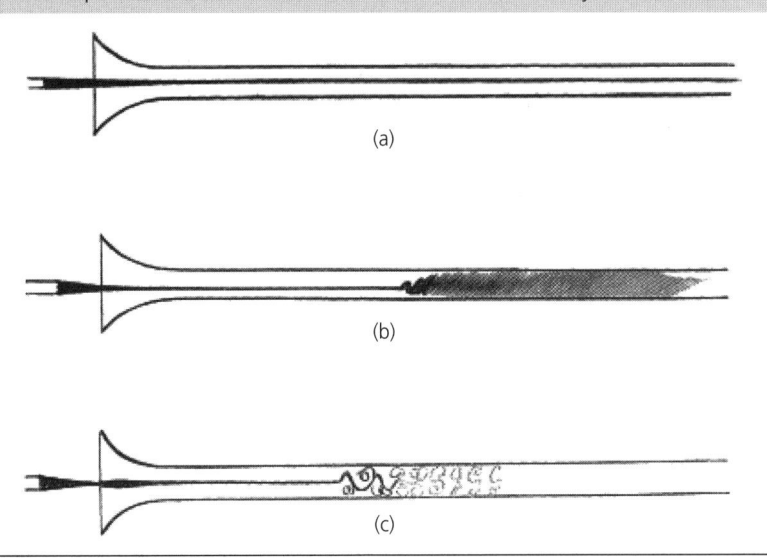

occur as the temperature increased, commenting that for water the kinematic viscosity of water at 5°C is double its value at 45°C. The non-dimensional Reynolds Number Re, representing the ratio of inertial to viscous forces, can be used as a guide to the type of flow that might be expected in a pipe of diameter D.

$$Re = \frac{\rho VD}{\mu} = \frac{VD}{\nu} \tag{3.8}$$

Various authors have investigated the critical values of Re since Reynolds, including Schiller and Eisner (1932). In round numbers laminar flow in pipes occurs at Re values less than about 2000 and turbulent flow at Re values greater than about 4000. Between 2000 and 4000 transitional flow can be expected.

3.3.2 Characteristics of laminar and turbulent flow

When fluid is flowing close to a bounding surface, such as the inside of a pipe, and momentum transfer is by molecular activity only, then the flow is laminar. In laminar flow, the forces of viscosity predominate over other forces such as fluid inertia. With stable laminar flow, it is possible to introduce any type of disturbance into the flow which will be dampened out by the forces of viscosity.

As velocity increases, the forces of inertia increase and instability increases, until the viscous forces can no longer damp a disturbance, however minor.

Once flow becomes unstable and eddies form, the instantaneous velocity at a given point fluctuates markedly with time as indicated in Figure 3.3. An eddy not only has rotational velocity, but also translational velocity, depending upon its history. It may move for a brief period of time in the general direction of the flow, and then move transversely into a region of different velocity.

Since the eddy is carrying with it the mean velocity of the region it came from, the new region will experience a drag force, either backwards or forwards. This interchange of eddies results in much more effective mixing and diffusion of momentum than in laminar flow.

With such mixing action taking place, it is to be expected that there is much shear and energy dissipation. Each eddy gradually dissipates its energy in viscous shear, blends into its new surroundings and loses its identity. New eddies are continually being formed, which ensure the creation and maintenance of fully developed turbulence throughout the flow system.

Turbulent flow is more typical than laminar flow within most practical civil engineering applications.

Figure 3.3 Variation of instantaneous velocity at a point with time

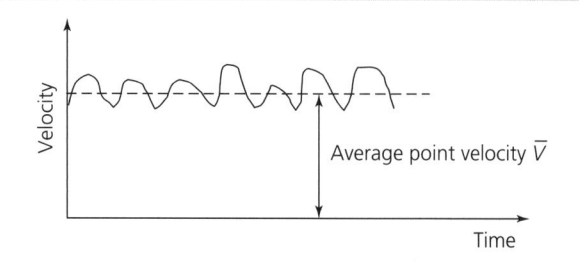

> **Revision points**
> - The terms laminar and turbulent flow are basically self explanatory.
> - Reynolds number can be used to determine the likely type of flow based on velocity, diameter and viscosity.
> - In most civil engineering applications, flow will be turbulent.

3.4. Modification of Bernoulli equation for head loss due to friction

A characteristic of flow within pipelines, which the examples in Chapter 2 did not take into account, is a significant loss of head through friction. As it is not possible to destroy energy, this implies some of the energy is converted to another form, mainly heat. The modified Bernoulli equation is

$$\frac{V_1^2}{2g} + \frac{P_1}{\rho g} + z_1 = \frac{V_2^2}{2g} + \frac{P_2}{\rho g} + z_2 + h_f \qquad (3.9)$$

The expression used to find h_f will depend on whether the flow is laminar or turbulent.

For laminar flow the head loss in a circular pipe is given by what has become known as the Hagen-Poiseuille equation, although Hagenbach (1860) and, as reported by Jacobson (1860), Neumann also researched this area. In current usage the equation is generally written as

$$h_f = \frac{32\nu LV}{gD^2} = \frac{32\mu LV}{\rho g D^2} \qquad (3.10)$$

where L is the length of pipe under consideration and other symbols are as previously used.

You may be surprised to see that the equation does not include a term for pipe roughness.

For turbulent flow, head loss is given by the Darcy–Weisbach equation developed by Fanning (1877) building on the work of Weisbach (1845) and Darcy (1857). In current UK usage this is generally written as

$$h_f = \frac{\lambda L}{D} \frac{V^2}{2g} \qquad (3.11)$$

where λ is a non-dimensional friction factor. Since

$$V = \frac{Q}{A} \qquad (3.12)$$

it is also possible to express the friction factor as

$$h_f = \frac{8\lambda L Q^2}{\pi^2 g D^5} \qquad (3.13)$$

Other versions of the equation use a friction factor f instead of λ, but care needs to be taken since there is inconsistency between UK and North American usage.

Example 3.2

A 2.5-km-long 500-mm-dia. pipeline is used to convey water between two reservoirs whose water surface elevations differ by 90 m. The λ value is 0.02. Calculate the velocity and discharge.

The calculation will require the use of the Bernoulli equation to establish the velocity in the pipeline and the continuity equation to obtain the discharge.

Applying the Bernoulli equation between the water surfaces in the two reservoirs

$$\frac{V_1^2}{2g} + \frac{P_1}{\rho g} + z_1 = \frac{V_2^2}{2g} + \frac{P_2}{\rho g} + z_2 + h_f \tag{3.14}$$

A characteristic of problems such as this one is that it can usually be assumed the reservoir is large, hence the velocity on the surface can be assumed to be zero and the elevation of water in the reservoir remains constant. The equation thus simplifies to

$$h_f = z_1 - z_2 \tag{3.15}$$

assuming turbulent flow

$$\frac{\lambda L}{D} \frac{V^2}{2g} = z_1 - z_2 \tag{3.16}$$

where V is the velocity of flow in the pipeline.

Hence by transposition

$$V = \sqrt{\frac{2gD(z_1 - z_2)}{\lambda L}} \tag{3.17}$$

Substituting the numerical values, ensuring that all lengths are in metres

$$V = \sqrt{\frac{2 \times 9.81 \times 0.5 \times 90}{0.02 \times 2500}} = 4.202\,142\,\text{m/s} \tag{3.18}$$

Using the continuity equation

$$Q = VA = 4.202\,142 \times \pi \times 0.25^2 = 0.825\,\text{m}^3/\text{s} \text{ (3 sig. figs)} \tag{3.19}$$

3.4.1 Pipes in 'parallel'

In the situation where there is more than one pipe between two points, the difference in head between the ends of each of the parallel pipes will be the same. Bernoulli's equation is separately applied to each pipe and the overall flow is obtained by adding the flows calculated in each pipe.

Example 3.3

Two large reservoirs 3 km apart are connected by two pipes. The difference in elevation of the reservoirs is 60 m. The first pipe is 0.5 m diameter with a λ value of 0.04. The second pipe is 0.6 m diameter with a λ value of 0.05. The two pipes follow different routes between the two reservoirs, the first pipe being 2.9 km long and the second pipe being 3.1 km long.

As only the discharge has been asked for, and making similar assumptions as in the previous example, we can use the following version of the head loss equation for each pipe.

$$\frac{8\lambda L Q^2}{\pi^2 g D^5} = z_1 - z_2 \tag{3.20}$$

Hence

$$Q = \sqrt{\frac{\pi^2 g D^5 (z_1 - z_2)}{8\lambda L}} \tag{3.21}$$

For the first pipe the following calculations apply.

The first pipe is 0.5 m in diameter with a λ value of 0.04.

$$Q = \sqrt{\frac{\pi^2 g \times 0.5^5 \times 60}{8 \times 0.04 \times 2900}} = 0.4423 \, \text{m}^3/\text{s} \tag{3.22}$$

For the second pipe the following calculations apply.

The second pipe is 0.6 m in diameter with a λ value of 0.05.

$$Q = \sqrt{\frac{\pi^2 g \times 0.6^5 \times 60}{8 \times 0.05 \times 3100}} = 0.6036 \, \text{m}^3/\text{s} \tag{3.23}$$

Total flow between the reservoirs $= 1.0459 \, \text{m}^3/\text{s}$ ($1.05 \, \text{m}^3/\text{s}$ to 3 sig. figs) \hfill (3.24)

3.4.2 Head losses at change of pipe section

Head losses also occur at sudden changes of pipe section as shown in Table 3.1. This loss results from the formation of eddies. Some of the values in the table have been determined by theory and some by experiment. The latter technique has to be used for commercial pipe fittings such as valves.

Hydraulics for Civil Engineers

Table 3.1 Head losses at change of pipe section

Situation	Head loss in terms of velocity	in terms of flow rate and pipe diameters
Sudden increase in diameter of a pipe	$h_L = \dfrac{(V_1 - V_2)^2}{2g}$	$h_L = \dfrac{8Q^2}{\pi^2 g D_1^4}\left(1 - \dfrac{D_1^2}{D_2^2}\right)^2$
Sudden decrease in diameter of a pipe	$h_L = \dfrac{0.44 V_2^2}{2g}$	$h_L = \dfrac{3.52 Q^2}{\pi^2 g D_2^4}$
Entry into a non-protruding pipe (tapered or rounded entries have lower values)	$h_L = \dfrac{0.5 V^2}{2g}$	$h_L = \dfrac{4 Q^2}{\pi^2 g D^4}$
Exit from a pipe	$h_L = \dfrac{0.5 V^2}{2g}$	$h_L = \dfrac{4 Q^2}{\pi^2 g D^4}$
90° elbow	$h_L = \dfrac{V^2}{2g}$	$h_L = \dfrac{8 Q^2}{\pi^2 g D^4}$

Example 3.4

(a) Verify that the two equations given in Table 3.1 for head loss at a sudden increase in pipe diameter are equivalent to each other.

(b) Water flows between two reservoirs whose top water levels differ by 20 m through a pipe whose diameter is 100 mm for the first 150 m and 200 mm for the final 400 m. The first section of pipe has $\lambda = 0.02$ and the final section has $\lambda = 0.04$. Determine the flow rate through the pipe.

Part (a)
Starting from the equation expressed in terms of velocity

$$h_L = \frac{(V_1 - V_2)^2}{2g} = \frac{V_1^2\left(1 - \dfrac{V_2}{V_1}\right)^2}{2g} \tag{3.25}$$

Using the continuity equation this becomes

$$h_L = \frac{\left(\dfrac{Q}{A_1}\right)^2\left(1 - \dfrac{Q}{A_2} \times \dfrac{A_1}{Q}\right)^2}{2g} = \frac{\left(\dfrac{Q}{A_1}\right)^2\left(1 - \dfrac{A_1}{A_2}\right)^2}{2g} = \frac{\dfrac{Q^2}{\pi^2 D_1^4}\left(1 - \dfrac{\dfrac{\pi D_1^2}{4}}{\dfrac{\pi D_2^2}{4}}\right)^2}{2g} = \frac{8Q^2}{\pi^2 g D_1^4}\left(1 - \dfrac{D_1^2}{D_2^2}\right)^2$$

$$\tag{3.26}$$

Part (b)

Considering a control volume extending between the top of each reservoir where pressure terms disappear and it can again be assumed that there is minimal velocity

$$z_1 - z_2 = \sum h_f + \sum h_L \tag{3.27}$$

Substituting for the losses from friction and at changes at section, this becomes

$$z_1 - z_2 = \frac{8\lambda_1 L_1 Q^2}{\pi^2 g D_1^5} + \frac{8\lambda_2 L_2 Q^2}{\pi^2 g D_2^5} + \frac{4Q^2}{\pi^2 g D_1^4} + \frac{8Q^2}{\pi^2 g D_1^4}\left(1 - \frac{D_1^2}{D_2^2}\right)^2 + \frac{4Q^2}{\pi^2 g D_2^4} \tag{3.28}$$

This can be simplified to

$$z_1 - z_2 = \frac{4Q^2}{\pi^2 g}\left(\frac{2\lambda_1 L_1}{D_1^5} + \frac{2\lambda_2 L_2}{D_2^5} + \frac{1}{D_1^4} + \frac{2}{D_1^4}\left(1 - \frac{D_1^2}{D_2^2}\right)^2 + \frac{1}{D_2^4}\right) \tag{3.29}$$

Substituting the numerical values this becomes

$$20 = \frac{4Q^2}{\pi^2 g}\left(\frac{2 \times 0.02 \times 150}{0.1^5} + \frac{2 \times 0.04 \times 400}{0.2^5} + \frac{1}{0.1^4} + \frac{2}{0.1^4}\left(1 - \frac{0.1^2}{0.2^2}\right)^2 + \frac{1}{0.2^4}\right) \tag{3.30}$$

This simplifies to

$$20 = \frac{4Q^2}{\pi^2 g}(600\,000 + 100\,000 + 10\,000 + 11\,250 + 625) \tag{3.31}$$

From which

$$Q = \sqrt{\frac{20 \times \pi^2 g}{4 \times 721\,875}} = 0.0259 \text{ m}^3/\text{s (3 sig. figs)} \tag{3.32}$$

If the minor losses were to be ignored a flow rate of 0.0263 m³/s would be obtained. Their small effect could be used to justify the name of *minor losses* sometimes applied to them in long pipeline situations.

Revision points

- In real situations, Bernoulli's equation needs to be modified to take account of the conversion of energy to less useful forms such as heat by the effect of friction.
- Not surprisingly for both laminar flow and turbulent flow the head losses are directly proportional to the length of pipe.
- Pipe roughness is only a factor in head loss in turbulent flow.
- Besides frictional losses in head, Bernoulli's equation can be modified to take account of losses due to eddying at changes in pipe section, including entry to, and exit from pipes.

3.5. Boundary layers in turbulent flow

Even though the overall flow within a pipe may be turbulent, adjacent to its sides lies a zone of slower moving liquid. Within the boundary layer there are three zones: the laminar sub layer, the transitional sub layer and the turbulent sub layer.

The extent to which protrusions on the side of the pipe extend through the boundary layer determines the type of turbulent flow that occurs. If the protrusions lie completely within the laminar sub layer, the overall flow is described as *smooth turbulent*. If they just pass into the transitional sub layer, the overall flow is *transitional turbulent*. Protrusions penetrating well beyond the laminar sub layer encourage eddying and the flow is described as *rough turbulent*.

3.6. Derivation of λ values and use in design charts

A number of authors have investigated λ values since Darcy. For smooth pipes Blasius (1913) established a relationship between λ and Reynolds number applicable at high *Re* values. Von Kármán (1930) developed a relationship, confirmed experimentally by Nikuradse (1933), which showed that for turbulent flow in rough pipes λ depended on the relative roughness, defined as k/D where k is the surface roughness.

The Colebrook–White (1937) developed Von Kármán's work to produce the following formula for ? covering the complete range of turbulent flow including the transition zone

$$\frac{1}{\sqrt{\lambda}} = -2\log\left(\frac{k}{3.7D} + \frac{2.51}{Re\sqrt{\lambda}}\right) \tag{3.33}$$

The first term within the brackets is derived from work on rough pipes and the second from work on smooth pipes.

A problem with this equation is that λ appears on both sides of the equation making direct solution difficult. This was tackled by Rouse (1943) and Moody (1944) who each produced design charts to enable the friction factor to be obtained if the Reynolds number is known.

Barr (1981) produced the approximate solution which, although daunting at first sight, once entered into a spreadsheet can be used to directly obtain a value of λ

$$\frac{1}{\sqrt{\lambda}} = -2\log\left[\frac{k}{3.7D} + \frac{5.02\log\left(\dfrac{Re}{4.518\log\left(\dfrac{Re}{7}\right)}\right)}{Re\left[1 + \dfrac{Re^{0.52}}{29\left(\dfrac{D}{k}\right)^{0.7}}\right]}\right] \tag{3.34}$$

Values of λ obtained from this equation are plotted in Figure 3.4. If the non-dimensional terms λ and *Re* in the Colebrook–White equation are replaced by their full equivalents (Hydraulics Research, 1990) the average pipe velocity in the direction of flow may be obtained using

$$V = -2\sqrt{2gDS}\log\left(\frac{k}{3.7D} + \frac{2.51\nu}{D\sqrt{2gDS}}\right) \tag{3.35}$$

where S is the hydraulic gradient.

Real flow in pipes

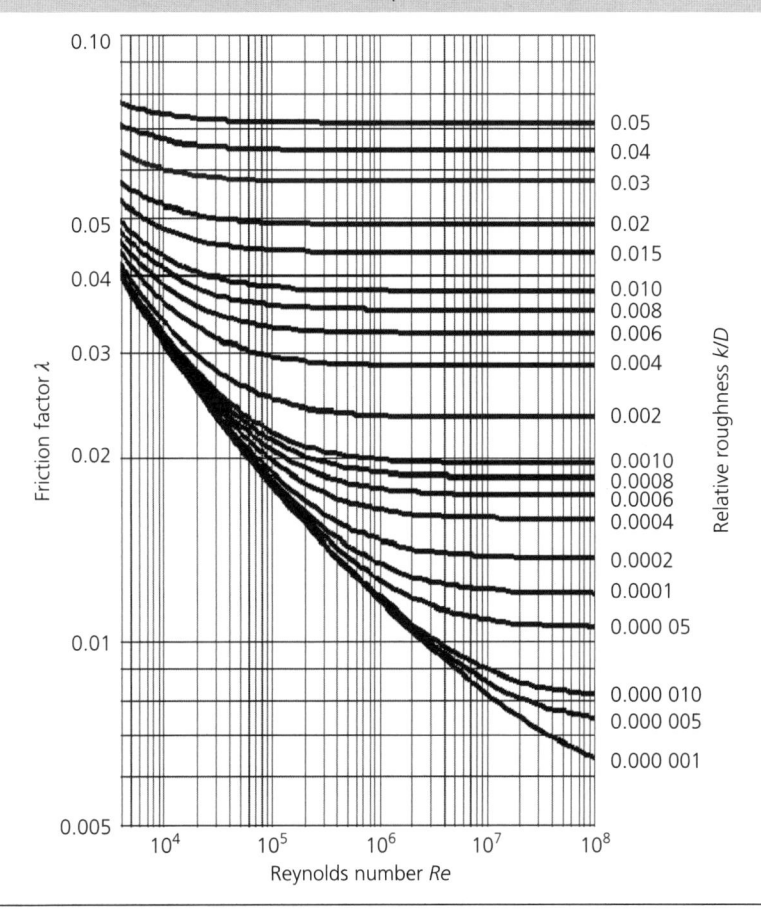

Figure 3.4 Values of friction factor λ based on Barr's equation

The Wallingford charts (Hydraulics Research, 1990) provide the solution to this equation graphically for pipes with surface roughness between 0.003 mm (applicable to Perspex) and 30 mm (typical of water mains severely attacked by tuberculation).

Example 3.5

A 1500-m-long 200-mm-dia. concrete pipeline is used to convey water from a reservoir. The outlet of the pipeline is 30 m below the inlet. Assuming the pipes have a surface roughness $k = 0.6$ mm, use Figure 3.5 to determine the velocity and the discharge.

A velocity of about 1.7 m/s and a discharge of about 55 l/s [0.055 m³/s] can be read off the design chart.

Views vary over whether it is preferable to use the equations or design charts. The facilities offered by spreadsheets may now tend to encourage the former.

Figure 3.5 Wallingford chart for $k = 0.6$ mm

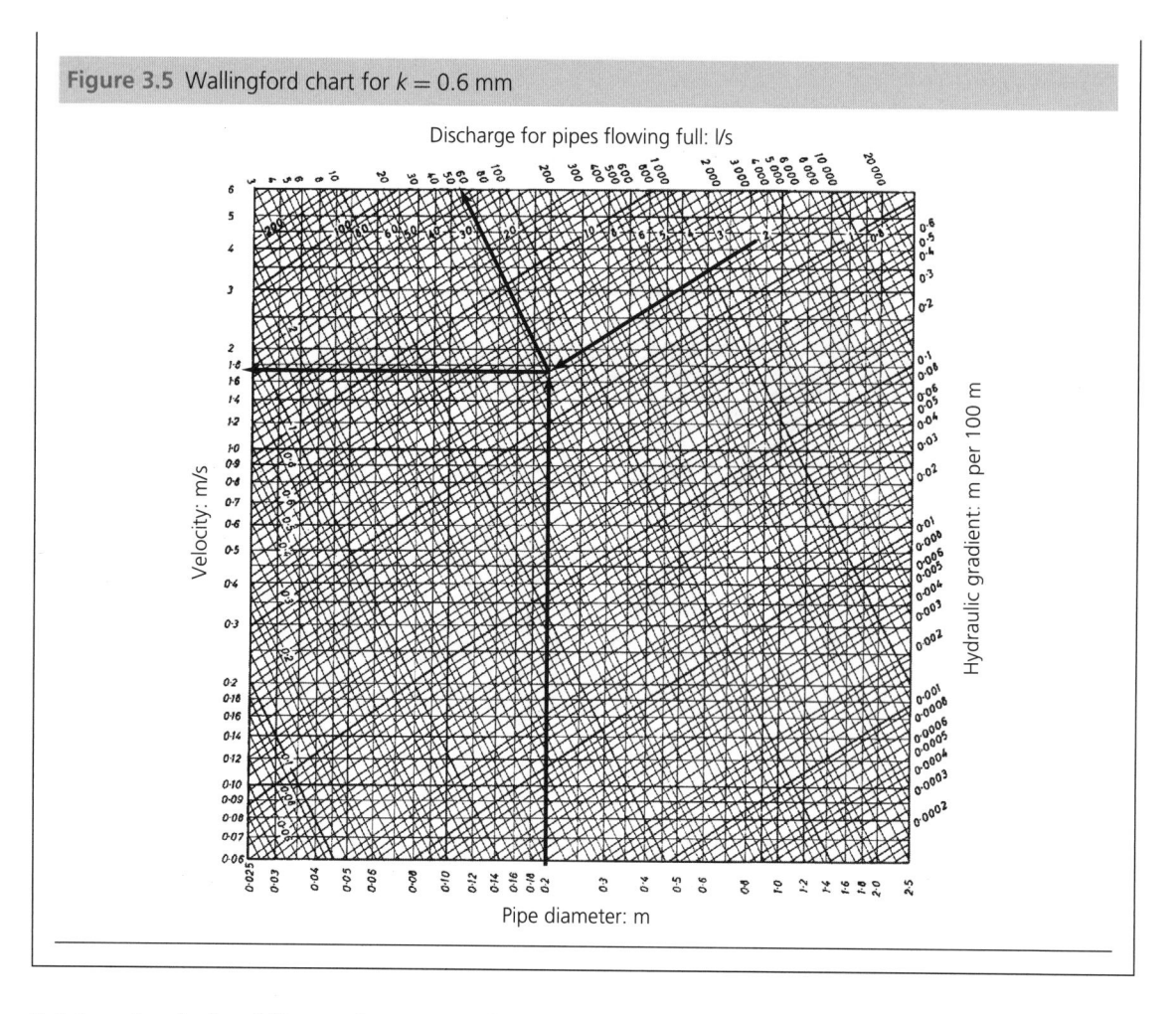

3.6.1 Analysis of flows pipe networks using the Hardy–Cross method

The Hardy–Cross method (Cross, 1936) is a simple manual iterative method, but you need to be aware that more sophisticated computer-based methods will be used in practice. Applications typically include analysis of flows in water supply networks.

The first stage is to assume flows Q within each pipe while respecting the continuity equation at each node.

From a knowledge of the pipe diameter D and assumed flow Q, the trial velocity V in each pipe is calculated and the trial head loss h_f in each pipe is calculated using the Darcy equation, modified to take account of flow direction

$$h_f = \frac{\lambda L V |V|}{2gD} \tag{3.36}$$

In using this equation λ values can be obtained from Figure 3.4 based on the relative roughness of the pipes. If the values of h_f sum to zero around a loop of pipes and the calculated head loss at any

Real flow in pipes

junction is the same regardless of the route to it, then the correct values for flow in each pipe have been selected.

If the values of h_f do not sum to zero, a correction factor δQ is applied to each value of flow where

$$\delta Q = -\frac{\sum h_f}{2 \sum (h_f/Q)} \qquad (3.37)$$

and the calculations repeated with the corrected values of flow. This is repeated until the error is reduced to a sufficiently low value.

A tabular approach to carrying out the calculations is recommended.

Example 3.6

$0.5 \text{ m}^3/\text{s}$ of water is supplied at junction A to a ring main ABCD. Water is drawn off at junctions B, C and D at rates of 0.35, 0.10 and 0.05 m^3/s respectively. All the pipes have a roughness of 0.6 mm. Pipes AB and DA are each 1000 m long, pipe BC is 2000 m long and pipe CD is 3000 m long. Pipes AB and CD are each 0.5 m in diameter. Pipes BC and DA are each 0.3 m in diameter. Assuming that the kinematic viscosity of water is $1.141 \times 10^{-6} \text{ m}^2/\text{s}$ determine the flow rate and its direction within pipe CD?

This example will be solved using the Hardy–Cross method. Basic properties of the pipes can be seen in Table 3.2.

Taking flows clockwise round the ring main to be positive and assuming as an initial trial that there is a flow rate of 0.25 m^3/s between junctions A and B allows the remaining flows within the pipes to be determined as shown in Figure 3.6.

For the first iteration the results seen in Table 3.3 are obtained.

The correction factor to be applied to each of the Q values in the next iteration

$$\delta Q = -\frac{\sum h_f}{2 \sum (h_f/Q)} = -\frac{-62.8224}{2 \times 404.5197} = 0.0851 \text{ m}^3/\text{s} \qquad (3.38)$$

Table 3.2

Pipe	Length: m	Diameter D: m	Cross-sectional area: m^2	Roughness k/D
A–B	1000	0.5	0.1963	0.0012
B–C	2000	0.3	0.0707	0.0020
C–D	3000	0.5	0.1963	0.0012
D–A	1000	0.3	0.0707	0.0020

47

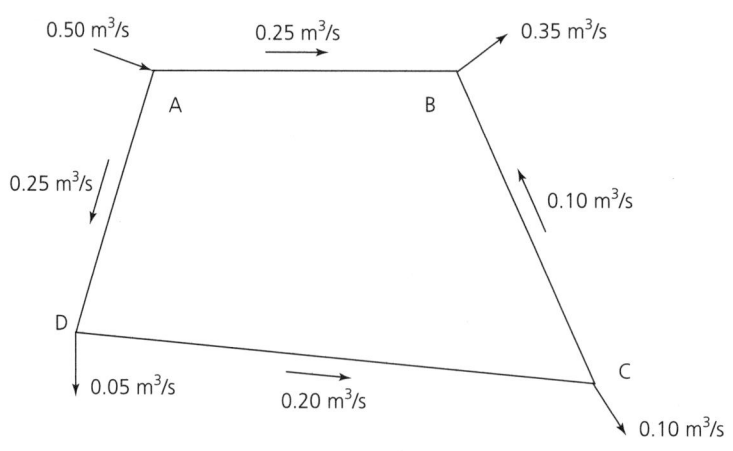

Figure 3.6 Hardy–Cross method for flows in a ring main showing initial trial flows

The calculations for the second iteration, with Q values corrected by the δQ obtained from equation (3.33), are shown in Table 3.4. From this table the following correction factor is obtained for the third iteration:

$$\delta Q = -\frac{\sum h_f}{2 \sum (h_f/Q)} = -\frac{-18.0742}{2 \times 192.0491} = 0.0471 \text{ m}^3/\text{s} \tag{3.39}$$

Table 3.3

	Q: m³/s	Velocity: m/s	Reynolds number	λ	h_f	h_f/Q
A–B	0.2500	1.2732	1.12E + 09	0.0205	3.3938	13.5752
B–C	−0.1000	−1.4147	1.24E + 09	0.0234	−15.9273	159.2730
C–D	−0.2000	−1.0186	8.93E + 08	0.0205	−6.5161	32.5805
D–A	−0.2500	−3.5368	3.10E + 09	0.0234	−49.7728	199.0911
					$\sum h_f = -68.8224$	$\sum h_f/Q = 404.5197$

Table 3.4

	Q: m³/s	Velocity: m/s	Reynolds number	λ	h_f	h_f/Q
A–B	0.3351	1.7065	1.50E + 09	0.0205	6.0963	18.1944
B–C	−0.0149	−0.2113	1.85E + 08	0.0234	−0.3552	23.7848
C–D	−0.1149	−0.5854	5.13E + 08	0.0205	−2.1519	18.7229
D–A	−0.1649	−2.3333	2.04E + 09	0.0234	−21.6635	131.3470
					$\sum h_f = -18.0742$	$\sum h_f/Q = 192.0491$

Table 3.5

	Q: m³/s	Velocity: m/s	Reynolds number	λ	h_f	h_f/Q
A–B	0.3821	1.9461	1.71E + 09	0.0205	7.9289	20.7495
B–C	0.0321	0.4544	3.98E + 08	0.0234	1.6435	51.1634
C–D	−0.0679	−0.3457	3.03E + 08	0.0205	−0.7505	11.0574
D–A	−0.1179	−1.6676	1.46E + 09	0.0234	−11.0655	93.8730
					$\sum h_f = -2.2436$	$\sum h_f/Q = 176.8434$

The calculations for the third iteration, with Q values corrected by the δQ obtained from equation (3.34), are shown in Table 3.5. From this table the following correction factor is obtained for the third iteration:

$$\delta Q = -\frac{\sum h_f}{2\sum (h_f/Q)} = -\frac{-2.2436}{2 \times 176.8434} = 0.0063 \, \text{m}^3/\text{s} \tag{3.40}$$

'The correction term found in equation (3.35) has diminished to a value such that further trials are not necessary and the flows with this final correction applied are shown in Figure 3.7.

Figure 3.7 Hardy–Cross method for flows in a ring main showing final flows

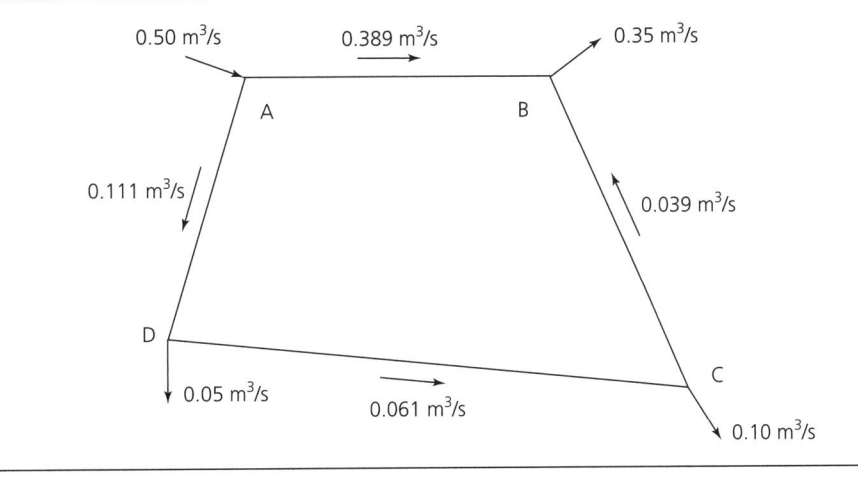

Hydraulics for Civil Engineers

> ### ✎ Revision points
>
> - The friction factor λ used in the determination of head loss in turbulent flow is not a constant: it depends on the relative roughness of the pipe and Reynolds number of the flow.
> - While the Colebrook–White equation expresses the relationship of λ to the other factors, its use is tedious since λ appears on both sides of the equation.
> - The Moody and Wallingford charts were developed to overcome the difficulties in direct calculations.
> - Barr's equation, while daunting in itself, can be used within spreadsheet applications to directly determine λ from the relative roughness of the pipe and Reynolds number of the flow.
> - The Hardy–Cross method uses an iterative approach to the manual calculation of flows in relatively simple pipe networks taking into account the values of λ and Reynolds number.

> ### ✓ Chapter summary
>
> - Dynamic viscosity is a direct measure of the internal resistance of a liquid to flow.
> - Kinematic viscosity is the dynamic viscosity divided by its density.
> - At low values of the dimensionless Reynolds number laminar flow occurs; at higher values of Reynolds number turbulent flow occurs.
> - Civil engineering applications will normally involve turbulent flow.
> - In real situations, Bernoulli's equation has to be modified to take account of frictional losses.
> - The friction factor λ in turbulent flow depends on relative pipe roughness and Reynolds number.

Question for practice

The discharge from an old sewer 365 m long when flowing full has been measured as 25 l/s. The pipe diameter is 225 mm and has an estimated surface roughness of 0.6 mm. Taking the kinematic viscosity as 1.14 mm^2/s, calculate the head loss in the pipe.

REFERENCES

Barr DIH (1981) Solution of the Colebrook–White function for resistance to uniform turbulent flow. *ICE (Institution of Civil Engineers) Proceedings* **71**: 529–535, http://dx.doi.org/10.1680/iicep.1981.1895.

Blasius H (1913) Das Ähnlichkeitsgesetz bei Reibungsvorgängen in Flüssigkeiten. *Forschungs-arbeit des Ingenieur-wesens*, Springer, Berlin, p. 131 (in German).

Colebrook C (1939) Turbulent flow in pipes with particular reference to the transition region between the smooth and rough pipe laws. *ICE Proceedings* **12**: 393–422, http://dx.doi.org/10.1680/ijoti.1939.13150.

Colebrook CF and White CM (1937) Experiments with fluid-friction in roughened pipes. *Proceedings of the Royal Society, London* **161**: 367–381, http://dx.doi.org/10.1098/rspa.1937.0150.

Cross H (1936) Analysis of flows in networks of conduits or conductors. *University of Illinois Engineering Experiment Station Bulletin* **286**.

Darcy H (1857) *Recherches Expérimentales Relatives au Mouvement de l'Eau dans les Tuyaux.* Mallet-Bachelier, Paris, France (in French).

Fanning JT (1877) *A Practical Treatise on Water-Supply Engineering.* Van Nostrand, New York, NY, USA.

Hagen G (1839) Ueber die Bewegung des Wassers in Engen Cylindrischen Röhren. *Annalen der Physik und Chemie* **46**: 423–442 (in German).

Hagenbach E (1860) Ueber die Bestimmung der Zähigkeit Einer Flüssigkeit Durch den Ausfluss aus Röhren. *Annalen der Physik und Chemie* **109**: 385–426.

Hydraulics Research (1990) *Charts for the hydraulic design of channels and pipes*, 6th edn. Thomas Telford, London, UK.

Jacobson H (1860) Beiträge zur. *Haemodynamik Archiv für Anatomie, Physiologie und wissenschaftliche Medicin* **80**: 80-113 (in German).

Moody LF (1944) Friction factors for pipe flow. *Trans. ASME* **66**: 671–678.

Nikuradse J. (1933) Strömungsgesetze in Rauhen Rohren. *Forschungs-Arbeit des Ingenieur-Wesens*, p. 361 (in German).

Poiseuille JL-M (1840a) Recherches expérimentales sur le mouvement des liquides dans les tubes de très petits diamètres. *Comptes Rendus*, **11**: 961–967 (in French).

Poiseuille JL-M (1840b) Recherches expérimentales sur le mouvement des liquides dans les tubes de très petits diamètres. *Comptes Rendus*, **11**: 1041–1048 (in French).

Poiseuille JL-M (1841) Recherches expérimentales sur le mouvement des liquides dans les tubes de très petits diamètres. *Comptes Rendus* **12**: 112–115 (in French).

Reynolds O (1883) An experimental investigation of the circumstances which determine whether the motion of water shall be direct or sinuous, and of the law of resistance in parallel channels. *Philosophical Transactions of the Royal Society* **174**: 935–982, http://dx.doi.org/10.1098/rspl.1883.0018.

Reynolds O (1884) On the two manners of motion of water. *Proceedings of the Royal Institution*, **11**: 44–52, 354–363.

Rouse H (1943) Evaluation of boundary roughness. *Proceedings of the Second Hydraulics Conference*, University of Iowa Studies in Engineering, Bulletin No. 27.

Schiller L and Eisner F (1932) *Strömungslehre der Rohre und Offenen Gerinne auf Experimenteller Grundlage.* Akademische Verlagsgesellschaft, Leipzig, Germany (in German).

Stokes GG (1845) On the internal friction of fluids in motion. *Transactions of the Cambridge Philosophical Society* **8**: 287–305, http://dx.doi.org/10.1017/CBO9780511702266.002.

von Kármán T (1930) Mechanische Aehnlichkeit und Turbulenz. *Proceedings of the Third International Congress for Applied Mechanics* (Oseen CW and Weibull W (eds)). Stockholm, Sweden, vol. 1, pp. 79–93 (in German).

Weisbach J (1845) *Lehrbuch der Ingenieur- und Maschinen-Mechanik.* Vol. 1. Vieweg und Sohn, Braunschweig, Germany (in German).

FURTHER READING

Jackson D and Launder B (2007) Osborne Reynolds and the publication of his papers on turbulent flow. *Annual Review of Fluid Mechanics* **39**: 19–35.

Hydraulics for Civil Engineers
ISBN 978-0-7277-5845-3

ICE Publishing: All rights reserved
http://dx.doi.org/10.1680/hce.58453.053

4
Turbines and pumps

Learning aims

After studying this chapter you should be able to

- explain the principal differences between impulse and reaction turbines and how this influences their selection for particular applications
- appreciate that the energy transformations that occur within turbines can be investigated using Bernoulli's equation
- explain the principal differences between centrifugal, axial and mixed-flow pumps and how this influences their selection for particular applications
- explain the concept of specific speed of pumps and turbines
- calculate the power output of turbines and power input of pumps, taking account of their efficiencies
- determine head–discharge relationships for rising mains and compare these with pump characteristics to obtain the duty points of a pump
- have an awareness of the mechanism of cavitation and the damage that this may cause to turbines and pumps.

4.1. Introduction

Turbines and pumps are machines that are designed to convert energy from one form to another. We will concentrate on machines involving mechanical energy that is rotary in nature. In the case of a turbine energy from a fluid is converted into mechanical energy and in the case of a pump the conversion is the other way round. A further conversion from or to electrical energy may also be involved.

4.2. Turbines
4.2.1 Impulse turbines

These rely on the transfer of momentum from the incoming jet to the buckets and include the original water wheels. The static pressure within impulse turbines is atmospheric.

A major improvement was achieved by Pelton in 1880. In the Pelton wheel a high speed jet of liquid strikes a series of buckets mounted around the circumference, called the runner, of a wheel (Figure 4.1). Only a single bucket is being struck at any point in time, unless multiple jets are included. A splitter ridge on each bucket divides the incoming jet into two equal parts that are sent by the bucket almost

Figure 4.1 Pelton wheel

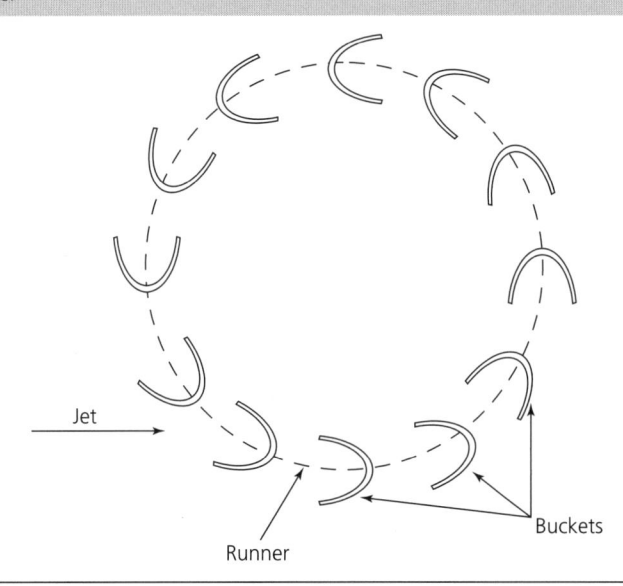

back in the opposite direction from the direction of the original jet, as indicated in Figure 4.2. In theory the maximum effect would be if the deflection angle θ was 180°, but there are practical difficulties in achieving this. In its original form, as with the traditional water wheels, the shaft is horizontal with a single jet. It is possible to use up to six jets if a vertical shaft is used.

The momentum equation is applied to a control volume of liquid to find the component of force exerted by the bucket on the fluid in the direction of the incoming jet. A complicating factor is that the bucket itself will be moving with a velocity V_b away from the jet. We therefore need to be careful to

Figure 4.2 Pelton wheel bucket

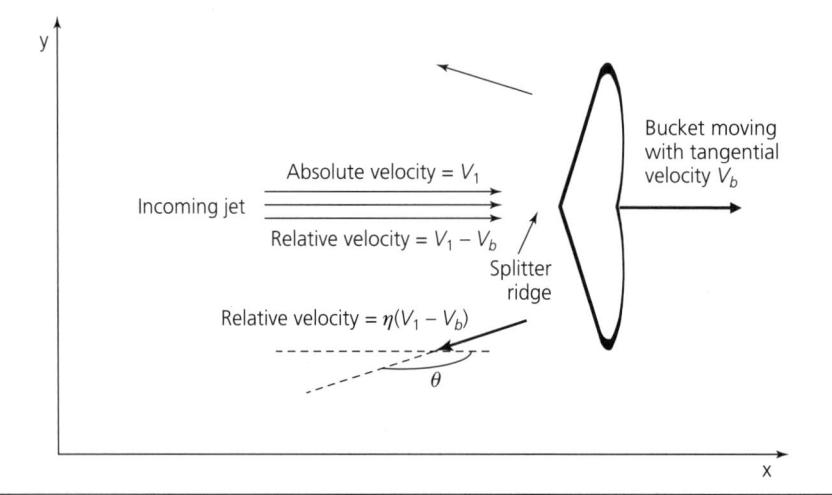

distinguish between absolute velocities and relative velocities. Using the coordinate system and sign convention shown in Figure 4.2, the momentum equation gives the force applied to the liquid by the bucket in the x direction as

$$-F_{RX} = \rho Q(V_{2Xr} - V_{1Xr}) \tag{4.1}$$

where V_{1Xr} and V_{2Xr} indicate the relative velocities between the fluid and the moving bucket before and after the jet strikes the bucket.

For the incoming jet

$$V_{1Xr} = V_1 - V_b \tag{4.2}$$

and for the liquid after deflection by the bucket

$$V_{2Xr} = -\eta(V_1 - V_b)\cos\theta \tag{4.3}$$

where η is the percentage of the original relative velocity maintained in the deflected jet.

Substituting these into the momentum equation we obtain

$$-F_{RX} = \rho Q[\eta(V_1 - V_b)\cos\theta - (V_1 - V_b)] \tag{4.4}$$

Since

$$Q = AV_1 \tag{4.5}$$

we can write

$$-F_{RX} = \rho A V_1[\eta(V_1 - V_b)\cos\theta - (V_1 - V_b)] = \rho A V_1(V_1 - V_b)(\eta\cos\theta - 1) \tag{4.6}$$

An equal and opposite force is exerted by the jet of fluid on the bucket.

The power generated by the force acting on the bucket is the rate of doing work. This is equivalent to the force times the bucket speed. Hence

$$\text{power} = \rho A V_1 V_b (V_1 - V_b)(\eta\cos\theta - 1) \tag{4.7}$$

Simple calculus shows that maximum power will be obtained if V_b equals $0.5V_1$. This would result in the absolute velocity of the liquid leaving the bucket being zero with the whole of the kinetic energy in the jet being transferred to the bucket.

4.2.2 Reaction turbines

These differ from impulse turbines in being completely under fluid pressure. Drawing on earlier work the Francis turbine was developed in the middle of the nineteenth century. This usually has a vertically mounted shaft with the fluid entering a spiral volute horizontally under pressure (Figure 4.3). From the volute stationary guide vanes direct the fluid onto the curved vanes of the central runner where kinetic energy is transferred to the runner. The cross-sectional area of the volute decreases round the spiral in

Figure 4.3 Francis turbine

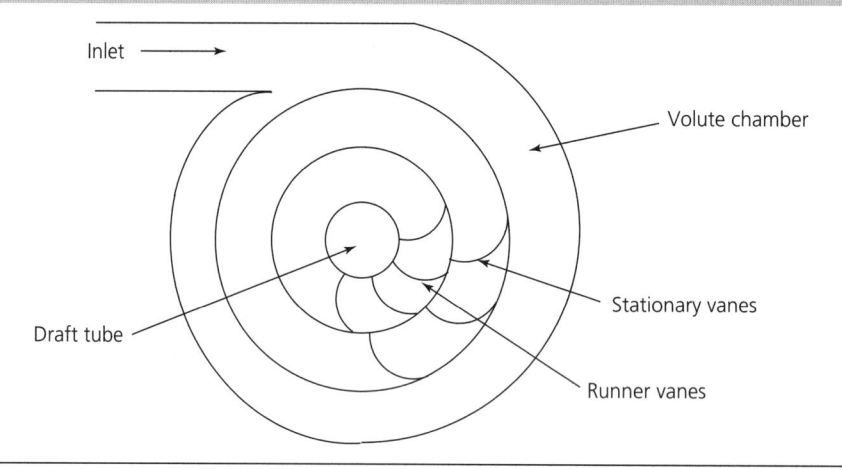

an attempt to maintain a constant radial velocity as some of the fluid passes through to the central draft tube. This vertical tube is submerged in fluid in the tail race to ensure the turbine remains full of fluid.

In the Kaplan turbine (Figure 4.4) the shaft is usually mounted vertically with the fluid entering horizontally. As with the Francis turbine, guide vanes deflect the flow towards the centre of the turbine. However the flow is then turned into the vertical direction where it passes through the runner which usually has four or six vanes. A characteristic of this type is the ability to adjust the pitch of the vanes for maximum efficiency.

Reaction turbines can be characterised by the energy E transferred to the fluid per unit weight of the fluid. Using subscript 1 to denote input conditions and subscript 2 to denote outlet conditions,

Figure 4.4 Kaplan turbine

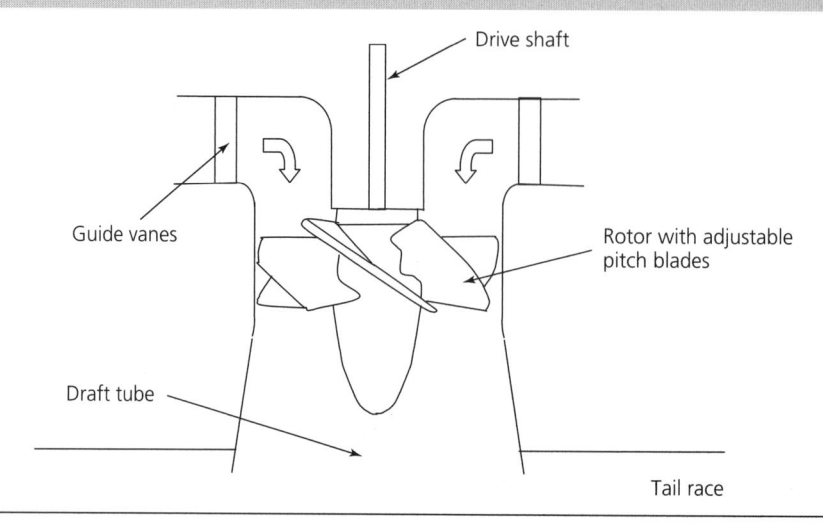

Bernoulli's equation becomes

$$\frac{P_1}{\rho g} + \frac{V_1^2}{2g} = E + \frac{P_2}{\rho g} + \frac{V_2^2}{2g} \tag{4.8}$$

Hence

$$E = \frac{P_1 - P_2}{\rho g} + \frac{V_1^2 - V_2^2}{2g} \tag{4.9}$$

with the first fraction representing the drop in static pressure in the fluid and the second fraction representing the drop in velocity head in the fluid.

4.2.3 Comparison of turbine types

Comparison of the three turbine types considered in this chapter are summarised in Table 4.1. The Pelton wheel needs high pressure difference to generate the high velocity jet. A practical limit to the head at which reaction turbines can operate is provided by the ability of seals to resist the internal pressures.

An aid to comparison is the specific speed N_s. It is defined as the speed of the turbine in rpm needed to develop a power of 1 kW when operating under a static head of 1 m. The power output of a turbine can be expressed in terms of the specific speed.

$$\text{Output power in kW} = \left(\frac{N_s}{N}\right)^2 H^{5/2} \text{ where } N \text{ is the runner speed in rpm} \tag{4.10}$$

There are various definitions of the efficiency of a turbine, for example hydraulic efficiency takes account of losses due to friction and shock effects. However the most useful is that of overall efficiency.

$$\text{Overall efficiency} \, \eta = \frac{\text{power output from shaft}}{\text{hydraulic power input}} \tag{4.11}$$

For an impulse turbine the power input is $0.5 \rho Q V_1^2$ and for a reaction turbine it is $\rho g H Q$ where V_1 is the velocity of the jet impinging on the impulse turbine bucket and H is the head difference between the inlet and the tailwater outlet of the reaction turbine.

Table 4.1 Comparison of turbines

	Pelton wheel	Francis turbine	Kaplan turbine
Suitable for heads	Typically 90 to 900 m unsuitable for low heads	Typically 10 to 400 m can be susceptible to leakage above 400 m	Typically 3 to 10 m but up to 50 m
Discharge	Low	Intermediate	High
Specific speed rpm	12 to 60	60 to 500	280 to 800
Typical power output	80 to 300 MW	10 to 300 MW	20 to 100 MW

Example 4.1

Turbines are to be installed as part of a hydro-electric scheme. The available head is 50 m and a flow rate of 15 m³/s of water is expected to be available for each turbine. The chosen Francis turbines will have a specific speed of 180 and will run at 500 rpm. Determine the efficiency of the turbines in this situation.

Hydraulic power input $= \rho g H Q = 1000 \times 9.81 \times 15 \times 50$ W $= 7357.5 \times 10^3$ W $=$ 7358 kW (4.12)

$$\text{Power output} = \left(\frac{N_s}{N}\right)^2 H^{5/2} = \left(\frac{180}{500}\right)^2 \times 75^{5/2} = 6313 \text{ kW} \qquad (4.13)$$

The overall efficiency is given by

$$\eta = \frac{\text{power output}}{\text{power input}} = \frac{6313}{7358} = 0.86 \qquad (4.14)$$

4.2.4 Use of turbines for power generation

The main use of turbines is in hydroelectric generation. The hydro-electric plant at Cragside in Northumberland in the UK was an early application. The world's largest hydro-electric scheme, the Three Gorges in China, like the earlier record holder, the Colorado scheme in the USA, uses Francis turbines. The large reservoirs needed to support such power generation schemes inevitably leads to environmental concerns.

In recent years there has been an increasing interest in the use of micro- and mini-hydroelectric power generation. These are generally 'run of the river' low head situations where Kaplan turbines are usually appropriate. Like their larger cousins, these are not immune from environmental concerns. While they are a renewable power source, their use needs to be balanced against possible impacts on flood defence, water ecology and fishery interests. The Environment Agency is still developing policies to achieve a balance between these sometimes conflicting issues.

Revision points

- Turbines are machines for converting energy of moving water into useful mechanical, and often ultimately electrical, energy.
- Impulse turbines, such as the Pelton wheel, operate at atmospheric pressure and rely on the transfer of momentum from incoming jet(s) of water to buckets mounted on a circular runner.
- Calculations using the momentum equation for an impulse turbine need to be based on the relative velocity between the incoming jet and the moving bucket rather than absolute velocities.
- In theory maximum power from an impulse turbine is obtained when the tangential velocity of the buckets is equal to half of that of the incoming jet.
- Reaction turbines, such as the Francis and Kaplan turbines, operate under fluid pressure.

- In the Francis turbine the inflowing water is directed towards vanes on a rotating runner. In the process of passing through the runner the direction of flow changes from radial to axial and a large proportion of the total head in the water is transferred as kinetic energy to the runner.
- In the Kaplan turbine flow is directed towards blades on an impeller.
- Turbines are characterised by their specific speed. Impulse turbines are low-discharge, high-head machines with a low specific speed. Kaplan turbines are high-discharge, low-head with a high specific speed. Francis turbines are intermediate between these.
- While turbines can provide renewable energy, they are not without their own environmental impacts.

4.3. Pumps
4.3.1 Centrifugal pumps

These, shown in Figure 4.5, are the equivalent of the Francis turbine. Liquid enters at the centre of the impeller from the suction tube and is thrown out into the outer part of the volute by the vanes of the rotating impeller. As the liquid enters the pump it has a high velocity and low pressure. As it flows through the pump the area of flow expands with a resulting drop in velocity and, as a consequence of Bernoulli's equation, an increase in hydraulic pressure. The outflow occurs at right angles to the input to the pump.

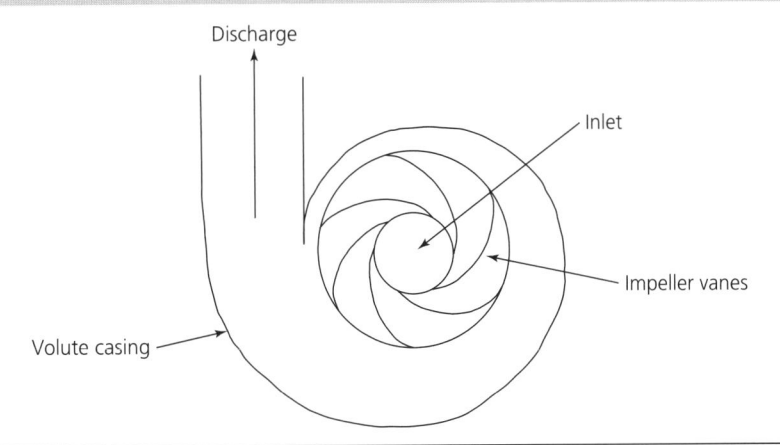

4.3.2 Axial flow pumps

These consist of a linear tube containing an impeller as illustrated in Figure 4.6. The liquid enters and leaves the pump along its axis. The blade angle of the impeller may be fixed or variable. However the former are only efficient over a narrow range of discharge. The fixed guide vanes at the outlet side of the impeller convert the rotational motion of the liquid imparted by the impeller back into axial flow. Sometimes guide vanes may also be provided on the inlet side, though these have a limited beneficial effect.

It is necessary to limit the amount of suction lift to avoid cavitation problems: see later section on cavitation in turbines and pumps.

Figure 4.5 Centrifugal pump

Figure 4.6 Axial flow pump

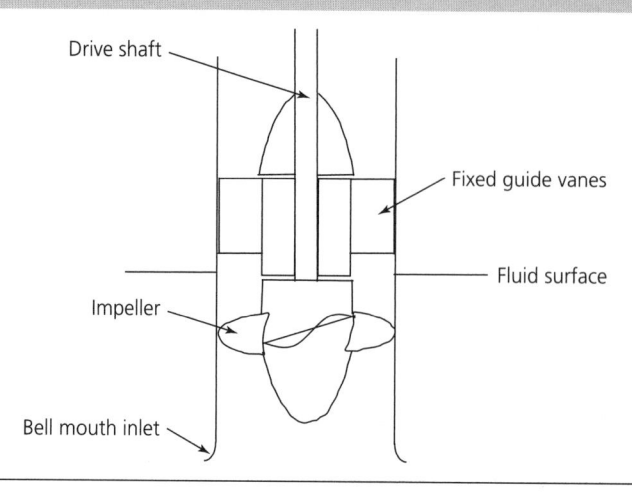

(Diagram showing: Drive shaft, Fixed guide vanes, Fluid surface, Impeller, Bell mouth inlet)

4.3.3 Mixed flow pumps

A third type of rotodynamic pump is a hybrid, mixed flow pump. In this the blades of the impeller are orientated so that although the fluid enters in a similar manner to that of an axial flow pump, it leaves with both radial and axial components.

Such pumps combine the ability of radial flow centrifugal pumps to work with high pressure with that of axial flow pumps to cope with high volumes. Some authors, for example Franzini and Finnemore (1997), classify these within the category of centrifugal pumps.

4.3.4 Comparison of pump types

Table 4.2 sets out the principle characteristics of the three types of rotodynamic pump. It needs to be appreciated that in reality these reflect a progression of impeller types, hence the variation in classification referred to in the preceding section.

As with turbines a useful term is the specific speed or type number of a pump. Unfortunately there are a number of different definitions of specific speed. One of the most commonly used is the speed in rpm

Table 4.2 Comparison of pumps

	Centrifugal radial flow	Mixed flow	Axial flow
Fluid entry direction	Axial	Axial	Axial
Discharge direction	Radial	Between axial and radial	Axial
Impeller type	Vanes	Mixture of vanes and impeller	Impeller
Operational speed	High	Intermediate	Low
Size	Small	Large	Very large
Head	High	Intermediate	Low
Discharge	Low	Intermediate	Large
Specific speed in rpm to achieve 1 m^3/s against a 1 m head	10 to 50	40 to 200	160 upwards

needed to discharge 1 m³/s under a 1 m head, which is given by

$$N_s = \frac{NQ^{1/2}}{H^{3/4}} \tag{4.15}$$

Having determined the specific speed requirement for a particular duty, the type of pump may be selected, using for example the information in the final row of Table 4.2.

Example 4.2

What type of pump is required to operate at 5000 rpm to produce a flow rate of 25 m³/s against a head of 3 m?

$$N_s = \frac{NQ^{0.5}}{H^{0.75}} = \frac{5000 \times 25^{0.5}}{3^{0.75}} = 11.0 \tag{4.16}$$

From Table 4.2, a centrifugal radial flow pump is appropriate.

4.3.5 Power required by a pump

$$\text{The power required by a pump} = \frac{\rho g H Q}{\eta} \tag{4.17}$$

where η is its overall efficiency. The efficiency is not a constant but varies with discharge and it is usual for pump manufacturers to supply efficiency against discharge curves.

4.3.6 Matching of pump to rising main characteristics

As well as efficiency plotted against discharge curves, manufacturers also supply graphs showing the head against discharge for their pumps. By plotting the head loss plotted against discharge for the pipe system into which the pump is to be introduced on the same graph, it is possible to determine the duty point and establish the efficiency and hence power requirement. The approach is illustrated in the following example.

Example 4.3

A pump is used to lift water from a river intake to a reservoir; the static lift is 22 m. The connecting pipeline is 2.5 km long, 300 mm diameter and the Darcy friction factor (λ) is assumed to be 0.033. [Strictly speaking, as outlined in Chapter 3, λ is not constant, depending on Reynolds number, and thus will not be independent of discharge. However common practice is to ignore the variation in pump design]. Pump characteristics are shown in Table 4.3.

Table 4.3

Discharge Q: m³/s	0	0.05	0.10	0.15	0.20	0.25
Pump head H: m	55.0	53.0	49.0	44.0	36.0	27.0
Efficiency η: %	0	47	73	77	62	29

Determine the discharge and head across the pump and hence the power input required.

The cross-sectional area of the pipe

$$A = \pi \times 0.15^2 = 0.070\,69 \text{ m}^2 \qquad (4.18)$$

Substituting

$$V = \frac{Q}{A} \qquad (4.19)$$

into

$$H = 22 + \frac{V^2}{2g} + \frac{\lambda L V^2}{2gD} \qquad (4.20)$$

gives the values shown in Table 4.4 for system head.

Table 4.4

Discharge Q: m³/s	0	0.05	0.10	0.15	0.20	0.25
System head H: m	22.0	29.0	50.2	85.3	134.6	198.0

The values of pump head, system head and efficiency against discharge are plotted in Figure 4.7. From this it can be seen that the duty point is a head of 50 m at a discharge of 0.10 m³/s. At this point the pump has an efficiency of about 73%.

Hence

$$\text{the input power required} = \frac{\rho g H Q}{\eta} = \frac{1000 \times 9.81 \times 50 \times 0.10}{0.73} = 67 \times 10^3 \text{ W [67 kW]} \qquad (4.21)$$

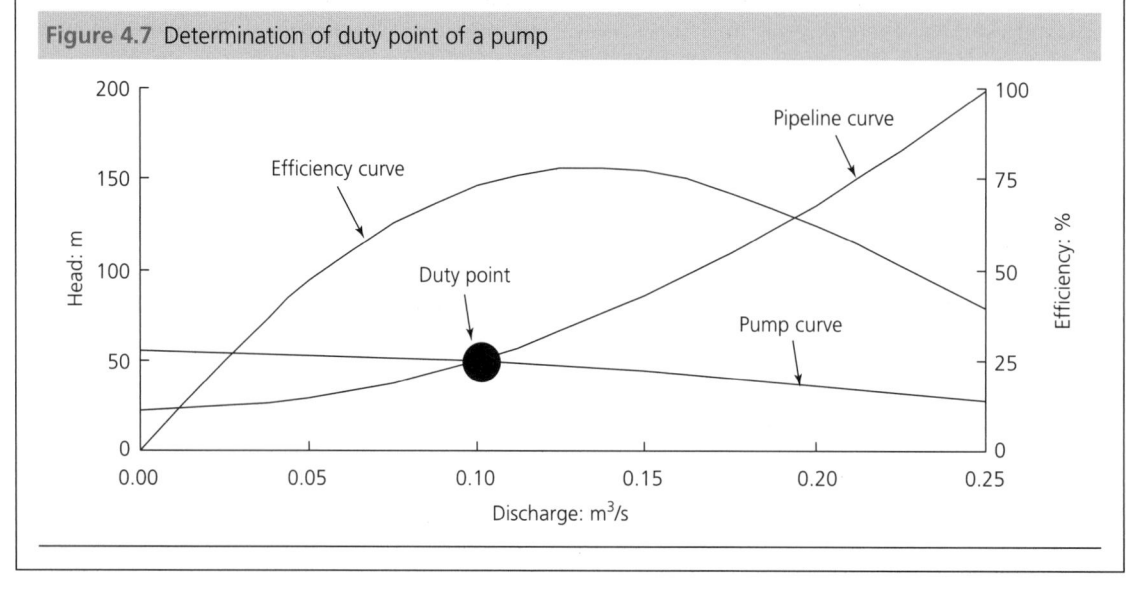

Figure 4.7 Determination of duty point of a pump

Revision points

- Pumps can be classified as centrifugal, axial flow or mixed flow.
- Centrifugal pumps operate at a high head with a low discharge.
- Axial flow pumps operate with high discharges at a low head.
- By comparing pump and system heads at different discharges, the duty point can be established.

4.4. Cavitation in turbines and pumps

Under reduced pressures, the boiling point of a fluid is reduced and bubbles of gas may form. These may suddenly collapse with the fluid rushing in to fill the cavity and high pressures being generated locally over short periods of time. This phenomenon is called cavitation. Continued cycles of the effect may cause failure of components.

Care must be taken to ensure that critical values of 'net positive suction head' do not develop within turbines and pumps. In turbines the effect is most likely to occur on the trailing edge of the turbine blades and in the draft tube. In pumps the most vulnerable area for the effect is at the inlet.

Chapter summary

- Turbines convert the energy of moving water into mechanical and often ultimately electrical energy.
- Low-discharge, high-head impulse turbines, including the Pelton wheel, rely on momentum transfer and can be analysed using the momentum equation.
- Francis and Kaplan turbines operate under fluid pressure, differing from each other in terms of flow directions through them.
- Kaplan turbines are high-discharge, low-head machines.
- Francis turbines are intermediate between Pelton wheels and Kaplan turbines in terms of discharge and operating head.
- Centrifugal pumps operate at a high head with low discharge.
- Axial flow pumps operate with high discharges at a low head.
- The duty point of a pump can be established by comparing pump and system heads at different discharges.
- Care needs to be taken to avoid cavitation resulting in damage to turbines and pumps.

Question for practice

To deliver 1 m^3/s of water against a head of 8.5 m, the energy input to a pump is 125 kW. At what overall efficiency is the pump operating?

REFERENCES

Engineering Services Data Unit (2003) *Radial, Mixed and Axial Flow Pumps: Introduction.* ESDU, London, UK.

Franzini JB and Finnemore EJ (1997) *Fluid Mechanics with Engineering Applications*, 9th edn. McGraw-Hill, New York, NY, USA.

Pelton LA (1880) *Water-wheel*. US Patent Office Patent No. 233692.

FURTHER READING

Girdhar P and Moniz O (2004) *Practical Centrifugal Pumps: Design Operation and Maintenance.* Newnes, Oxford.

Layton ET (1992) *From Rule of Thumb to Scientific Engineering: James B. Francis and the Invention of the Francis Turbine* (NLA Monograph Series). Research Foundation of the State University of New York, Stony Brook, NY.

Renewables First (2013) *Hydropower Learning Centre.* Available at http://www.renewablesfirst.co.uk/hydro-learning-centre/(accessed/08/13).

Hydraulics for Civil Engineers
ISBN 978-0-7277-5845-3

ICE Publishing: All rights reserved
http://dx.doi.org/10.1680/hce.58453.065

5
Steady uniform flow in open channels

> **Learning aims**
>
> After studying this chapter you should be able to
>
> - appreciate aesthetic and environmental issues related to channel design
> - derive basic parameters to describe flow in open channels
> - make use of Manning's equation to calculate velocities and discharge rates for simple and compound cross-sections
> - proportion dimensions of a channel to produce economically efficient cross-sections.

5.1. Introduction

Open channel applies to any passage through which liquid is flowing when the free surface of the liquid is open to atmospheric pressure. This will include rivers as well as man-made structures such as spillways and, when they are not flowing full, sewer pipes.

Flow in open channels has certain similarities to flow in pipes which are flowing full. The boundary of the channel transmits a shearing force, converting energy into heat and resulting in a heat loss.

The analysis of open channel flows is generally more complex than pipes since there is an infinite variety of shapes and sizes, types of boundary and complex flow patterns. Flow in open channels is generally assumed to be turbulent. As in pipe flow, although velocity of flow will vary at different points in the cross-section, all calculations will generally be based on the mean velocity of flow.

The concepts of steady and uniform flow will again be needed for considering open channel situations. We saw earlier that steady flow is constant over time and uniform flow is flow through a constant cross-sectional area. This chapter will be based on such conditions. Under these conditions the depth of flow is termed the normal depth. The following chapter will consider the effect of changes in cross-section. In both this and the following chapter the fluid in the channels under consideration is water.

5.2. Sustainable design of river channels

In designing river channels the engineer can have a large influence on the human and natural environment. The tendency in the past has been to concentrate solely on hydraulic performance leading in urban areas to the production of straight regular-sectioned concrete or steel-lined channels. This is monotonous from an aesthetic aspect and environmentally damaging. In urban areas such an

Figure 5.1 Concrete-lined channel through urban area (River Can, Chelmsford, UK)

approach has also encouraged development up to the edge of the river but facing away from it with the river being treated as something 'to hide away in the back yard'. Figure 5.1 shows such a canalised river, during a period when the water level was lowered for maintenance purposes, and indicates how it has been used as a dumping ground for supermarket trolleys and the like. In rural areas the emphasis for a long time was on efficient drainage to increase agricultural production, linked with a lowering of the water table and the removal of hedges along the river banks. The impact of such approaches were explored by Purseglove (1988) who also pointed out that imposing artificial courses on rivers could lead to long-term maintenance problems, citing not only well-known large-scale effects such as on the Mississippi, but also smaller-scale problems such as those that occurred on the Afon Trannon in Wales following engineering works in the 1970s. He drew attention to the need to work with, rather than against, nature and drew attention to the need for river engineering design to consider more than just the hydraulic aspects that are the subject of this and the following chapter. A need to be aware of ecological and geomorphological processes (Leeks *et al.*, 1988) is also needed. Examples of approaches to river engineering that were sympathetic to the environment were contained in Lewis and Williams (1984). The need for an integrated approach to river management has been given further emphasis by the introduction of the European Union's Water Framework Directive. To support this directive the Environment Agency commissioned an online design guide to fluvial design.

The concluding message of this section is that, although much of this and the next chapter consider regularly shaped channels to illustrate principles of hydraulic design of river channels, this does not mean the channels you design have to be trapezoidal or rectangular in cross-section, all lined with concrete or steel!

Steady uniform flow in open channels

Figure 5.2 Hydraulic radius for some common channel cross-sections

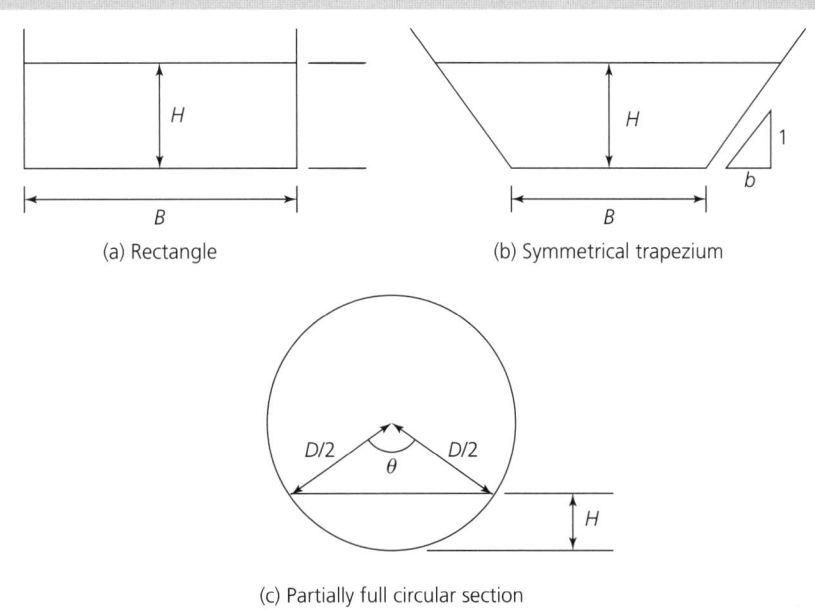

(a) Rectangle

(b) Symmetrical trapezium

(c) Partially full circular section

5.3. Basic definitions
5.3.1 Wetted perimeter and hydraulic radius

Figure 5.2 illustrates these for some simple channel cross-sections. For a rectangular section of width B and water depth H, the wetted perimeter $P = B + 2H$ and the hydraulic radius R is defined by the equation $R = A/P$, where A is the cross-sectional area of the channel. This leads to

$$R = \frac{BH}{B + 2H} \tag{5.1}$$

For a symmetrical trapezoidal section where the bottom width is B and the sides slope at an angle of 1 in b to the horizontal, the wetted perimeter is

$$P = B + 2H\sqrt{1 + b^2} \tag{5.2}$$

the cross-sectional area

$$A = (B + bH)H \tag{5.3}$$

and the hydraulic radius

$$R = \frac{A}{P} = \frac{(B + bH)H}{B + 2H\sqrt{1 + b^2}} \tag{5.4}$$

For a circular pipe of diameter D filled to a depth H the wetted perimeter may be found from the standard arc length formula as

$$P = \frac{\theta D}{2} \tag{5.5}$$

where the angle θ in radians is shown in Figure 5.2(c).

The area of the water filled segment is

$$A = \frac{1}{2}(\theta - \sin \theta) \times \left(\frac{D}{2}\right)^2 = \frac{1}{8}D^2(\theta - \sin \theta) \tag{5.6}$$

The hydraulic radius is

$$R = \frac{A}{P} = \frac{\frac{1}{8}D^2(\theta - \sin \theta)}{\frac{\theta D}{2}} = \frac{D}{4\theta}(\theta - \sin \theta) \tag{5.7}$$

It can also be shown that

$$\theta = 2\cos^{-1}\left(1 - \frac{2H}{D}\right) \tag{5.8}$$

The hydraulic radius has significance in the calculation of flow rates described later in this chapter.

5.3.2 Hydraulic mean depth

The hydraulic mean depth m is defined as the ratio of the cross-sectional area to the width of the water surface. For a channel of rectangular cross-section, this will be the same as the actual depth H.

5.3.3 Froude number and flow type

Many aspects of open channel flow can be characterised by the Froude number. This is a non-dimensional term derived from the ratio of the stream velocity to the velocity (or celerity) at which the wave form resulting from a surface disturbance would be propagated. From this ratio, the following expression for the Froude number is obtained

$$Fr = \frac{V}{\sqrt{gm}} \tag{5.9}$$

A value of Fr equal to unity defines what is known as the critical condition. The critical depth is when

$$Fr = 1.0 \tag{5.10}$$

For subcritical flow (Fr less than 1) the flow can be described as tranquil or streaming. Should a disturbance occur, by for example an object placed into the water, the resulting wave will be propagated upstream.

For supercritical flow (*Fr* greater than 1) the flow can be described as rapid or shooting. In this case a disturbance cannot be propagated upstream since the velocity of the flowing water is greater than the celerity of the wave.

Subcritical flow is associated with mild slopes and supercritical flow with steep slopes. The relationship between the type of flow and energy will be explored later in the chapter.

Example 5.1

A river has a bed width of 3 m wide and the banks slope uniformly at a gradient of 1 in 2.5. If the flow rate is 7 m³/s and the flow velocity is 2 m/s, determine the depth of flow and establish whether the flow is sub or supercritical.

From the continuity equation

$$A = \frac{Q}{V} = \frac{7}{2} = 3.5 \, m^2 \tag{5.11}$$

the cross-sectional area of a trapezoidal section is

$$A = (B + nH)H \tag{5.12}$$

Substituting the bed width of 3 m and the now known area of flow of 3.5 m² gives

$$3.5 = (3 + 2.5 \times H)H \tag{5.13}$$

hence

$$2.5H^2 + 3H - 3.5 = 0 \tag{5.14}$$

Using the quadratic formula

$$H = \frac{-3 \pm \sqrt{3^2 - 4 \times 2.5 \times (-3.5)}}{2 \times 2.5} \tag{5.15}$$

the only positive and hence meaningful root is

$$H = 0.727 \, m \tag{5.16}$$

the width of the water surface $= 3 + (2 \times 2.5/0.727) = 9.878 \, m$ (5.17)

the hydraulic mean depth $m = \dfrac{9.878}{3.5} = 2.822 \, m$ (5.18)

the Froude number

$$Fr = \frac{V}{\sqrt{gm}} = \frac{2}{\sqrt{9.81 \times 2.822}} = 0.380 \tag{5.19}$$

As this value is less than unity, the flow is subcritical.

> **Revision points**
>
> - Under conditions of steady flow and uniform flow, the depth of flow is called the normal depth.
> - The type of flow in an open channel can be characterised by the Froude number. A Froude number less than unity is subcritical and can be described as tranquil. A Froude number greater than unity indicates supercritical rapid flow conditions.

5.4. Discharge equations
5.4.1 Development of Chézy's and Manning's equations

Early work investigating discharge, predating investigations of flow in pipes, was carried out by Chézy (1769) when he was designing channels to supply water to Paris. By considering the equilibrium of forces parallel to the sloping bed on an uniformly flowing fluid, the shear stress was derived as

$$\tau_0 = \rho g R S_0 \tag{5.20}$$

where R is the hydraulic radius and S_0 is the bed slope expressed as a fraction.

The derivation assumes that τ_0 is constant across the wetted perimeter. While this may be true for engineered channels, it is likely that the variation of surface materials, especially between the bed and banks, of natural watercourses is likely to lead to inaccuracy. The derivation also assumes that S_0 is small.

A further assumption is that the shear stress is related to velocity by

$$\tau_0 = KV^2 \tag{5.21}$$

where K is a coefficient of roughness and leads to

$$V = \sqrt{\frac{\rho g}{K} R S_0} \tag{5.22}$$

$\sqrt{\rho g/K}$ can be replaced by the Chézy coefficient C to give

$$V = C\sqrt{R S_0} \tag{5.23}$$

It should be noted that, although described as a coefficient, C is not dimensionless. This is particularly significant when reading texts of North American origin. In the SI system, C has units of $m^{0.5}/s$.

A number of suggestions have been made for working values of C. The most widely accepted is that of Manning (1891 and 1895)

$$C = \frac{R^{1/6}}{n} \tag{5.24}$$

where n is what is now called Manning's roughness coefficient. This is often quoted without units but the caution on the use of North American texts again applies. The SI unit for n is $s/m^{1/3}$. Typical values of n are given in Chow (1981).

Substituting Manning's suggestion for C into Chézy's version gives

$$V = \frac{1}{n} R^{2/3} S_0^{1/2} \tag{5.25}$$

This is widely known as Manning's equation.

5.4.2 Use of Manning's equation for steady uniform flow in channel of simple geometry

Under these conditions the water surface is parallel to the bed of the channel with the depth of flow remaining constant. The depth of flow is called the normal depth and the hydraulic gradient is equal to the bed gradient.

Example 5.2

A water-conveying channel of constant symmetrical cross-section 0.9 m deep has top and bottom widths of 1.7 m and 0.5 m. The normal depth of flow is 0.75 m. The bed slope is 1 in 2600. Manning's n for the channel is 0.035 s/m$^{1/3}$. Calculate the steady flow rate in the channel.

The cross-section is sketched in Figure 5.3.

Figure 5.3 Flow in trapezoidal channel

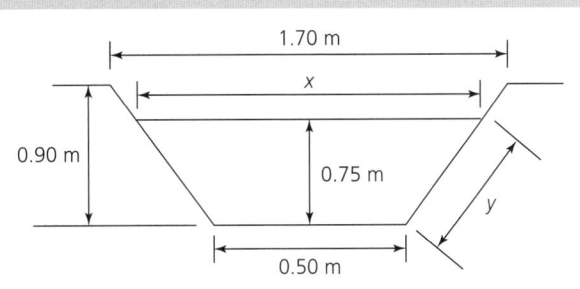

From the sketch it can be seen that the width of the top water surface is

$$x = 0.5 + 2\left(\frac{0.75}{0.90} \times 0.6\right) = 1.5\,\text{m} \tag{5.26}$$

and that the length of the wetted side slope is

$$y = \sqrt{0.75^2 + 0.50^2} = 0.9014\,\text{m} \tag{5.27}$$

Hence

the length of the wetted perimeter $P = 0.50 + 2 \times 0.9014 = 2.303$ m (5.28)

and the cross-sectional area of flow

$$A = 0.75\left(\frac{1.7 + 0.5}{2}\right) = 0.8250\,\text{m}^2 \tag{5.29}$$

The hydraulic radius

$$R = \frac{A}{P} = \frac{0.8250}{2.303} = 0.3582 \, \text{m} \tag{5.30}$$

Combining the continuity equation with Manning's equation gives

$$Q = \frac{A}{n} R^{2/3} S_0^{1/2} \tag{5.31}$$

or substituting the numerical values

$$Q = \frac{0.8250}{0.035} \times 0.3582^{2/3} \times \left(\frac{1}{2600}\right)^{1/2} = 0.23 \, \text{m}^3/\text{s} \tag{5.32}$$

As Manning's n was only given to two significant figures, it is not possible to rely on a value of flow rate beyond the same precision.

5.4.3 Use of Manning's equation for steady uniform flow in compound channels

In practice, channels are not usually simple rectangles or trapezoids in cross-section. Typically there may be a combination of low-flow and high-flow sections. The velocity of flow will not be constant across the channel due to both variations in depth and differing values of Manning's n.

For such circumstances it is necessary to divide the cross-section into a number of subsections. Traditionally vertical boundaries between subsections have been used as for example in Chadwick and Morfett (1998) and Hamill (2011). However there are other possibilities. A review was conducted by Fischenich (1997). Figure 5.4 shows by dashed lines possible approaches to division of the section: horizontally as line 1–1, inclined as lines 1–2 or vertically as lines 1–3. A further question is whether or not the divisions within the water are included within the wetted perimeter of the main channel. Based largely on work by Wormleaton and Merrett (1990) and earlier work by Wormleaton and co-workers, Fischenich concluded that for floodplain flow depths less than one third of the depth of the main channel horizontal division including the division surface within the wetted perimeter was preferable. However, for greater floodplain flow depths, the inclined divisions, excluding the division surfaces from the wetted perimeter, was appropriate.

Figure 5.4 Subdivision of a compound section

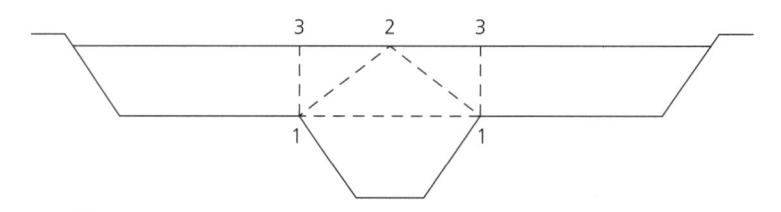

Example 5.3

Figure 5.5 shows a concrete lined channel through a town centre. The channel is 0.85 km long and is laid to an even fall along its length with a difference in level between each end of 1.3 m. Manning's n for the low-flow channel is 0.015 s/m$^{1/3}$ and for the remainder of the section is 0.020 s/m$^{1/3}$.

Figure 5.5 Example of a compound channel

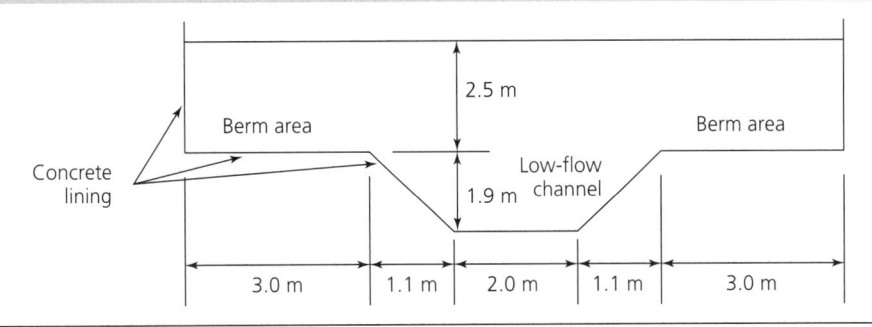

Using vertical subdivisions, determine the discharge

(a) when flow remains within the low-flow channel
(b) under flood conditions, when the depth of water across the berm areas is 2.5 m.

Longitudinal gradient $s_0 = 1.3/850 = 0.001\,529$ (5.33)

(a) For flow confined to the low-flow channel

inclined length of sloping bank $= \sqrt{1.1^2 + 1.9^2} = 2.195\,\text{m}$ (5.34)

$P = (2 \times 2.195) + 2 = 6.391\,\text{m}$ (5.35)

$A = 2 \times (1.9 + 1.1)/2 + (2 \times 1.9) = 6.80\,\text{m}^2$ (5.36)

$R = A/P = 6.80/6.391 = 1.064\,\text{m}$ (5.37)

$Q = \dfrac{A}{n} \times R^{2/3} \times s_0^{1/2} = \dfrac{6.80}{0.015} \times 1.064^{2.3} \times 0.001\,529^{1/2} = 18.5\,\text{m}^3/\text{s}$ (3 sig. figs)   (5.38)

(b) When the flow extends over the berms, we need to consider separately the central zone and the zones above the berm areas.

For the central zone

$A = 6.80 + 2.5 \times 3.0 = 14.3\,\text{m}^2$ (5.39)

under the traditional approach, the wetted perimeter is confined to the interface between the water and the bed, so P remains as 6.391 m

$$R = \frac{A}{P} = \frac{14.3}{6.391} = 2.237 \text{ m} \tag{5.40}$$

$$Q = \frac{A}{n} \times R^{2/3} \times s_0^{1/2} = \frac{14.3}{0.015} \times 2.237^{2/3} \times 0.001\,529^{1/2} = 63.8 \text{ m}^3/\text{s} \text{ (3 sig. figs)} \tag{5.41}$$

For the zones above the berm areas

$$A = 2 \times (3 \times 2.5) = 15.6 \text{ m}^2 \tag{5.42}$$

$$P = (2 \times 3) + (2 \times 2.5) = 11 \text{ m} \tag{5.43}$$

$$R = \frac{A}{P} = \frac{15.6}{11} = 1.418 \text{ m} \tag{5.44}$$

$$Q = \frac{A}{n} \times R^{2/3} \times s_0^{1/2} = \frac{15.6}{0.020} \times 1.418^{2/3} \times 0.001\,529^{1/2}$$

$$= 780 \times 1.26217 \times 0.039\,10 = 38.5 \text{ m}^3/\text{s} \tag{5.45}$$

Hence

the total flow under flood conditions $= 63.8 + 38.5 = 102.3 \text{ m}^3/\text{s}$ \hfill (5.46)

> **Revision points**
> - With steady uniform flow the water surface is parallel to the channel bed.
> - Manning's equation can be used to derive velocity of flow in open channels. With the additional use of the continuity equation discharge rates can be found.

5.5. Velocity variation over channel cross-section

We have so far assumed that velocity is constant in open channel flow. However, as with pipe flow, in reality it varies across the section. The frictional resistance of the boundaries causes the liquid to slow down near the bed and the sides, while the frictional resistance between the atmosphere and the liquid cause a slight reduction in velocity at the free surface. The maximum velocity occurs on the channel centre line, a little below the liquid surface as indicated for a rectangular section in Figure 5.6. The mean velocity occurs at about $0.4H$ above the bed and is about 85 per cent of the velocity at the surface.

5.6. Most economically efficient section
5.6.1 Principle

The most economical section will be that which gives the maximum discharge for a given volume of excavation. As discharge is proportional to velocity × cross-sectional area and excavation is proportional to cross-sectional area, the proportions of the most economical section are found by

Figure 5.6 Variation in velocity across channel cross-section

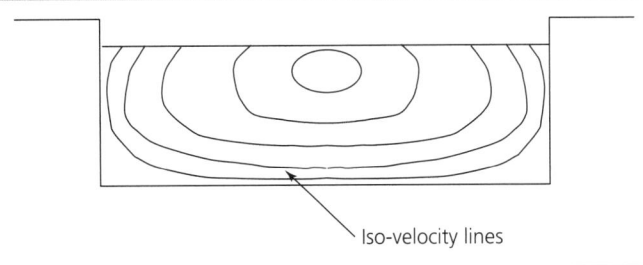

assuming the area to be constant and finding depth to give maximum velocity. This occurs when the wetted perimeter is a minimum.

5.6.2 Rectangular channel
For a channel as shown in Figure 5.2(a), the wetted perimeter is

$$P = B + 2H \tag{5.47}$$

But since the cross-sectional area

$$A = BH \tag{5.48}$$

$$P = A/H + 2H \tag{5.49}$$

Differentiation gives

$$\frac{dP}{dH} = \frac{-A}{H^2} + 2 \tag{5.50}$$

Putting this to zero and substituting

$$A = BH \tag{5.51}$$

gives

$$B = 2H \tag{5.52}$$

Thus the most economically efficient rectangular section giving maximum discharge for a given cross-sectional area is one having its width twice its depth.

5.6.3 Trapezoidal channel
It was shown earlier for the channel shown in Figure 5.2(b) that

$$A = (B + bH)H \tag{5.53}$$

Hence

$$B = \frac{A - bH^2}{H} = \frac{A}{H} - bH \tag{5.54}$$

Substituting this value in

$$P = B + 2H\sqrt{1+b^2} \tag{5.55}$$

gives

$$P = \frac{A}{H} - bH + 2H\sqrt{1+b^2} \tag{5.56}$$

Differentiating gives

$$\frac{dP}{dH} = \frac{-A}{H^2} - b + 2\sqrt{1+b^2} \tag{5.57}$$

Again substituting for A and placing this equal to zero gives the analysis yields

$$B + 2bH = 2H\sqrt{1+b^2} \tag{5.58}$$

The left-hand side of this equation may be recognised as the width of the top of the water surface and the right-hand side as the length of the wetted side slope.

5.6.4 Circular channel

The derivation of optimum depths for this case is more complicated. Unlike rectangular and trapezoidal sections, the area cannot be taken as a constant. Douglas *et al.* (1995) point out that there will come a point where the wetted perimeter increases rapidly compared to the increase in area. This results in the maximum velocity occurring when the depth of flow $H = 0.81D$ but with the maximum discharge occurring at $H = 0.95D$.

5.7. Specific energy
5.7.1 Introduction

For this and the subsequent chapter it is useful to look at the variation in energy along a channel. An adaptation of Bernoulli's equation is used.

Bakhmeteff (1912) introduced the concept of specific energy. The approach is similar to using the Bernoulli equation but instead of having an arbitrary horizontal datum, energies are calculated relative to the sloping bed of the channel.

The specific energy

$$E = H + \frac{\alpha V^2}{2g} \tag{5.59}$$

where α is a velocity distribution coefficient, usually taken as unity but having values up to 1.5 in natural watercourses. Throughout the rest of this book a value of 1.0 will be assumed giving the approximate equation

$$E = H + \frac{V^2}{2g} \tag{5.60}$$

Figure 5.7 Specific energy profile along an open channel

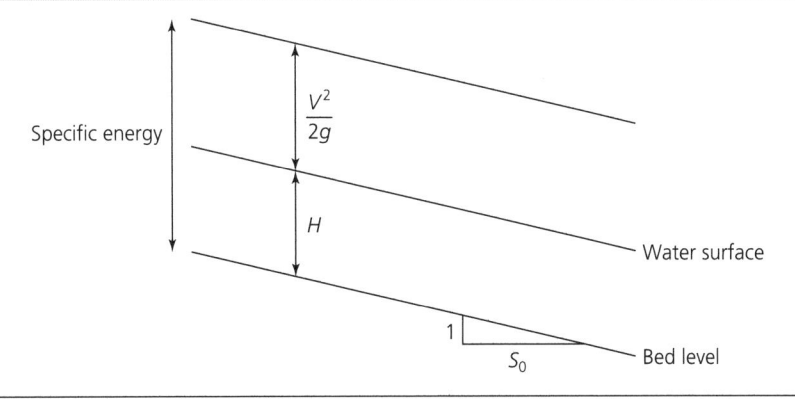

The specific energy may also be expressed in terms of the flow rate as

$$E = H + \frac{Q^2}{2gA^2} \tag{5.61}$$

For steady flow the energy gradient will be parallel to the bed as shown in Figure 5.7.

5.7.2 Critical depth and minimum value of specific energy of a rectangular channel and re-arranging for *H*

For a given channel section and flow rate there are two alternate values of depth that can lead to a particular value of specific energy. Under critical conditions these alternatives coincide and the specific energy has a minimum value.

The critical condition occurs when the Froude number

$$Fr = \frac{V}{\sqrt{gm}} = 1 \tag{5.62}$$

Using the specific energy equation expressed in terms of discharge

$$E = H + \frac{Q^2}{2gA^2} \tag{5.63}$$

and substituting

$$A = BH \tag{5.64}$$

$$E = H + \frac{Q^2}{2gB^2H^2} = H + \frac{Q^2 H^{-2}}{2gB^2} \tag{5.65}$$

Differentiating gives

$$\frac{dE}{dH} = 1 - \frac{Q^2}{gB^2 H^3} \tag{5.66}$$

Hydraulics for Civil Engineers

For a minimum value of E

$$\frac{Q^2}{gB^2H^3} = 1 \tag{5.67}$$

and re-arranging for H

$$H = \sqrt[3]{\frac{Q^2}{gB^2}} \tag{5.68}$$

This particular value is called the critical depth H_c.

It can be useful, as a first approximation, to consider wide channels as rectangular in cross-section, even though they actually have sloping sides.

Example 5.4

A wide channel conveys water at 8 m³/s per m width (q). Assuming the velocity distribution coefficient is unity, plot the variation between depth of flow and specific energy for flow depths between 0.5 m and 4.0 m. Determine the critical depth and verify that at this depth the Froude number is unity.

The calculation, assuming that we may treat the wide channel as rectangular in section, are summarised (see Table 5.1).

Table 5.1 Calculation of specific energy

H: m	$V = q/H$: m/s	$V^2/2g$: m	$E = H + V^2/2g$: m
0.50	16.000	13.048	13.548
0.75	10.660	5.800	6.550
1.00	8.000	3.262	4.262
1.50	5.333	1.450	2.950
2.00	4.000	0.815	2.815
2.50	3.200	0.522	3.022
3.00	2.667	0.362	3.362
3.50	2.286	0.266	3.766
4.00	2.000	0.204	4.204

The relationship is plotted in Figure 5.8 from where it can be seen that any particular value of specific energy can be achieved with two different values of water depth.

Replacing qB for Q gives

$$H_c = \sqrt[3]{\frac{q^2 B^2}{gB^2}} = \sqrt[3]{\frac{q^2}{g}} \tag{5.69}$$

Figure 5.8 Specific energy plotted against flow

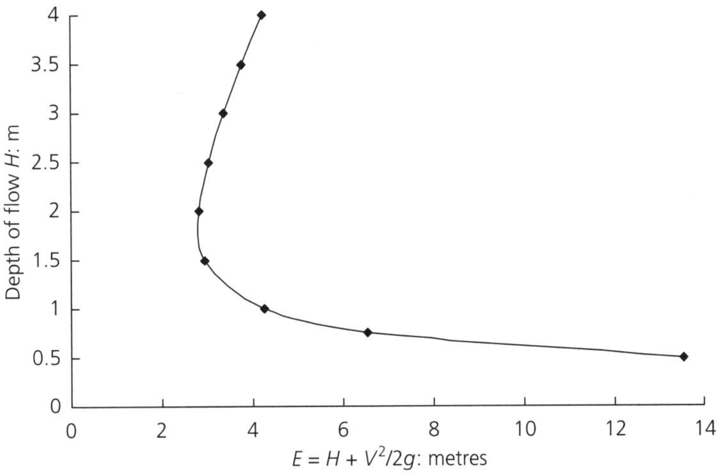
4
3.5
3
2.5
2
1.5
1
0.5
0
Depth of flow H: m
0
2
4
6
8
10
12
14
E = H + V²/2g: metres

and substituting the numerical values

$$H_c = \sqrt[3]{\frac{8^2}{9.81}} = 1.868\,\text{m}\,(3\,\text{sig. figs}) \tag{5.70}$$

The Froude number

$$Fr = \frac{V}{\sqrt{gm}} \tag{5.71}$$

For a rectangular channel the hydraulic mean depth m is equal to the actual depth, in this case H_c.

$$V = Q/A = qB/(BH_c) = q/H_c \tag{5.72}$$

This enables the Froude number to be restated as

$$Fr = \frac{q}{H_c\sqrt{gH_c}} \tag{5.73}$$

or substituting the numerical values

$$Fr = \frac{8}{1.868\sqrt{9.81 \times 1.868}} = 1 \tag{5.74}$$

5.7.3 Relationship between critical depth and minimum specific energy for rectangular section

Since the Froude number

$$Fr = \frac{V}{\sqrt{gH_c}} = 1 \qquad (5.75)$$

we can write

$$V^2 = gH_C \qquad (5.76)$$

Hence the specific energy at the critical depth

$$E = H_C + \frac{gH_C}{2g} = 1.5H_C \qquad (5.77)$$

or

$$H_C = \tfrac{2}{3}E \qquad (5.78)$$

Applying this to the previous example

$$E = 1.5H_C = 1.5 \times 1.868 = 2.802 \text{ m} \qquad (5.79)$$

This is compatible with the plot shown in Figure 5.8.

5.7.4 Avoiding critical flow

In practice when the normal flow is close to critical conditions, small changes in flow rate can cause oscillations between sub and supercritical conditions. This can cause problems such as bank erosion. It is generally advisable therefore to design channels so that flows are clear of the anticipated critical region.

> **Revision points**
> - For uniform steady flow the energy gradient is parallel to the bed slope.
> - Specific energy is measured relative to the bed of the channel.
> - For any given channel section and flow rate there are two depths giving the same specific energy: one is subcritical and one is supercritical.
> - At the critical depth the specific energy has its minimum value.
> - Small variations in flow rate close to critical conditions can cause undesirable oscillations between subcritical and supercritical flow.

> **Chapter summary**
> - Application of simplifying design assumptions should not be allowed to result in river channels of poor ecological or aesthetic value.
> - The normal depth is that occurring under steady uniform conditions.

- The Froude number distinguishes between subcritical tranquil flow and supercritical rapid flow.
- In steady uniform flow the water surface is parallel to the channel bed.
- Manning's equation can be used to derive flow velocity in open channels.
- Specific energy is measured relative to the bed of the channel.
- For any given channel section and flow rate there are two depths giving the same specific energy: one is subcritical and one is supercritical.
- The specific energy is a minimum at the critical depth.
- Flows close to critical conditions can be unacceptably unstable.

Questions for practice

(a) A concrete lined trapezoidal channel has a uniform bed width of 3 m and side slopes of 1 in 1. The longitudinal gradient is 1 in 1250. Assuming Manning's n for the channel is 0.012 s/m$^{1/3}$, determine the hydraulic radius and discharge when the depth of flow is 1.5 m.

(b) A trapezoidal channel has a uniform bed width of 4 m. The banks slope at an angle of 64.3° to the horizontal. The bed slope is 0.0008 and Manning's n is 0.025 s/m$^{1/3}$. Find the normal depth when the flow rate is 15 m^3/s and establish whether this is subcritical or supercritical.

REFERENCES

Bakhmeteff BA (1912) *O Neravnomernom Dwijenii Jidkosti v Otkrytom Rusle*, St Petersburg, Russia, reprinted in English in Bakhmeteff BA (1932) *Hydraulics of Open Channels*. New York, NY, USA (in Russian).

Chadwick A and Morfett J (1998) *Hydraulics in Civil and Environmental Engineering*, 3rd edn, Spon, London, UK, http://dx.doi.org/10.4324/9780203235454.

Chézy A (1769) *Mémoires sur la Vitesse de l'Eau Conduit dans une Rigole Donée*. Dossier 847 (MS 1915) of the manuscript collection of the Ecole des Ponte et Chaussées, Paris (in French).

Chow VT (1981) *Open-Channel Hydraulics*. McGraw Hill, Tokyo, Japan.

Douglas JF, Gasiorek JM and Swaffield JA (1995) *Fluid Mechanics*, 3rd edn. Longmans, Harlow, UK.

Fischenich JC (1997) *Hydraulic Impacts of Riparian Vegetation: Summary of the Literature* (Technical Report EL-97-9) Washington, DC, USA: US Army Corps of Engineers.

Hamill L (2011) *Understanding Hydraulics*, 3rd edn, Palgrave Macmillan, Basingstoke, UK.

Leeks GJ, Lewin J and Newson MD (1988) Channel change, fluvial geomorphology and river engineering: the case of the Afon Trannon, Mid-Wales. *Earth Surface Processes and Landforms* **13**: 207–223, http://dx.doi.org/10.1002/esp.3290130303.

Lewis G and Williams G (1984) *Rivers and Wildlife*. Royal Society for the Protection of Birds, Sandy, UK.

Manning R (1891) On the flow of water in open channels and pipes. *Transactions of the Institution of Civil Engineers of Ireland*, vol. 20, pp. 161–207.

Manning R (1895) On the flow of water in open channels and pipes: Supplement. *Transactions of the Institution of Civil Engineers of Ireland*, vol. 24, pp. 179–207.

Purseglove J (1988) *Taming the Flood*. OUP, Oxford, UK.

Wormleaton PR and Merrett DJ (1990) An improved method of calculation for steady uniform flow in prismatic main channel/flood plain sections. *Journal of Hydraulic Research* **28**: 157–174, http://dx.doi.org/10.1080/00221689009499084.

FURTHER READING

Environment Agency (2009) *The Fluvial Design Guide*, available at http://evidence.environment-agency.gov.uk/FCERM/en/FluvialDesignGuide/Chapter_1_Background.aspx (accessed 12/06/2013).

Herschel C (1897) On the origin of the Chézy formula. *J. Assoc. Eng. Soc.* **18**: 363–369.

6
Open channel flow with varying conditions

Learning aims
After studying this chapter you should be able to

- appreciate that a change in cross-section or gradient will result in a change in flow depth
- appreciate that energy changes will generally be small when flow was originally subcritical
- appreciate that the transition from supercritical to subcritical flow will require the formation of a hydraulic jump and that there will be significant energy loss
- apply principles of continuity and energy conservation to common situations where there is a change to initially subcritical flow
- use conjugate depth and energy loss equations in the analysis of hydraulic jumps
- apply specific energy equations to applications of flow measurement
- calculate water surface profiles in situations of gradually varied flow.

6.1. Changes to flow regime
6.1.1 Introduction
The preceding chapter examined flow under an assumption that the flow was uniform. Uniform flow requires the cross-section and gradient of the channel to remain constant. However in practice changes may occur from place to place, for example passage over a weir, under a sluice gate, through a contraction caused by bridge piers, or into a flatter bed at the end of a spillway from a dam.

The effect that such changes may have on flow characteristics will depend on whether the flow is initially subcritical or supercritical. In some cases the changes may result in a transition between the two types of flow, subcritical and supercritical.

6.1.2 Subcritical to supercritical transition
For situations where the flow is initially subcritical, there is a smooth transition of the water surface between the two types of flow with little loss in energy. Such a condition may occur where there is an increase in bed slope. Problems may be approached using a combination of the continuity equation with the principle of conserving specific energy.

6.1.3 Supercritical to subcritical transition and formation of the hydraulic jump
For situations where the flow was initially supercritical, a smooth transition is not possible. This can be explained by examination of the relationship between specific energy and flow depth introduced in the

Figure 6.1 Specific energy plotted against flow at hydraulic jump

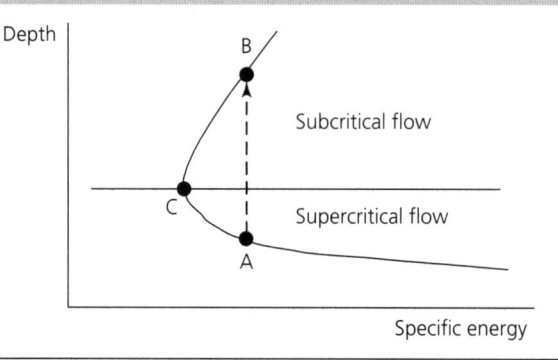

preceding chapter. Consider flow in a channel with the specific energy and depth initially represented by Point A on Figure 6.1. If there were to be a smooth transition to subcritical flow the path A–C–B would need to be followed to get to the alternative subcritical depth B. However the reality is that the flow changes directly from that represented by Point A to that represented by Point B with the formation of a standing wave known as a hydraulic jump. In the process turbulence results in a significant loss of energy.

Because of the energy losses, it is not possible to use conservation of energy in analysing flow depths across a hydraulic jump. The following analysis for a rectangular channel of width B is attributed to Bélanger (1841).

Applying the momentum equation to a control section extending just before to just after the jump, illustrated in Figure 6.2, gives

$$\tfrac{1}{2}\rho g B H_1^2 - \tfrac{1}{2}\rho g B H_2^2 = \rho Q (V_2 - V_1) = \rho A_1 V_1 (V_2 - V_1) = \rho B H_1 V_1 (V_2 - V_1) \tag{6.1}$$

hence

$$\tfrac{1}{2}g(H_1^2 - H_2^2) = H_1 V_1 (V_2 - V_1) \tag{6.2}$$

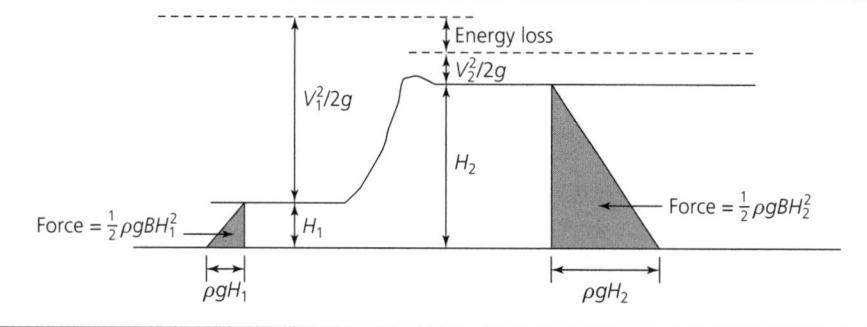

Figure 6.2 Analysis of the hydraulic jump

But the continuity equation gives

$$Q = BH_1V_1 = BH_2V_2 \quad \text{or} \quad V_2 = V_1\frac{H_1}{H_2} \tag{6.3}$$

hence

$$\frac{1}{2}g(H_1^2 - H_2^2) = H_1V_1\left(\frac{V_1H_1}{H_2} - V_1\right) = V_1^2H_1\left(\frac{H_1 - H_2}{H_2}\right) = V_1^2\left(\frac{H_1}{H_2}\right)(H_1 - H_2) \tag{6.4}$$

This can be rewritten as

$$\frac{1}{2}g(H_1 + H_2)(H_1 - H_2) = V_1^2\left(\frac{H_1}{H_2}\right)(H_1 - H_2) \tag{6.5}$$

Therefore

$$(H_1 + H_2) = \frac{2V_1^2}{g}\frac{H_1}{H_2} \tag{6.6}$$

But the Froude number prior to jump in the rectangular section

$$Fr_1 = \frac{V_1}{\sqrt{gH_1}} \tag{6.7}$$

from which

$$V_1^2 = Fr_1^2 gH_1 \tag{6.8}$$

and substituting into equation (6.6) gives

$$(H_1 + H_2) = \frac{2Fr_1^2 gH_1}{g}\frac{H_1}{H_2} \tag{6.9}$$

$$H_1H_2 + H_2^2 - 2Fr_1^2H_1^2 = 0 \tag{6.10}$$

This is a quadratic in H_1 and H_2.

Using the formula for the solution of a quadratic equation leads to

$$H_2 = \frac{-H_1 \pm \sqrt{H_1^2 - 4 \times 1 \times (-2Fr_1^2H_1^2)}}{2 \times 1} = \frac{-H_1 \pm \sqrt{H_1^2 + 8Fr_1^2H_1^2}}{2} \tag{6.11}$$

The negative root is physically meaningless, so

$$H_2 = \frac{H_1}{2}\left(-1 + \sqrt{1 + 8Fr_1^2}\right) \tag{6.12}$$

Similarly

$$H_1 = \frac{H_2}{2}\left(-1 + \sqrt{1 + 8Fr_2^2}\right) \tag{6.13}$$

H_1 and H_2 are known as 'conjugate depths'.

Note that the conjugate depth equations can be expressed in other forms such as

$$H_2 = -\frac{H_1}{2} + \sqrt{\frac{H_1^2}{4} + \frac{2Q^2}{gB^2H_1}} \tag{6.14}$$

Once H_1 and H_2 have been determined the energy loss across the jump

$$\Delta E = H_1 + \frac{V_1^2}{2g} - \left(H_2 + \frac{V_2^2}{2g}\right) \tag{6.15}$$

This can be shown to be the same as

$$\Delta E = \frac{(H_1 - H_2)^3}{4H_1 H_2} \tag{6.16}$$

This energy loss will be transferred to the bed and banks of the channel. This can lead to problems of scour and erosion. It is important therefore to know where hydraulic jumps will occur and provide protection against these effects. On the other hand engineers may deliberately induce the formation of a hydraulic jump in a stilling basin to remove energy from the system.

Peterka (1958) reported on experimental investigations into hydraulic jumps carried out by the US Bureau of Reclamation. He characterised forms of jumps based on their Froude number as summarised in Table 6.1. The length of channel occupied by a hydraulic jump can be difficult to determine, especially for low Froude numbers. It is related to the Froude number immediately prior to the jump.

Revision points

- Changes in channel cross-section will lead to changes in flow depth.
- A reduction in cross-section under subcritical flow conditions will lead to reduced water level and increased velocity.
- Transition from subcritical to supercritical flow occurs without appreciable loss of energy.
- The transition from subcritical to supercritical conditions can be investigated using a combination of the continuity and specific energy equations.
- Transition from supercritical to subcritical flow involves the formation of a hydraulic jump with appreciable energy loss.
- The depth of water immediately prior to a hydraulic jump can be determined from the normal depth after the jump by use of the momentum derived conjugate depths equation.
- Protection to the beds and banks may be required to prevent erosion at hydraulic jumps.
- A hydraulic jump may be deliberately introduced to induce energy reduction in a hydraulic system.

Open channel flow with varying conditions

Table 6.1 Types of hydraulic jump (based on Peterka (1958))

Froude number immediately before jump Fr_1	Description	Energy dissipation	Length of jump
1.0–1.7	Slight ruffle on water surface	>5%	Difficult to determine
1.7–2.5	Small rollers on water surface	5–15%	$4.0H_2$ at $Fr_1 = 1.7$ $4.3H_2$ at $Fr_1 = 2.0$ $4.9H_2$ at $Fr_1 = 2.5$
2.5–4.5	Irregular oscillations producing rough water surface	15–45%	$4.9H_2$ at $Fr_1 = 2.5$ $5.2H_2$ at $Fr_1 = 3.0$ $5.6H_2$ at $Fr_1 = 3.5$ $5.8H_2$ at $Fr_1 = 4.0$ $5.9H_2$ at $Fr_1 = 4.5$
4.5–9.0	Stable, well-defined	45–70%	$5.9H_2$ at $Fr_1 = 4.5$ $6.0H_2$ at $Fr_1 = 5.0$ $6.1H_2$ at $Fr_1 = 5.5$ to 9.0
>9	Rough	70–85%	$6.1H_2$ at $Fr = 9.0$ $6.0H_2$ at $Fr = 14.0$ $5.5H_2$ at $Fr = 20.0$

6.2. Examples of flow changes
6.2.1 Spillway

Figure 6.3 illustrates the transitions of flow that may occur along a spillway. The bed initially has a mild slope along which the flow is subcritical. The depth of flow here is the normal depth for the flow rate in the mild channel. There is then a smooth transition to the normal depth associated with the steep channel. From the toe of the steep channel, the depth gradually increases until it becomes equal to H_1, whose value is related by Bélanger's equation to its conjugate H_2, the normal depth for the downstream mild slope. The water surface profile between the toe of the steep channel and the point at which the hydraulic jump occurs can be found using methods for gradually varied flow described later in this chapter.

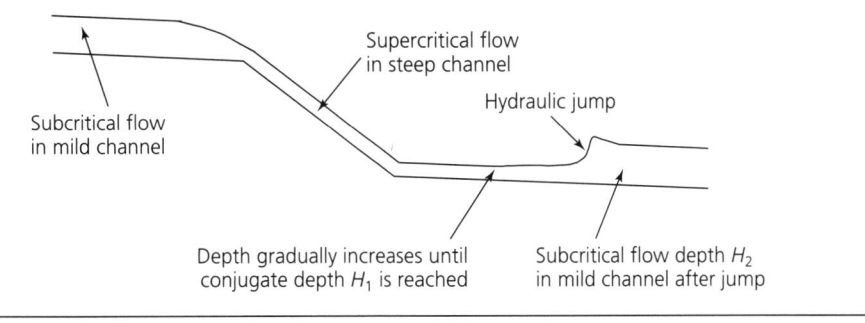

Figure 6.3 Flow transitions along a spillway

Example 6.1

A 4-m-wide steep spillway of rectangular cross-section discharges into a channel of similar cross-section but having a mild slope.

Table 6.2

	Steep channel	Mild channel
Slope	1 in 30	1 in 850
Manning's n	0.015 s/m$^{1/3}$	0.015 s/m$^{1/3}$

Parameters for the two channels are shown in Table 6.2

(a) Calculate the flow rate if the depth in the steep channel is 0.8 m.
(b) Confirm that the flow in the steep channel is supercritical.
(c) Calculate the depth and velocity of flow after the hydraulic jump.
(d) Calculate the depth, velocity and Froude number at the start of the jump.
(e) Calculate the energy loss at the jump.
(f) Estimate the length of the hydraulic jump.

Part (a)
Cross-sectional area of flow

$$A = 0.8 \times 4 = 3.2 \text{ m}^2 \tag{6.17}$$

length of wetted perimeter

$$P = 4 + (2 \times 0.8) = 5.6 \text{ m} \tag{6.18}$$

hence

$$\text{hydraulic radius } R = \frac{A}{P} = \frac{3.2}{5.6} = 0.571\,43 \text{ m} \tag{6.19}$$

Using Manning's equation

$$Q = \frac{A}{n} R^{2/3} S_0^{1/2} = \frac{3.2}{0.015} \times 0.571\,43 \times \left(\frac{1}{30}\right)^{1/2} = 26.821 \text{ m}^3/\text{s} \tag{6.20}$$

Part (b)
Velocity in steep channel

$$V = \frac{Q}{A} = \frac{26.821}{3.2} = 8.3815 \text{ m/s} \tag{6.21}$$

Froude number

$$Fr = \frac{V}{\sqrt{gH}} = \frac{8.3815}{\sqrt{9.81 \times 0.8}} = 2.9919 \qquad (6.22)$$

The Froude number is greater than unity, therefore flow is supercritical.

Part (c)
The 26.821-m³/s flow calculated earlier for the steep channel also has to pass through the mild channel.

Applying Manning's equation again but with Normal depth H after the

hydraulic jump unknown

$$26.821 = \left(\frac{4H}{0.015}\right) \times \left(\frac{4H}{4+2H}\right)^{2/3} \times \left(\frac{1}{850}\right)^{1/2} \qquad (6.23)$$

Successive approximation leads to

H for mild channel $= 2.679$ m $\qquad (6.24)$

Velocity after jump

$V = Q/A = 26.821/(4 \times 2.679) = 2.503$ m/s $\qquad (6.25)$

Part (d)
The depth immediately before the jump can be found using the conjugate depth equation

$$H_1 = \frac{H_2}{2}\left(-1 + \sqrt{1 + 8Fr_2^2}\right) \qquad (6.26)$$

where suffix 1 refers to a position immediately before the jump and suffix 2 refers to a position after the jump.

$$Fr_2 = \frac{V}{\sqrt{gH}} = \frac{2.503}{\sqrt{9.81 \times 2.679}} = 0.4882 \qquad (6.27)$$

$$H_1 = \frac{2.679}{2}\left(-1 + \sqrt{1 + 8 \times 0.4882^2}\right) = 0.9442 \text{ m} \qquad (6.28)$$

Velocity at this location $= Q/A = 26.821/(4 \times 0.9442) = 7.102$ m/s $\qquad (6.29)$

$$Fr_1 = \frac{7.102}{\sqrt{9.81 \times 0.9442}} = 2.334 \qquad (6.30)$$

Part (*e*)
The energy loss

$$\Delta E = \frac{(H_2 - H_1)^3}{4H_1 H_2} = \frac{(2.679 - 0.944)^3}{4 \times 0.944 \times 2.679} = 0.516 \,\text{m} \tag{6.31}$$

Part (*f*)
From Table 6.1, for

$$Fr_1 = 2.33 \tag{6.32}$$

the length of the hydraulic jump is about

$$4.6H_2 = 4.6 \times 2.679 = 12 \,\text{m} \tag{6.33}$$

(greater accuracy is not justified).

6.2.2 Narrowing of a channel

In order for specific energy to remain constant, there will be a reduction in the depth of flow. As the overall flow rate Q remains the same, the flow per unit width q must increase. Figure 6.4 shows the specific energy–depth relationships in the original and in a constricted channel. The effect will depend on whether the flow is initially subcritical or supercritical.

If the flow is originally supercritical (below the dashed line in Figure 6.4), to maintain the energy value E between the original and restricted channels, H_2 in the restricted channel must be greater than H_1 in the original channel. However if the original flow was subcritical, H_2 will have to be less than H_1 to maintain a constant value of E.

Figure 6.4 Effect of constriction in bed width on flow depth

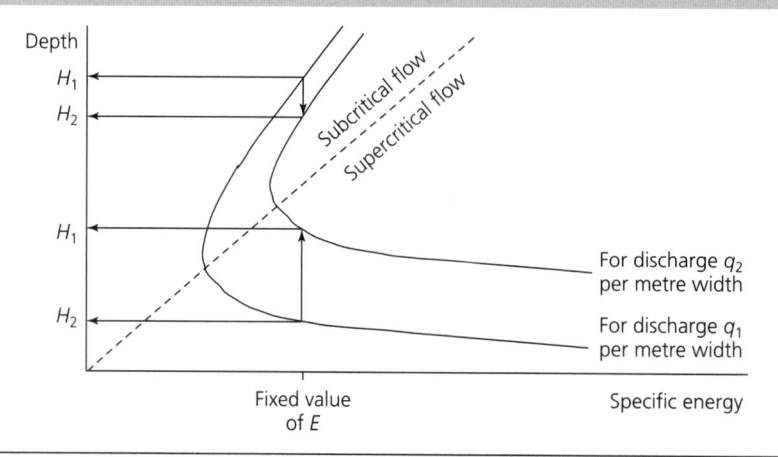

Since

$$H_c = \sqrt[3]{\frac{Q^2}{gB^2}} \tag{6.34}$$

the change in channel width will also increase the critical depth at the restriction. This, coupled with the decreased depth of flow when conditions are initially subcritical, means that the possibility of a change from subcritical to supercritical flow is increased.

Chow (1981, pp. 43 and 47–49) points out that for initially subcritical flow there will be two possible depths at the narrowed section of the channel: one representing subcritical and one representing supercritical conditions. The former is associated with gradual changes in cross-section and the latter with abrupt changes.

Example 6.2

A 5-m-wide rectangular channel is carrying a 1.5-m depth of water at a rate of 10 m³/s. As the channel passes between a pair of bridge piers its width is decreased to 3.5 m. What is the depth of flow at the narrowed section?

The velocity of flow upstream of the bridge is

$$V = Q/A = 10/(5 \times 1.5) = 1.333 \text{ m/s} \tag{6.35}$$

and the critical depth

$$H_c = \sqrt[3]{\frac{Q^2}{gB^2}} = \sqrt[3]{\frac{10^2}{9.81 \times 5 \times 5}} = 0.639 \text{ m} \tag{6.36}$$

Our depth of flow of 1.5 m is greater than this, so conditions are initially subcritical. This can also be checked by finding the Froude number.

$$Fr = \frac{V}{\sqrt{gH}} = \frac{1.333}{\sqrt{9.81 \times 1.5}} = 0.348 \tag{6.37}$$

As this is less than unity, subcritical conditions are confirmed.

The specific energy in this upstream location is

$$E = H + \frac{V^2}{2g} = 1.5 + \frac{1.333^2}{2 \times 9.81} = 1.5906 \text{ m} \tag{6.38}$$

At the location of the bridge the critical depth

$$H_c = \sqrt[3]{\frac{Q^2}{gB^2}} = \sqrt[3]{\frac{10^2}{9.81 \times 3.5 \times 3.5}} = 0.941 \text{ m} \tag{6.39}$$

Denoting the depth of flow at the bridge as H_b,

the area of flow in this restriction $= 3.5 H_b$ (6.40)

and the continuity equation gives

the velocity of flow here $= 10/3.5 H_b = 2.857/H_b$ (6.41)

Applying the principle of conservation of specific energy between the two locations

$$1.5906 = H_b + \frac{\left(\frac{2.857}{H_b}\right)^2}{2 \times 9.81} \qquad (6.42)$$

Multiplying each term by (2×9.81) gives

$$31.208 = 19.62 H_b + \left(\frac{8.1624}{H_b^2}\right) \qquad (6.43)$$

Multiplying each term by H_b^2 to remove the final fraction and re-arranging gives

$$31.208 H_b^2 - 19.62 H_b^3 - 8.1633 = 0 \qquad (6.44)$$

This equation is satisfied by the values

$$H_b = 1.368 \text{ m} \qquad (6.45)$$

and

$$H_b = 0.674 \text{ m} \qquad (6.46)$$

representing subcritical and supercritical conditions respectively. The degree of abruptness of the change in cross-section will determine which of these occurs.

6.2.3 Raised bed

A sudden rise in the bed depth will reduce the area of flow as well as reducing the specific energy by the difference in level of the bed. If the height of the projection in the bed level is h_p, then the specific energy equation becomes

$$H_1 + \frac{V_1^2}{2g} - h_p = H_2 + \frac{V_2^2}{2g} \qquad (6.47)$$

where the subscripts 1 and 2 refer to conditions before and after the rise in bed level respectively.

As was the case with the narrowed section considered earlier, V_2 is greater than V_1 if the flow was initially subcritical and V_2 is less than V_1 if the flow was originally supercritical.

In the case of flow that was initially subcritical, there will be a limit on the extent to which the water surface is drawn down over the raised bed. This limit is reached when the depth of flow over the raised bed H_2 is equal to the critical depth H_c.

Example 6.3

A rectangular channel 4.5 m wide runs through a factory site. A rectangular cable duct 0.5 m high has been laid across the bed of the channel. On a particular day the average velocity of flow some distance upstream of the duct was measured as 0.8 m/s and the depth of flow was 2.2 m. Calculate the depth of flow over the duct.

By finding the Froude number we can ascertain whether the flow was initially subcritical or supercritical.

$$Fr_1 = \frac{V_1}{\sqrt{gH_1}} = \frac{0.8}{\sqrt{9.81 \times 2.2}} = 0.172 \tag{6.48}$$

As this is less than unity, subcritical flow is indicated. This will mean that the water surface will lower and the velocity increase over the duct.

Substituting into the specific energy equation gives

$$2.2 + \frac{0.8^2}{2g} - 0.5 = H_2 + \frac{V_2^2}{2g} \tag{6.49}$$

This leads to

$$V_2^2 = 33.994 - 19.62 H_2 \tag{6.50}$$

Continuity also gives

$$0.8 \times 2.2 = H_2 V_2 \tag{6.51}$$

from which

$$V_2 = \frac{1.76}{H_2} \tag{6.52}$$

This can be placed back into the specific energy equation giving

$$\left(\frac{1.76}{H_2}\right)^2 = 33.994 - 19.62 H_2 \tag{6.53}$$

Hence

$$33.994 H_2^2 - 19.62 H_2^3 - 3.0976 = 0 \tag{6.54}$$

Successive approximation leads to

$$H_2 = 1.676 \text{ m (subcritical)} \tag{6.55}$$

or

$$H_2 = 0.336 \text{ (supercritical)} \tag{6.56}$$

As H_2 cannot be less than H_c, the relevant solution is

$$H_2 = 1.676 \text{ m} \tag{6.57}$$

6.2.4 Flow below a vertical underflow sluice gate

If conditions are such as to hold back water as in Figure 6.5, a situation is generated where there is subcritical flow upstream, and supercritical flow immediately downstream, of the gate. The area of flow initially converges to a minimum at the *vena contracta* and the depth gradually increases until it is sufficient for a hydraulic jump to form.

Figure 6.5 Flow beneath vertical underflow sluice gate

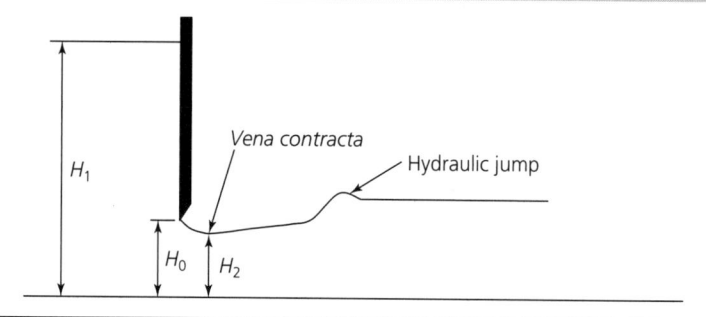

The discharge under the gate can be expressed as

$$Q = K_s H_0 B \sqrt{2gH_1} \tag{6.58}$$

where K_s is the sluice coefficient (Rouse, 1950). Values of K_s typically lie between 0.55 and 0.60. This relationship together with the specific energy and continuity equations can be used to determine the depth of flow at the *vena contracta*.

Example 6.4

An underflow sluice gate occupies the full width of a 1.0-m-wide rectangular channel. It is lifted 0.8 m from the closed position. Once stable conditions have been achieved a hydraulic jump is observed to occur a little way beyond the sluice and the depth upstream of the sluice is 1.3 m. If the sluice coefficient is 0.6, establish the depth of flow and velocity at the *vena contracta*.

The discharge is

$$Q = 0.6 \times 0.8 \times 1.0 \times \sqrt{2 \times 9.81 \times 1.3} = 2.4242 \, \text{m}^3/\text{s} \tag{6.59}$$

and the velocity upstream of the sluice is given by

$$V_1 = \frac{Q}{A_1} = \frac{2.4242}{1.0 \times 1.3} = 1.8647 \, \text{m/s} \tag{6.60}$$

and the velocity at the *vena contracta*

$$V_2 = \frac{Q}{A} = \frac{2.4242}{1.0 H_2} = \frac{2.4242}{H_2} \tag{6.61}$$

Substituting into the specific energy equation gives

$$1.3 + \frac{1.8647^2}{2 \times 9.81} = H_2 + \frac{\left(\frac{2.4242}{H_2}\right)^2}{2 \times 9.81} \tag{6.62}$$

This simplifies to

$$19.62 H_2^3 - 28.983 H_2^2 + 5.877 \tag{6.63}$$

Successive approximation leads to

$$H_2 = 0.577 \, \text{m} \tag{6.64}$$

and

$$V_2 = 2.4142/0.577 = 4.18 \, \text{m/s} \tag{6.65}$$

Revision points

The flow down a steep spillway is likely to be supercritical; the supercritical flow continuing until a hydraulic jump occurs in the milder receiving channel.

Narrowing of a channel by, for example, intrusion of bridge piers will cause a reduction in the depth of initially subcritical flow: this could extend to a transition to supercritical conditions.

A rise in the bed causes a reduction in specific energy.

If an underflow sluice constricts flow, subcritical flow occurs upstream and supercritical flow occurs under and immediately downstream of the sluice with the formation of a hydraulic jump.

6.3. Flow rate measurement based on changes in section
6.3.1 The Venturi flume

This is analogous to the Venturi meter used in the determination of flow rates in pipes. It relies on the changes in energy make up as water passes through a narrowed section of channel of rectangular cross-section. The flume was developed in the United States early in the twentieth century (Cone, 1917).

The depth of water H_1 upstream of the constriction and the depth at the constriction itself H_2 are recorded. By applying together the equations of conservation of specific energy and continuity, it is possible to express the theoretical flow rate as

$$Q = B_2 H_2 \sqrt{\frac{2g(H_1 - H_2)}{1 - \left(\frac{H_2 B_2}{H_1 B_1}\right)^2}} \tag{6.66}$$

where B_1 and B_2 are the widths at the unrestricted and restricted sections of channel. In practice there is some loss of energy between the measurement points and it is necessary to apply a coefficient of discharge to the value obtained by this equation to obtain the actual flow rate. Typically streamlining the approach to the narrowed throat section results in a value of the coefficient between 0.95 and 0.99.

6.3.2 The standing wave flume

This is similar to a Venturi flume but with a low water surface downstream of the narrowed throat. This results in critical conditions being developed within the throat and, assuming that the upstream velocity head is negligible, it can be shown from a consideration of the specific energy equation that theoretically

$$Q = 1.705 B_2 H_1^{3/2} \tag{6.67}$$

Again in practice this value has to be modified by a discharge factor of about 0.95 to 0.99.

6.3.3 Broad-crested weir

Broad-crested weirs are intended to provide a means of determining flow in relatively wide rivers.

Provided the dimensions of the weir are appropriate (the length of weir is greater than three times the upstream head, and the weir is of sufficient height), the flow will adjust itself for maximum discharge and will pass through its critical depth as it crosses the weir with a hydraulic jump forming downstream of it.

The height of the weir h_p shown in Figure 6.6 needs to be such that the equation

$$H_1 + \frac{V_1^2}{2g} - h_p = H_c + \frac{V_c^2}{2g} \tag{6.68}$$

can be satisfied.

At the critical depth the Froude number is unity, hence

$$V^2 = g H_c \tag{6.69}$$

Open channel flow with varying conditions

Figure 6.6 Broad-crested weir

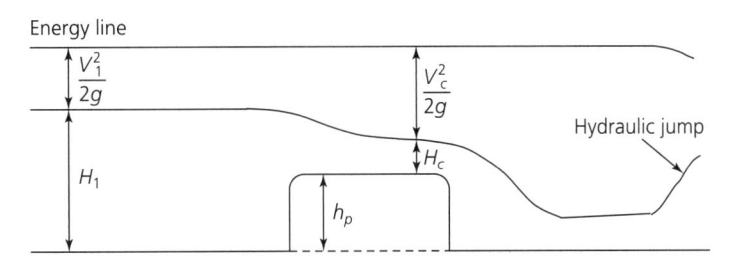

and it was shown earlier that for a channel of rectangular cross-section

$$H_c = \sqrt[3]{\frac{Q^2}{gB^2}} \tag{6.70}$$

This enables the equation to be satisfied to be rewritten as

$$H_1 + \frac{V_1^2}{2g} - h_p = 1.5 \times \sqrt[3]{\frac{Q^2}{gB^2}} \tag{6.71}$$

and, making h_p the subject,

$$h_p = H_1 + \frac{V_1^2}{2g} - 1.5 \times \sqrt[3]{\frac{Q^2}{gB^2}} \tag{6.72}$$

In using the weir to ascertain the flow rate, we need to use the rearranged version of the equation

$$Q = 1.705B \left(H_1 - h_p + \frac{V_1^2}{2g} \right)^{3/2} \tag{6.73}$$

The $V_1^2/2g$ term tends to be omitted as being insignificant, giving

$$Q = 1.705B(H_1 - h_p)^{3/2} \tag{6.74}$$

which is similar in form to the expression stated earlier for the standing wave flume.

Example 6.5

A 5-m-wide channel with a slope of 1 in 5000 carries 7.5 m³/s of water. Manning's n is 0.015 s/m$^{1/3}$.

(a) What is the normal depth in the channel?
(b) A broad crested weir is to be placed across the channel. What is the minimum height of the weir to ensure that critical flow develops over it at this flow rate?

(c) On a different occasion the depth of water upstream of the weir is 2 m. What is the flow rate on this occasion?

(a) Manning's equation gives

$$7.5 = \left(\frac{5H_1}{0.015}\right) \times \left(\frac{5H_1}{5+2H_1}\right)^{2/3} \times \left(\frac{1}{5000}\right)^{1/2} \tag{6.75}$$

where H_1 is the normal depth.

Successive approximation leads to $H_1 = 1.613$ m and by substitution into the continuity equation

$$V_1 = 7.5/(5 \times 1.613) = 0.930 \text{ m/s} \tag{6.76}$$

(b) Placing these values into

$$h_p = H_1 + \frac{V_1^2}{2g} - 1.5 \times \sqrt[3]{\frac{Q^2}{gB^2}} \tag{6.77}$$

gives

$$h_p = 1.613 + \frac{0.930^2}{2 \times 9.81} - 1.5 \times \sqrt[3]{\frac{7.5^2}{9.81 \times 5^2}} = 0.709 \text{ m} \tag{6.78}$$

(c) Using

$$Q = 1.705 B (H_1 - h_p)^{3/2} \tag{6.79}$$

we obtain

$$Q = 1.705 \times 5 \times (2 - 0.709)^{3/2} = 12.5 \text{ m}^3/\text{s} \tag{6.80}$$

Revision points

- Changing the channel section can form a convenient method of flow measurement.
- The Venturi flume causes a reduction in cross-sectional area by restricting the channel width. Flow rates can be found from calculations based on depths of water upstream and at the throat of the flume.
- The standing wave flume results in the formation of critical flow conditions and allows the flow rate to be established based on the depth upstream of the flume.
- By providing a raised hump of sufficient height in the channel bed, critical conditions are induced over a broad crested weir allowing flow rates to be determined based on the water depth upstream of the weir.

6.4. Gradually varied flow

So far in this chapter we have considered changes in flow that could be considered rapid. There can also be a gradual change in flow, for example the rising water surface that occurs between the bottom of a spillway and the start of the ensuing hydraulic jump.

A fundamental characteristic of such gradually varying non-uniform flow is that the water surface and total energy lines are not parallel to the bed so it is necessary to work in terms of total energy rather than specific energy. The slope of the total energy line depends on the friction gradient S_F. This is not a constant so in reality the total energy line is curved. Figure 6.7 shows the changes in components of energy between two sections distance ΔL apart. The total energies at sections 1 and 2 are related by

$$Z_1 + E_1 = Z_2 + E_2 + \overline{S_F}\Delta L \tag{6.81}$$

where

$$E_1 = H_1 + \frac{V_1^2}{2g} \quad \text{and} \quad E_2 = H_2 + \frac{V_2^2}{2g} \tag{6.82}$$

and $\overline{S_F}$ is the average friction gradient between the sections. A simple approach, which can be justified provided ΔL is not too great is to assume that

$$\overline{S_F} = (S_{F1} + S_{F2})/2 \tag{6.83}$$

We can replace $Z_1 - Z_2$ by $S_0 \Delta L$ and rearrange to obtain

$$\Delta L = \frac{E_2 - E_1}{S_0 - \overline{S_F}} \tag{6.84}$$

Figure 6.7 Energy variation along channel in gradually varied flow

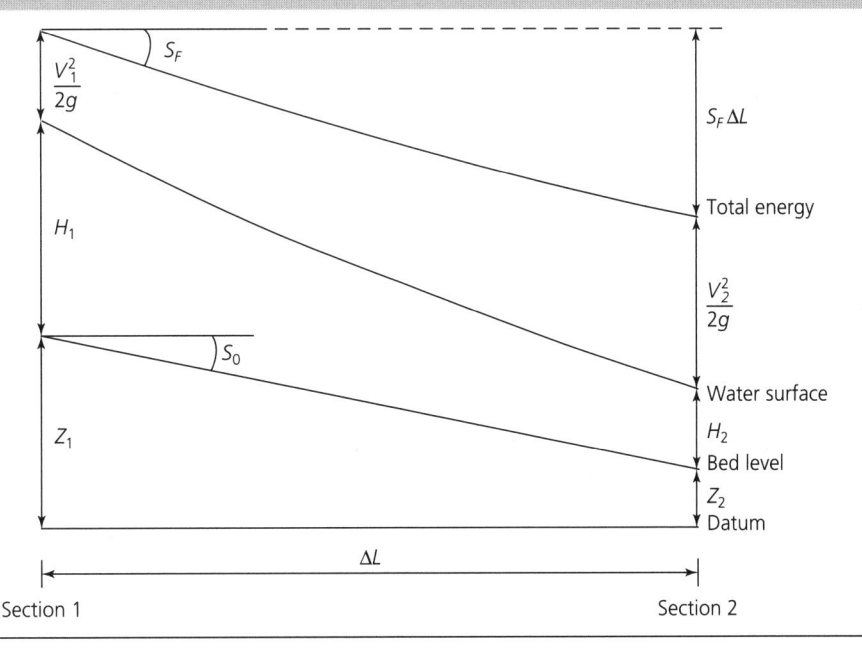

A numerical integration approach is used. The starting point is where the position of the water surface is known. Examples of such control points are the *vena contracta* downstream of an underflow sluice, the toe of a spillway or the location of a dam. Working as appropriately upstream or downstream from the control point, the channel is divided into sections. Note that for subcritical flow, a control point will affect the profile upstream, while for supercritical flow it is the profile downstream that is affected. There are two basic ways of carrying out the calculations: the direct step and standard step methods.

In the direct step method the length of sections is the distance required for the water level to change by a chosen amount ΔH so that

$$H_2 = H_1 \pm \Delta H \tag{6.85}$$

the sign depending on whether it is a situation where the depth is increasing or decreasing away from the control point.

In the standard step method, the sections of channel considered are of selected length and the average depth of water within each of the sections is found. This method requires an iterative approach with trial values of H_2 used until the energy equation is balanced.

Although there is an implication that the increments of depth in the direct step method and distance in the standard step method should remain constant, there is no reason why variations from this cannot be made.

The iteration needed in the standard step method is a slight disadvantage. However the method can accommodate changes in bed characteristics such as bed roughness, gradient and width. This is not possible with the direct step method.

Whichever method is used, it is useful to have a knowledge of the normal and critical depths of flow because for example, when working upstream from a dam, the backwater curve for the zone of gradually varied flow will approach the normal depth asymptotically. Both methods have been aided considerably by the availability of spreadsheets and are best illustrated by example.

The two methods can also be based on the alternative equation

$$\frac{\Delta H}{\Delta L} = \frac{S_0 - S_F}{1 - Fr^2} \tag{6.86}$$

Example 6.6

In an example earlier in this chapter we considered a steep spillway discharging into a mild channel. We found that a rate of 26.82 m^3/s produced a depth of flow of 0.8 m in the steep channel. We also found that in the mild channel a hydraulic jump would occur once the depth of flow was 0.944 m.

It would complete our knowledge of the hydraulics at this location if we knew the water surface profile from the junction between the steep and mild channels to the start of the hydraulic jump.

The control point in this case is the depth of 0.8 m at the change in bed slope and we work downstream from this location.

Either the direct step or standard step methods may be used and the results, summarised in Tables 6.3 and 6.4, indicate that the flow depth of 0.944 m at which the hydraulic jump occurs about 34.5 m from the toe of the spillway.

Revision points

- In gradually varied non-uniform flow the water surface and bed are not parallel to each other.
- Problems of gradually varied flow have to be analysed in terms of total, rather than specific, energy.
- A numerical integration method is generally used working upstream from a control point in subcritical flow or downstream from a control point in supercritical flow.

Chapter summary

- A reduction in cross-sectional area under subcritical flow will lead to reduced depth and increased velocity.
- Transition from subcritical to supercritical flow occurs without significant energy loss and can be investigated using a combination of the continuity and specific energy equations.
- Transition from supercritical to subcritical flow involves the formation of a hydraulic jump with appreciable energy loss and may be investigated using the conjugate depths equation.
- Critical flow may be deliberately induced in flumes and weirs to provide methods of flow measurement.
- In gradually varied non-uniform flow the water surface and bed are not parallel to each other.
- Gradually varied flow is analysed in terms of total energy using numerical integration.

Questions for practice

(a) A broad-crested weir is constructed across a 4.2 m wide rectangular channel. The upstream velocity of flow is 0.94 m/s and the depth upstream of the weir is 1.95 m.
Find:
(i) The height the weir would need to be to produce critical flow over it at the stated flow rate
(ii) the depth of water over the weir at this flow rate if the weir height was 0.43 m.

(b) A 6-m-wide channel of rectangular cross-section carries a flow of 10 m^3/s. The channel is 6 m wide and the bed slope is 1 in 5000. Manning's n of the bed is 0.015 s/m$^{1/3}$.
(i) Find the normal depth of flow.
(ii) It is proposed to construct a barrier across the channel. At the barrier the water level will be maintained at 2 m above bed level. Determine the backwater profile upstream of the barrier.

Table 6.3 Calculations of depth of flow from bottom of spillway to start of hydraulic jump, using direct step method

Depth: m	Area: m²	Velocity: m/s	Hyd. radius: m	H_1: m	$V_1^2/2g$: m	E_1: m	H_2: m	$V_2^2/2g$: m	E_2: m	S_{F1}	S_{F2}	S_{FBAR}	$S_0 - S_{FBAR}$	ΔL: m	Distance from control point: m
0.8	3.200	8.382	0.571	–	–	–	–	–	–	–	–	–	–	–	0.000
0.82	3.280	8.177	0.582	0.800	3.581	4.381	0.820	3.408	4.228	0.033	0.031	0.032	-0.031	4.922	4.922
0.84	3.360	7.982	0.592	0.820	3.408	4.228	0.840	3.248	4.088	0.031	0.029	0.030	-0.029	4.881	9.803
0.86	3.440	7.797	0.601	0.840	3.248	4.088	0.860	3.098	3.958	0.029	0.027	0.028	-0.027	4.837	14.640
0.88	3.520	7.620	0.611	0.860	3.098	3.958	0.880	2.959	3.839	0.027	0.025	0.026	-0.025	4.790	19.431
0.9	3.600	7.450	0.621	0.880	2.959	3.839	0.900	2.829	3.729	0.025	0.024	0.024	-0.023	4.741	24.172
0.92	3.680	7.288	0.630	0.900	2.829	3.729	0.920	2.707	3.627	0.024	0.022	0.023	-0.022	4.690	28.862
0.94	3.760	7.133	0.639	0.920	2.707	3.627	0.940	2.593	3.533	0.022	0.021	0.021	-0.020	4.635	33.497
0.944	3.776	7.103	0.641	0.940	2.593	3.533	0.944	2.572	3.516	0.021	0.021	0.021	-0.019	0.921	34.417

Table 6.4 Calculations of depth of flow from bottom of spillway to start of hydraulic jump, using standard step method

Distance: m	ΔL: m	Depth: m	Area: m²	Velocity: m/s	Hyd. radius: m	H_1: m	$V_1^2/2g$: m	E_1: m	H_2: m	$V_2^2/2g$: m	E_2: m	S_{F1}	S_{F2}	S_{FBAR}	$\Delta L (S_{FBAR} - S_0)$: m	Balancing error: m
0	–	0.800	3.200	8.382	0.571	–	–	–	–	–	–	–	–	–	–	–
5	5	0.820	3.281	8.174	0.582	0.800	3.581	4.381	0.820	3.405	4.226	0.033	0.031	0.032	0.155	0.000
10	5	0.841	3.363	7.976	0.592	0.820	3.405	4.226	0.841	3.242	4.083	0.031	0.029	0.030	0.144	0.001
15	5	0.861	3.446	7.784	0.602	0.841	3.242	4.083	0.861	3.088	3.950	0.029	0.027	0.028	0.133	0.000
20	5	0.882	3.529	7.600	0.612	0.861	3.088	3.950	0.882	2.944	3.826	0.027	0.025	0.026	0.124	0.000
25	5	0.903	3.614	7.422	0.622	0.882	2.944	3.826	0.903	2.808	3.711	0.025	0.023	0.024	0.115	0.000
30	5	0.925	3.699	7.251	0.632	0.903	2.808	3.711	0.925	2.680	3.604	0.023	0.022	0.023	0.107	0.000
31	1	0.929	3.716	7.217	0.634	0.925	2.680	3.604	0.929	2.655	3.584	0.022	0.022	0.022	0.020	0.000
32	1	0.933	3.734	7.183	0.636	0.929	2.655	3.584	0.933	2.630	3.563	0.022	0.021	0.021	0.020	0.000
33	1	0.938	3.751	7.150	0.638	0.933	2.630	3.563	0.938	2.605	3.543	0.021	0.021	0.021	0.020	0.000
34	1	0.942	3.769	7.117	0.640	0.938	2.605	3.543	0.942	2.581	3.523	0.021	0.021	0.021	0.020	0.000
34.5	0.5	0.944	3.778	7.100	0.641	0.942	2.581	3.523	0.944	2.569	3.514	0.021	0.021	0.021	0.010	0.000

REFERENCES

Bélanger JB (1841) *Notes sur l'Hydraulique*. Ecole Royale des Ponts et Chaussées, Paris, France (in French).

Chow VT (1981) *Open-Channel Hydraulics*. McGraw-Hill, Tokyo, Japan.

Cone VM (1917) The Venturi flume. *Journal of Agricultural Research* **9**: 115–129.

Peterka AJ (1958) *Hydraulic Design of Stilling Basins and Energy Dissipaters*. US Bureau of Reclamation, Denver, CO, USA.

Rouse H (1950) *Engineering Hydraulics*. Wiley, New York, NY, USA.

# 7
Hydrology of river flow

> ### Learning aims
> After studying this chapter you should be able to
>
> - estimate values of flows of particular return periods based on annual maximum flow records and consider the limitations of the approach
> - outline the peak over threshold method and use the application of this and the *Flood Estimation Handbook* to obtain the median annual maximum flood
> - describe the hydrograph method of flow prediction, including the separation of base flow and surface runoff, and explain the production of a unit hydrograph
> - outline the design storm hydrograph method contained in the *Flood Estimation Handbook*.

7.1. Introduction
Hydrology is a discipline in its own right. Shaw *et al.* (2011) define it as 'a multidisciplinary subject, dealing with the occurrence, circulation and distribution of the waters of the Earth'. In this and the following chapter the author can only present an outline of the subject as it relates to rainfall and flows in rivers and drainage systems. There are two basic approaches to the prediction of flow rates in rivers: return periods and hydrographs. Full details are contained in the *Flood Studies Report* (Natural Environment Research Council, 1975) and the *Flood Estimation Handbook* (*FEH*) (Institute of Hydrology, 1999). A potential source of confusion is that hydrologists use the word 'flood' to describe a high flow event whether or not this causes flooding in the sense the public would recognise. In this chapter I have used the word 'flow' rather than 'flood' except where this conflicts with the specific *FEH definition of QMED as the median annual maximum flood*.

7.2. Return period approach
This is a statistically based technique in which extreme values of flood flows are predicted based on extrapolation from collected records. It is usual for records to be based on a water year, rather than a calendar year. In Great Britain the water year starts on 1 October.

7.2.1 Extrapolated annual maxima method
This is based on original work by Gumbel (1931). In practice the method has become more sophisticated as described in Robson and Reed (1999).

The 1 in T year event is the event that on average will only be equalled or exceeded once in T years. The probability P of the 1 in T event being exceeded in any year is given by

$$P = 1/T \tag{7.1}$$

The N years of records are ranked into size order with the largest record being assigned rank

$$r = 1 \tag{7.2}$$

While for a large number of records it would be possible to assign the probability of each year's flow being exceeded using

$$P = r/N \tag{7.3}$$

this is not reliable for short record periods. A number of ways of overcoming this difficulty have been suggested by, *inter alia* Weibull (1939) who used

$$P = \frac{r}{N+1} \tag{7.4}$$

and Gringorten (1963) who used

$$P = \frac{r - 0.44}{N + 0.12} \tag{7.5}$$

These have been compared by a number of authors and it is generally agreed (Shaw et al., 2011, p. 260) that Gringorten is the more reliable for this application.

If the data conform to a Gumbel distribution, a plot of annual maximum flows against $-\ln(-\ln(1-P))$ gives a straight line which by interpolation, or more often extrapolation, enable the value of flood flow having a particular return period to be predicted.

Example 7.1

The following show the annual maximum flows for a river. Estimate the value of the 1-in-30-year flow using each approach for the determination of P (Table 7.1).

Table 7.1

Year	1	2	3	4	5	6	7	8	9	10
Max. flow: m³/s	5.3	31.2	35.0	13.7	15.4	19.1	17.6	24.2	14.5	24.5

Year 3 has the highest flow of 35.0 m³/s. It is therefore assigned rank

$$r = 1 \tag{7.6}$$

Year 1 has the lowest value and is given

$$r = 10 \tag{7.7}$$

with the other years having intermediate ranks.

Hydrology of river flow

Typical calculations for year 3 are

Weibull $P = \dfrac{r}{N+1} = \dfrac{1}{10+1} = 0.090\,909$

leading to $-\ln(-\ln(1 - 0.090\,909)) = 2.3506$ (7.8)

Gringorten $P = \dfrac{r - 0.44}{N + 0.12} = \dfrac{1 - 0.44}{10 + 0.12} = 0.055\,336$

leading to $-\ln(-\ln(1 - 0.055\,336) = 2.8660$ (7.9)

and for year 1

Weibull $P = \dfrac{r}{N+1} = \dfrac{10}{10+1} = 0.909\,091$

leading to $-\ln(-\ln(1 - 0.909\,091)) = 0.8746$ (7.10)

Gringorten $P = \dfrac{r - 0.44}{N + 0.12} = \dfrac{10 - 0.44}{10 + 0.12} = 0.944\,664$

leading to $-\ln(-\ln(1 - 0.944\,664) = -1.0628$ (7.11)

Figure 7.1 shows the plot of flow against $-\ln(-\ln(1 - P))$ using both equations with straight line extrapolations. The 1-in-30-year flow can be found by using

$P = 1/30 = 0.033\,33$ (7.12)

Using this value of P gives

$-\ln(-\ln(1 - P)) = 3.395$ (7.13)

The corresponding values of flow are about 45 m³/s using the Weibull plotting positions and 40 m³/s using the Gringorten plotting positions. The considerable difference between the two is probably a function of the short series of records available. However the physical situation should never be overlooked. Factors that may cause non-linearity include possible upstream obstruction

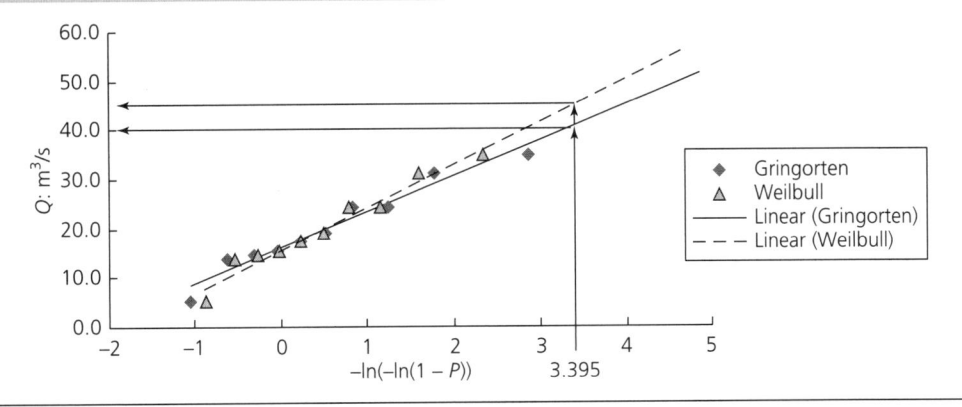

Figure 7.1 Extrapolation of flow records to find 1 in 30 year event

to higher flows or gauging stations being by-passed by out of bank flow. The method does not take account of changes in the catchment characteristics such as urbanisation or different agricultural activity that may have occurred over the period of the records. Note that in practice a longer period of record than used in this example is desirable.

The example assumed that there was a straight line relationship between $\ln(-\ln(1-P))$ and the observed annual maximum flow rate. This Gumbel distribution is termed an extreme value 1 (EV1) relationship. Other possibilities are shown in Figure 7.2.

The *Flood Studies Report* (NERC, 1975) found that catchments in Great Britain tended to exhibit the EV2 pattern. This was most pronounced in East Anglia and the South East of England.

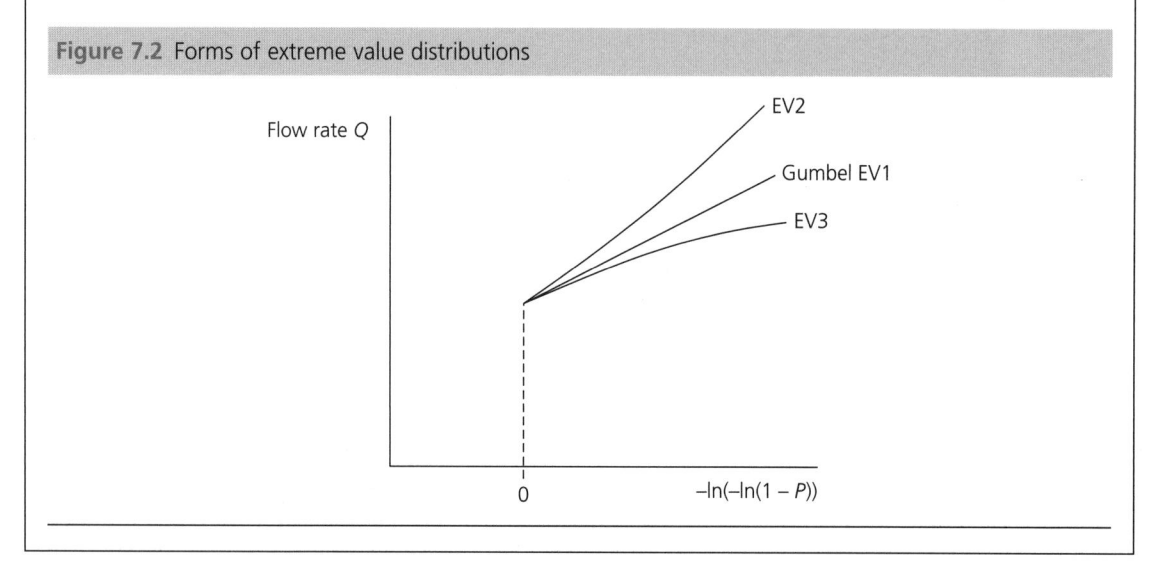

Figure 7.2 Forms of extreme value distributions

7.2.2 Peak over threshold method

A problem with the annual maximum flows approach is that a significant event may be discarded because there is a larger event in the same year, even though the two events are spaced sufficiently far apart as to be clearly independent of each other.

In the peak over threshold method the peak flows taken into account are divorced from the years in which they occur. Figure 7.3 illustrates this with two peaks above the threshold value occurring in both Years 1 and 4 but with no peaks above this value occurring in Year 2. The *Flood Estimation Handbook* (IOH, 1999) recommendation is that the threshold value is selected so that generally in each year there are about five peaks above the threshold.

The peak over threshold method comes with a problem of its own that does not occur in the annual maximum method: can it be guaranteed that two peaks close together are truly independent of each other?

7.2.3 *FEH* method

The *FEH* (IOH, 1999) points out that a gauged record twice as long as the target is desirable for obtaining a good estimate of the true flood frequency. The *FEH* approach is to standardise the annual

Figure 7.3 Peaks over threshold method

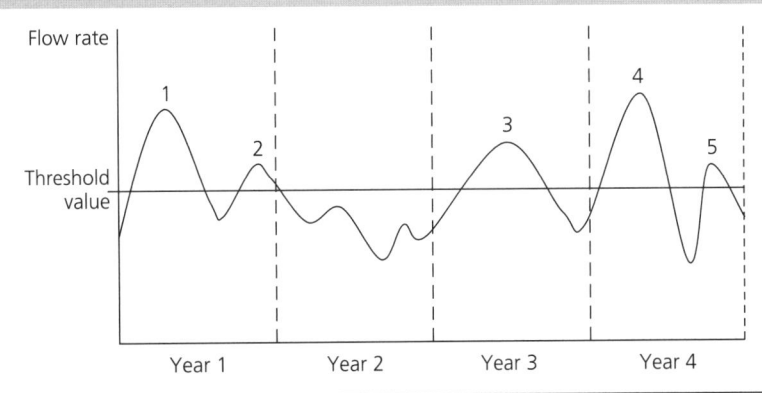

maximum flows by dividing each of them by the median annual maximum flow ($QMED$), also called the index flow. $QMED$ is the flow that on average is exceeded in half of all years. It therefore has an annual probability of exceedance P of 0.5 and a return period T of 2 years. The distribution of values obtained as a result of the standardisation process is called a flood growth curve. The growth curves have a similar form as the curves shown in Figure 7.2, but are expressed in terms of the growth factor. The *FEH* and software based on it use the generalised logistic distribution, rather than the earlier generalised extreme value distribution, to produce its curves. The growth curves have a value of 1.0 at the 2-year return period. An advantage of using the growth curves rather than the actual flow values is that, because of the standardisation process, growth curves from more than one gauging station can be combined to produce a larger data set. Having obtained the growth curve, a growth factor can be established for the target return period. By multiplying this growth factor by $QMED$, the flow rate for the watercourse at that return period is obtained.

For catchment records in excess of 13 years the *FEH* recommends that $QMED$ is obtained directly as the median of the recorded annual maximum flow values and for a catchment record less than 2 years data transfer from a donor or analogue catchment is suggested. For a record between 2 and 13 years, the *FEH* recommends obtaining $QMED$ from peaks over threshold data using the following relationship.

$$QMED = wQ_i + (1 - w)Q_{i+1} \tag{7.14}$$

which applied to records that have been placed in order of decreasing flow rate Q. The ith and $(i + 1)^{th}$ positions as well as a weighting factor w depend on the record length as shown in Table 7.2.

Example 7.2

The following peak over threshold flow values in m³/s were obtained for a watercourse over a 6-year period

89.9   91.0   78.5   65.9   149.6   73.6   61.7   68.3   114.8   77.1   86.9   60.0

Use these to obtain an estimate of the $QMED$.

Placing the records in descending size order gives

149.6   114.8   91.0   89.9   86.9   78.5   77.1   73.6   68.3   65.9   61.7   60.0

From Table 7.2 for a 6-year record we obtain

$$i = 5 \tag{7.15}$$

$$i + 1 = 6 \tag{7.16}$$

and

$$w = 0.725 \tag{7.17}$$

Hence

$$Q_i = 86.9 \text{ m}^3/\text{s} \tag{7.18}$$

and

$$Q_{i+1} = 78.5 \text{ m}^3/\text{s} \tag{7.19}$$

Hence

$$QMED = wQ_i + (1 - w)Q_{i+1} = 0.725 \times 86.9 + (1 - 0.725) \times 78.5 = 84.6 \text{ m}^3/\text{s} \tag{7.20}$$

Table 7.2 Positions and weights for *QMED* estimation from peak over threshold data for record lengths from three to 13 years

Record length: years	i^{th} position	$(i + 1)^{th}$ position	Weight: w
3	2	3	0.100
4	3	4	0.298
5	4	5	0.509
6	5	6	0.725
7	6	7	0.945
8	6	7	0.147
9	7	6	0.349
10	8	9	0.557
11	9	10	0.769
12	10	11	0.983
13	10	11	0.185

Source: *Flood Estimation Handbook* (IOH, 1999)

> ### ✏️ Revision points
>
> - The 1 in T year event is the event that on average will only be equalled or exceeded once in T years.
> - The probability P of the 1 in T event being exceeded in any year is given by
>
> $$P = 1/T \tag{7.21}$$
>
> - If the annual maximum flow data conform to a Gumbel distribution, a plot of annual maximum against $-\ln(-\ln(1-P))$ gives a straight line which by interpolation or extrapolation, enable the value of flood flow having a particular return period to be predicted.
> - The peak over threshold method allows the median annual maximum flood to be determined.
> - By standardising data, the *FEH* version of the peak over threshold method allows records from several catchments to be combined into a larger record.

7.3. Hydrograph approach
7.3.1 Outline of the approach

The flow in a river is made up of contributions from groundwater and surface water. The contribution from groundwater is called the river's baseflow and tends to provide a reasonably steady source of water to the river. The effective rainfall, that is the rainfall that is not lost by evaporation or has not infiltrated into the ground, forms the surface runoff. There is a time lag between rain falling on a catchment and its contribution to the flow of the river.

The contributions of base flow and surface runoff to the flow of the river during and after a rainfall event are illustrated in the hydrograph in Figure 7.4. Eventually the direct effect of surface runoff ceases but the final baseflow contribution has increased because of the recovery of some water that had infiltrated the ground during the rainfall event.

The concept of a unit hydrograph was introduced by Sherman (1932). The principles behind it, based on the assumption of uniform net rainfall occurring across the whole of a catchment are that, for that catchment

- rainfall of a given duration will produce runoff of a specific duration, regardless of the rainfall intensity
- the ratio of runoffs for rainfall events of equal durations over a catchment, are the same as the ratios of rainfall intensity
- the principal of superposition may be used to combine the effects of several rainfall events. This can be used to divide a storm that varies in intensity over time into sub-events.

Based on these principles a standardised graph can be produced (the unit hydrograph) which can be scaled for rainfall events of different durations and intensities.

In essence the approach used is that contributions of baseflow and runoff are separated. The unit hydrograph is combined with the selected rainfall profile to produce the surface runoff hydrograph. The process of combination of the unit hydrograph with rainfall prediction is called convolution. Baseflow is then added back in to obtain the outflow hydrograph.

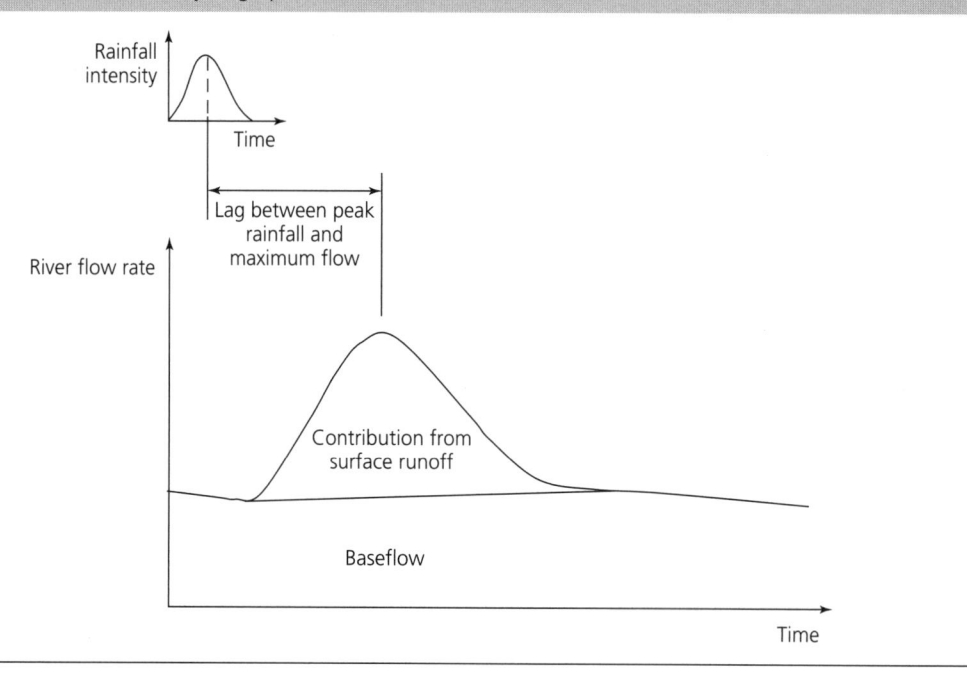

Figure 7.4 Relation between hydrograph, baseflow and rainfall event

In practice there are a number of complicating factors in the unit hydrograph method.

- The effective runoff will vary according to the state of the catchment before the rainfall event starts. This will depend on the time since previous rainfall events.
- Storms are rarely uniform in intensity across a catchment and indeed may not cover the whole of the catchment.

The use of computers has increased the extent to which models can take account of such effects. Examples include the probability distributed model described by Moore and Clark (1981) and subsequent development of it (Moore, 2007).

7.3.2 FEH design storm hydrograph method

The *FEH* flood unit hydrograph method (Houghton-Carr 1999) is based on a single event-based rainfall-runoff model. An outline of the process is shown in Figure 7.5.

Houghton-Carr (1999, p. 37) notes that the 1 in *T* rainfall and 1 in *T* flood events do not coincide with each other, principally because of the effects of catchment characteristics and the degree of antecedent wetness, and includes the design chart, here shown as Figure 7.6, to relate the rainfall and flood return periods.

The storm duration is given by

$$\text{duration} = T_P\left(1 + \frac{SAAR}{1000}\right) \tag{7.22}$$

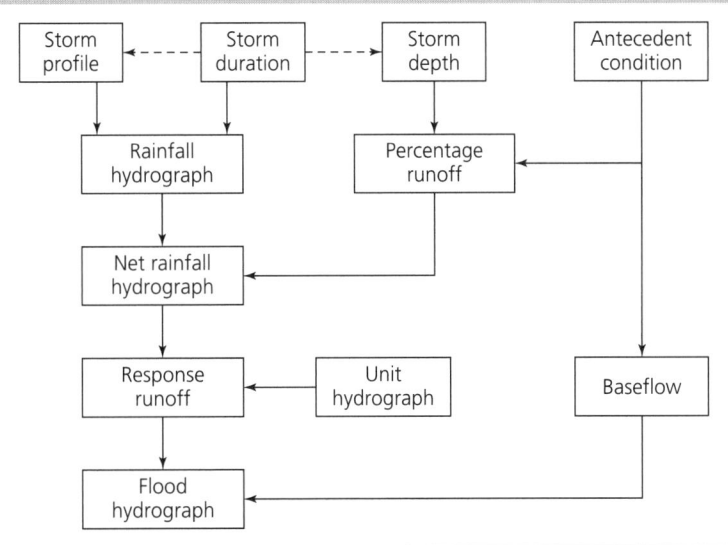

Figure 7.5 Outline of *Flood Estimation Handbook* hydrograph method
Modified from: Houghton-Carr (1999)

where T_P is the unit hydrograph estimated time to peak for the catchment and $SAAR$ is the standard average annual rainfall between 1961 and 1990.

The storm depth is established using location specific depth–duration–frequency (DDF) charts. An example is shown in Figure 7.7. The total depth of rainfall is then distributed using the appropriate storm profile. The theoretical basis and use of DDF charts are described in Faulkner (1999, pp. 4–6). The plots do not consist of a single straight line for each return period: there are breaks in the slopes at durations of 12 hours and 48 hours. The change at 12 hours represents a change from

Figure 7.6 Relationship between return periods of rainfall and flooding
Source: Houghton-Carr (1999) © NERC (CEH)

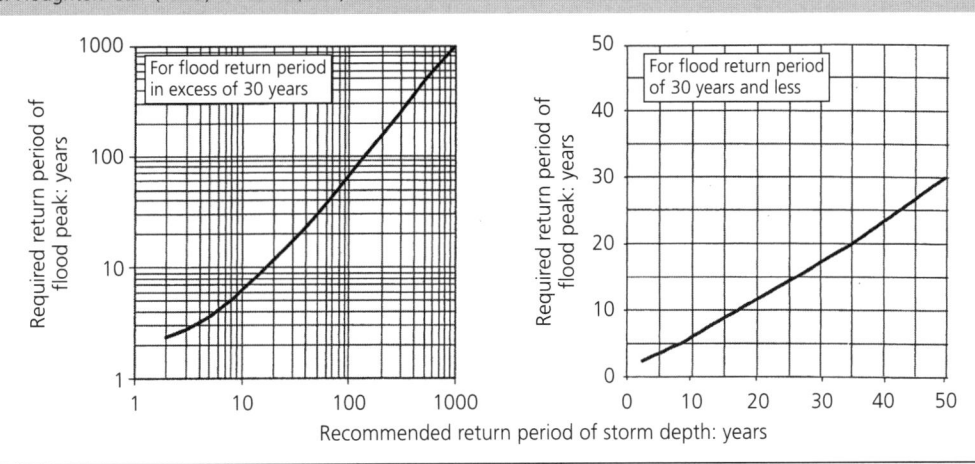

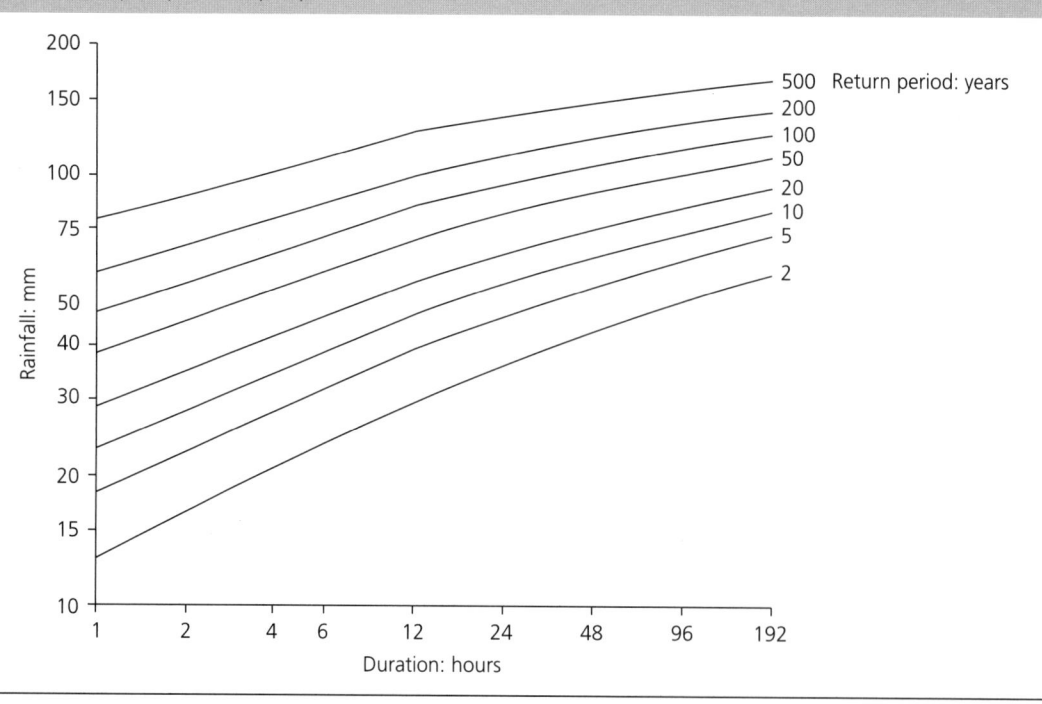

Figure 7.7 Example of *FEH* rainfall depth–duration–frequency (DDF) relationship (for Leicester, UK)
Source: Faulkner (1999) © NERC (CEH)

convective to frontal rainfall. The change at 48 hours reflects the fact that depressions typically pass over Britain in less than two days.

The total storm depth is next distributed according to the design storm profile. Faulkner (1999, p. 13) explains that these are symmetric single peaked bell-shaped curves whose shapes do not vary with location or storm duration. They are divided into winter and summer profiles and are classified by percentage peakedness. In the absence of specific information, the profile choice depends on the degree of urbanisation of the catchment (Figure 7.8). Rural catchments usually encounter floods in the winter. For these the design profile is the 75 per cent winter profile, defined as the profile which on average is more peaky than 75 per cent of UK winter storms. In urban catchments, floods normally result from summer thunderstorms and a 50 per cent summer profile is used. It can be noted that the Institution of Civil Engineers (1996) has criticised such approaches as too simplistic, especially for large catchments with reservoirs and recommended the use of the profile of the severest locally recorded sequence of storms and the complexities that occur in practice are recognised by the *FEH* (Houghton-Carr, 1999, pp. 39–40).

The *FEH* states that baseflow is only important on highly permeable catchments. The baseflow index *BFI* is a measure of a river's long term runoff and derives from stored, mainly groundwater sources. It is expressed as the ratio of the total flow hydrograph to the baseflow hydrograph.

The percentage runoff *PR* is made up of a number of elements: the standard percentage runoff component, *SPR*, the normal capacity of the catchment to generate rainfall; DPR_{CWI}, a dynamic

Figure 7.8 *FEH* recommended design storm profiles
Source: Houghton-Carr (1999) © NERC (CEH)

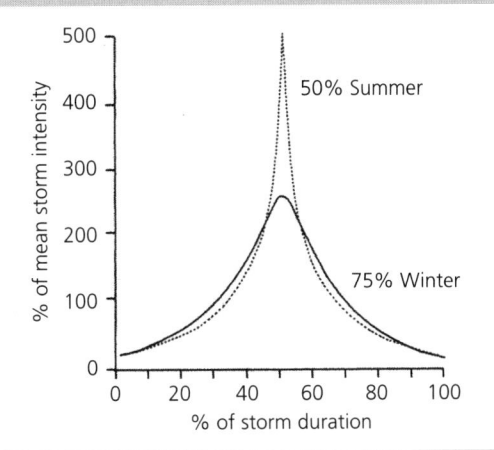

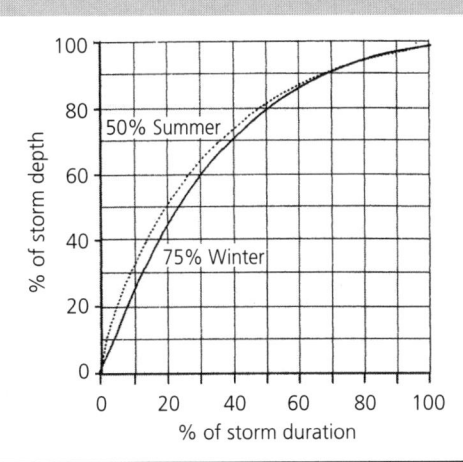

component dependent on the catchment wetness index, *CWI*; and another dynamic component, DPR_{RAIN}, dependent on the design storm depth.

SPR can be found in a number of ways. The ideal is for it to be based on the analysis of at least five past flood events. It can also be found from its relationship to the baseflow index, *BFI*,

$$(SPR = 72.0 - 66.5 BFI) \tag{7.23}$$

by transfer from a donor catchment or, as a last resort, from catchment descriptors.

DPR_{CWI} is given by

$$DPR_{CWI} = 0.25(CWI - 125) \tag{7.24}$$

DPR_{RAIN} is zero when the design storm depth is 40 mm or less. If the design storm depth is greater than 40 mm,

$$DPR_{RAIN} = 0.45(P - 0.40)^{0.7} \tag{7.25}$$

The *PR* for a rural catchment is then found by substituting these values into

$$PR_{RURAL} = SPR + DPR_{CWI} + DPR_{RAIN} \tag{7.26}$$

This can then be adjusted for the extent of urbanisation *URBEXT* in the catchment to give

$$PR = PR_{RURAL}(1.0 - 0.615 URBEXT) + 70(0.615 URBEXT) \tag{7.27}$$

The assumption behind this is that 61.5 per cent of the urbanised area is impervious and gives 70 per cent runoff.

The FEH assumes a triangular shaped hydrograph in which the rising and falling limbs are straight lines. The basewidth of the hydrograph is $2.52T_P$ and, if T_P is measured in hours, the maximum flow rate, or unit hydrograph peak U_p, is $2.2/T_P$ m^3/s per 10 mm of net rainfall over a 1 km^2 area.

Revision points

- Flow in a river can be separated into baseflow and surface runoff.
- There is a time lag between rain falling and the effect on river flow.
- A standardised unit hydrograph can be scaled for rainfall events of different intensities and durations.
- The principal of superposition can be used to model a storm that varies in intensity over time into sub-events.
- The *FEH* provides a hydrograph approach for the modelling of catchments in the UK.
- In general within the UK, flooding in rural catchments results from long-lasting winter rainfall and flooding in urban catchments from short-duration thunderstorms.

Chapter summary

- The 1 in T year event is the one that on average will only be equalled or exceeded once in T years.
- The probability P of the 1 in T year event being exceeded in any year is given by $P = 1/T$.
- The assumption of a Gumbel distribution allows the value of a flood flow having a particular return period to be estimated.
- The peak over threshold method allows the determination of the median annual maximum flood.
- The hydrograph method allows the prediction of flows based on separation of contributions from base flow and surface runoff.
- The unit hydrograph can be scaled for rainfall events of different intensities and durations and the principle of superposition allows the modelling of a storm that varies over time.

REFERENCES

Faulkner D (1999) *Rainfall Frequency Estimation.* (vol. 2 of the *Flood Estimation Handbook*). Institute of Hydrology (IOH), Wallingford, UK.

Gringorten II (1963) A plotting rule for extreme probability paper. *Journal of Geophysical Research* **68**: 813–814, http://dx.doi.org/10.1029/JZ068i003p00813.

Gumbel EJ (1931) The return periods of flood flows. *The Annals of Mathematical Statistics* **12**: 163–190, http://dx.doi.org/10.1214/aoms/1177731747.

Houghton-Carr H (1999) *Restatement and Application of the Flood Studies Report Rainfall–Runoff Method* (vol. 4 of the *Flood Estimation Handbook*). IOH, Wallingford, UK.

Institute of Hydrology [IOH] (1999) *Flood Estimation Handbook* (5 volumes). IOH, Wallingford, UK.

Institution of Civil Engineers (1996) *Floods and Reservoir Safety*, 3rd edn, Thomas Telford, London, UK, http://dx.doi.org/10.1680/fars3e.25035.

Moore RJ (2007) The PDM rainfall-runoff model. *Hydrology and Earth System Sciences* **11**: 483–499, http://dx.doi.org/10.5194/hess-11-483-2007.

Moore RJ and Clarke RT (1981) A distribution function approach to rainfall-runoff modelling. *Water Resources Research* **17**: 1367–1382, http://dx.doi.org/10.1029/WR017i005p01367.

Natural Environment Research Council (NERC) (1975) *Flood Studies Report* (5 volumes) NERC, London, UK.

Robson A and Reed D (1999) *Statistical Procedures for Flood Frequency Estimation.* (Volume 3 of Flood Estimation Handbook). IOH, Wallingford, UK.

Shaw EM, Bevan KJ, Chappell A and Lamb R (2011) *Hydrology in Practice.* 4th edn. Spon Press, Abingdon, UK.

Sherman LK (1932) Streamflow from rainfall by the unit graph method. *Engineering News Record* **108**: 501–505.

Weibull W (1939) The statistical theory of the strength of materials. *Proceedings of the Royal Swedish Institute for Engineering Research* No. 151.

8
Hydrology of surface water drainage

> **Learning aims**
>
> After studying this chapter you should be able to
>
> - appreciate the relevance of rainfall intensity for the design of surface water drainage systems
> - select appropriate pipe diameters for simple drainage networks using the Lloyd-Davis rational method
> - appreciate the role of computer modelling in the design of more complex drainage systems
> - be aware of the environmental and technical advantages of using sustainable drainage systems
> - describe typical elements of sustainable drainage systems and the concept of linking these within a management train
> - appreciate the past obstacles to the implementation of sustainable drainage systems and the moves to overcome these
> - use the CIRIA Report C635 approach to estimate excess run off as the result of

8.1. Introduction

A study of the effects of urbanisation was made by Packman (1980). By increasing the percentage of impervious surface, it reduces the opportunity for natural infiltration into soil with a resulting increase in peak flows and a decrease in the time to peak flow. There is almost instantaneous runoff into piped drainage systems where the concern is usually over relatively short duration high intensity rainfall that is likely to occur during summer storms.

8.2. Short duration rainfall intensity

Several formulae have taken the form

$$i = \frac{a}{t+b} \tag{8.1}$$

where i is the rainfall intensity, t is the storm duration and a and b are constants. These include the Ministry of Health (1930) formulae to give i in mm/h as follows

$$i = \frac{750}{t+10} \tag{8.2}$$

Figure 8.1 Bilham's classification of rainfall for events less than two hours long

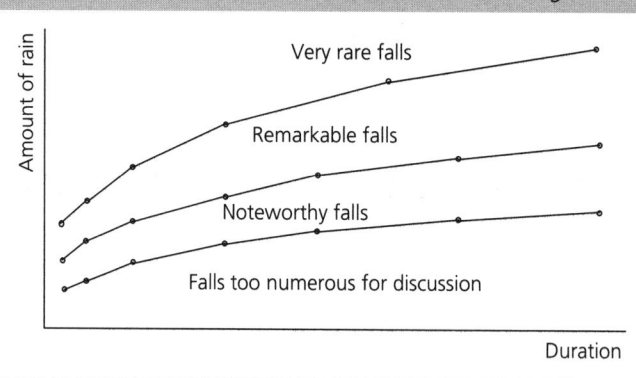

when t is between 5 and 20 minutes; and

$$i = \frac{1000}{t + 20} \tag{8.3}$$

when t is between 20 and 100 minutes.

The Ministry of Health formulae were shown by Norris (1948) to be applicable to storms having a return period of 1 year.

Bilham (1935) studied the relationship between length of storms and rainfall intensity from 12 locations. He grouped rainfall events into four categories as shown in Figure 8.1. Based on 10 years of records his formula

$$N = 1.25t\left(\frac{RD}{25.4} + 0.1\right)^{-3.55} \tag{8.4}$$

relates the number of occurrences of the event of a given duration and intensity within a 10-year period. He also suggested that there was no relation between short-term events and average annual rainfall. In Bilham's formulae RD is the rainfall depth in mm and t is the storm duration in hours.

A modified version of Bilham's formula was given by Holland (1964):

$$N = t\left(\frac{RD}{25.4}\right)^{-3.14} \tag{8.5}$$

Rainfall intensity formulae for various return periods included in the Wallingford procedure (Standing Technical Committee on Sewers and Water Mains, 1981) are shown in Table 8.1.

The Met Office have published tables of rainfall in mm/hr for a range of durations and return periods for various locations and Figures NA2 to NA6 of BS EN 752 (BSI, 2008) present maps showing intensities for storms of 5 minutes' duration for return periods between one in 1 year and one in 500 year as well as maximum intensity for the same duration.

Table 8.1 Formulae for rainfall intensity: mm/h

Return period T: years	Storm duration t between 4 and 20 min	Storm duration t between 20 and 120 min
1	$i = \dfrac{690}{t+7}$	$i = \dfrac{1000}{t+19}$
2	$i = \dfrac{950}{t+8}$	$i = \dfrac{1210}{t+16}$
5	$i = \dfrac{1230}{t+8}$	$i = \dfrac{1530}{t+15}$

8.3. Hydraulic design of surface water sewers

The *Flood Estimation Handbook* (Houghton-Carr, 1999) recommends that, for very heavily urbanised catchments, sewer design methods are more appropriate than the models contained within the *FEH*.

A number of design approaches have been devised, including

- Lloyd-Davies rational method
- TRRL hydrograph method
- constant runoff model (previously called the Wallingford procedure)
- variable runoff model
- fixed percentage runoff model.

It is often a matter of economics (and politics) to decide what return period storm should be designed for. However the National Annex to BS EN 752 (BSI, 2008) recommends for simple methods, such as the Rational Method, designing for a 1-in-2-year event for residential areas and a 1-in-5-year event for city centres.

Only the Lloyd-Davis rational method will be described in detail here as the others require the use of computer modelling.

8.3.1 The Lloyd-Davies rational method and derivatives

This method (Lloyd-Davies, 1906) is applicable to small systems of pipe size 600 mm diameter. It is a simple approach based on the Colebrook–White equation and assuming a uniform rainfall intensity lasting up to 15 minutes which demonstrates the principles involved. However for complex catchments computer modelling would be necessary.

The basic Lloyd-Davis equation is

$$Q_P = CiA \tag{8.6}$$

where C is a dimensionless runoff coefficient and i is the rainfall intensity during the time of concentration. There is some inconsistency over the use of A. Annex E to BSI (2008) uses it to represent the total catchment area. It further comments that for the design of paved car parks, roads and footpaths, the effective catchment area is typically taken to be equal to the plan paved area plus an allowance for any sloping or vertical surfaces draining on to it. Other use is to take it to represent only the area of impermeable surfaces within the catchment.

Several different developments of the basic method have been described as 'the modified rational method'. Perhaps the most common of these (National Water Council, 1981) separates C into two separate components C_V and C_R where C_V is a volumetric runoff coefficient and C_R is a routing coefficient.

$$C_V = PR/100 \tag{8.7}$$

where

$$PR = 0.829 PIMP + 25.0 SOIL + 0.078 UCWI - 20.7 \tag{8.8}$$

and

PR = percentage runoff

$PIMP$ = impermeable area as a percentage of the total catchment area

$SOIL$ = an index of the water holding capacity of the soil, varying between 0.15 and 0.5. The following values are given in the Flood Studies Report (NERC, 1975): 0.15 for well-drained sand, 0.30 for intermediate sandy soil, 0.40 for intermediate silty soil, 0.45 for poorly drained clayey soil and 0.50 for steep rocky areas; and

$UCWI$ = urban catchment wetness index

Typically C_V has a value varying between 0.6 on catchments with very pervious soils and 0.9 on catchments with heavy clay soils.

C_R varies with catchment shape and the peakedness of the rainfall event. National Water Council (1981) recommends that for the UK a value of 1.3 is used.

Taking this value together with the commonly used average value of C_V of 0.75 allows the equation for runoff to be simplified to

$$Q_P = iA \tag{8.9}$$

To avoid very small numbers, where it is easy to miscount the number of places after the decimal point, it is convenient to express i in mm/h and A in hectares (ha). Q_p in l/s can then be found from

$$Q_P = \frac{iA}{0.360} \quad \text{or} \quad Q_P = 2.78 iA \tag{8.10}$$

It is assumed that the peak discharge occurs when the whole catchment contributes to the discharge. The time of concentration t_C is the time taken for rain falling at the most remote part of the contributing catchment to arrive at the point of design interest in the drainage network. It is made up of two components, the time of entry t_E and the time of flow t_F.

The time of entry depends on the distance to the point of entry, the slope of the ground surface and the rainfall intensity. In the original rational method the usual practice was to take a value of 2 min. for

Hydrology of surface water drainage

normal urban areas up to 4 min. for areas with exceptionally large paved areas with small gradients. In the Modified Rational Method higher values, up to 8 min. for a storm of one-in-1-year return period, are used.

The time of flow is determined from the pipe length and velocity of flow.

The design approach is to ensure that the capacity of the pipe when flowing full at the design point is greater than the flow being contributed from the catchment upstream of this point. For surface water drains k has been found to be about 0.6 mm. The velocity of flow and pipe capacity can conveniently be determined from Figure 3.5.

The rainfall intensity for the desired return period and the time of concentration for each pipe is found using one of the sources mentioned in the previous section.

Example 8.1

Figure 8.2 shows the layout for a surface water sewage system for a small development. Details of pipe lengths, gradients and effective catchment areas, along with initial proposed pipe diameters, are shown in Table 8.2. Using rainfall intensities from Table 8.1 for a 1-in-1-year rainfall event and establishing the average velocity in the pipes when flowing full using either

$$V = -2\sqrt{2gDS}\log\left(\frac{k}{3.7D} + \frac{2.51\nu}{D\sqrt{2gDS}}\right) \qquad (8.11)$$

or the Wallingford chart (Figure 3.5), select suitable pipe sizes. Pipes of 225 mm, 300 mm, 375 mm and 450 mm diameter are available. Assume that the viscosity is as follows.

For pipe 1.1
   The gradient (column 4)

$$S = 0.030 \qquad (8.12)$$

Figure 8.2 Plan of drainage layout to be investigated

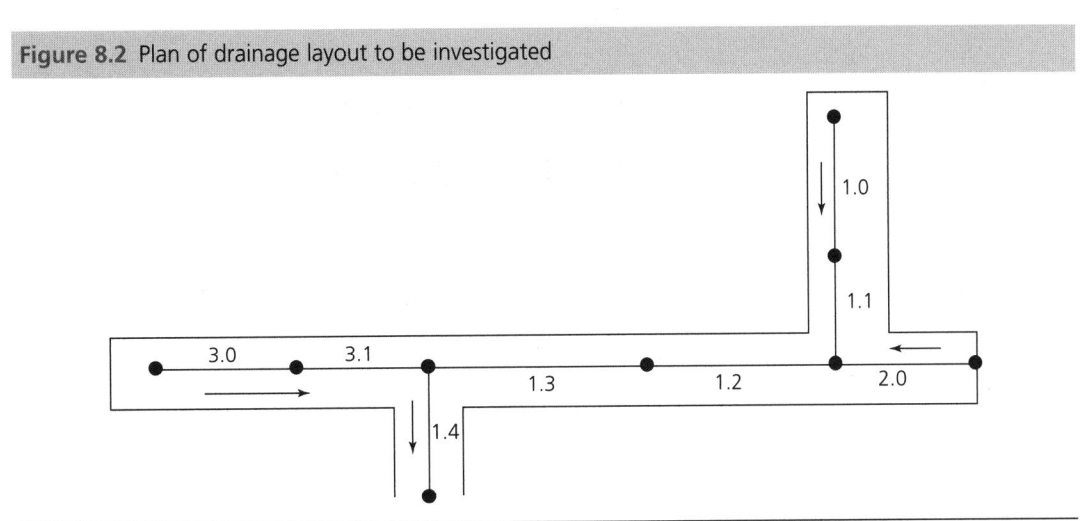

Hydraulics for Civil Engineers

Table 8.2 Details of proposed surface water drainage system

1	2	3	4	5	6	7	8	9	10	11	12	13	14
Pipe reference number	Difference in level: m	Length: m	Gradient	Pipe diameter: mm	From Colebrook–White equation Velocity: m/s	Flow capacity: l/s	Time of flow: min	Time of concentration: min	Rate of rainfall: mm/h	Contributing area: ha Direct	Cumulative	Peak rate of flow: l/s	Suitable size?
1.0	1.4	46.2	0.0303 or 1 in 33	225	2.27	90.2	0.34	2.34	73.9	0.195	0.195	40.1	40.1 < 90.2 ok
1.1	0.59	49.1	0.0120 or 1 in 83.2	225 300	1.43 1.72	56.8 121.5	0.57 0.48	2.91 2.82	69.6 70.3	0.145	0.340	65.8 66.4	65.8 > 56.8 too small 66.4 < 121.5 ok
2.0	0.97	48.5	0.0200 or 1 in 50	225	1.85	73.5	0.44	2.44	73.1	0.120	0.120	24.4	24.4 < 73.5 ok
1.2	1.65	54.3	0.0304 or 1 in 32.9	300	2.73	192.8	0.33	3.15	68.0	0.174	0.634	119.9	119.9 < 192.8 ok
1.3	0.72	84.7	0.0085 or 1 in 117.6	300 375	1.44 1.66	102.0 183.8	0.98 0.85	4.13 4.00	62.0 62.7	0.081	0.715	123.2 124.6	123.3 > 102.0 too small 124.6 < 183.8 ok
3.0	1.1	61.2	0.0180 or 1 in 55.6	225	1.75	69.7	0.58	2.58	72.0	0.121	0.121	24.2	24.2 < 69.7 ok
3.1	1.12	65.9	0.0170 or 1 in 58.8	225	1.70	67.7	0.65	3.23	67.4	0.185	0.306	57.3	57.3 < 67.7 ok
1.4	1.22	27.7	0.0440 or 1 in 22.7	375	5.25	579.8	0.09	4.09	62.2	0.359	1.380	238.6	238.6 < 579.8 ok

Storm frequency one in 1 year. Roughness coefficient 0.6 mm. Time of entry two minutes

This can also be expressed as 1 in 33, although the former version is more appropriate for substitution into the formula.

An initial trial pipe diameter D of 225 mm (column 5) has been used. Substituting relevant values into the formula gives a velocity of 2.27 m/s (column 6).

The flow capacity (column 7) $= VA = 2.27 \times \pi \times 0.1125^2 = 0.0902 \text{ m}^3/\text{s} = 90.2 \text{ l/s}$ (8.13)

The time of flow $t_f = 46.2/(2.27 \times 60) = 0.34 \text{ min}$ (8.14)

The time of concentration $t_c = t_e + t_f = 2 + 0.34 = 2.34 \text{ min}$ (8.15)

Using Table 8.1 the average intensity of a 1-in-1-year return period storm of this duration

$$i = \frac{690}{t+7} = \frac{690}{2.34+7} = 73.9 \text{ mm/h} \quad (8.16)$$

The cumulative contributing area to this first pipe $= 0.195 \text{ ha}$ (8.17)

The peak flow $Q_P = 2.78iA = 2.78 \times 73.9 \times 0.195 = 40.1 \text{ l/s}$ (column 13) (8.18)

Comparing this value with the capacity indicated in column 6 indicates that the selected pipe diameter is satisfactory.

Pipe 1.1
An initial trial diameter of 225 mm has been selected for this pipe. The calculation approach up to column 8 is similar to that for Pipe 1.0 and will not be detailed here.

The time of concentration for this pipe is the time of entry plus the total time of flow within pipes 1.0 and 1.1.

As the peak flow of 65.8 l/s is greater than the capacity of 56.8 l/s, the selected pipe is not large enough. The calculations are therefore repeated using a pipe of 300 mm diameter, which is found to be adequate.

Pipe 2.0
This pipe forms a new run. This is reflected in the time of concentration (column 9) and the cumulative area (column 12). The selected pipe diameter is found to be adequate.

Pipe 1.2
This pipe receives flow from both pipes 1.1 and 2.0. The time of concentration is taken as the time of flow within pipe 1.2 added to the larger of the times of concentrations of pipes 1.1 and 2.0. The cumulative area is the sum of all upstream areas. The selected pipe diameter is found to be adequate.

Pipe 1.3

This pipe receives flow from Pipe 1.2. The initial pipe selection is too small. A diameter of 375 mm is found to be adequate.

Pipe 3.0

This is the start of a new run, reflected in the entries in columns 9 and 12. The initial selection of diameter is found to be adequate.

Pipe 3.1

This receives flow from Pipe 3.0. This is taken into account in the time of concentration and the cumulative impermeable area. The initial pipe selection is found to be adequate.

Pipe 1.4

This receives flow from the entire network. The time of concentration is the time of flow within the pipe itself added to the larger of the times of concentration of the two pipes 1.3 and 3.1 immediately upstream of it. The initially selected pipe diameter of 375 mm is adequate. It is worth noting that this is the same diameter as that finally selected for Pipe 1.3, but has a much greater capacity because of its steeper gradient.

The rational method has a number of limitations including that it

- is only applicable to pipes of up to 600 mm diameter
- is only suitable for small catchments
- assumes different rainfall intensity for the catchment of each pipe
- does not allow for variation in intensity with time
- assumes (apart from some allowance made with the C_V and C_R factors in the modified method) that in urban environments there is 100 per cent runoff from paved surfaces and none from pervious areas
- tends to overestimate peak flows
- has no ability to consider the situation once the pipe network is full.

8.3.2 The TRRL hydrograph method

This method which was described by Watkins (1962) takes account of variations in rainfall intensity over time. An effective rainfall intensity for each time interval is obtained taking into account a runoff coefficient that allows for infiltration. Figure 8.3 shows the boundaries of a catchment with three subdivisions.

Figure 8.3 TRRL hydrograph method: sub-division of catchment area

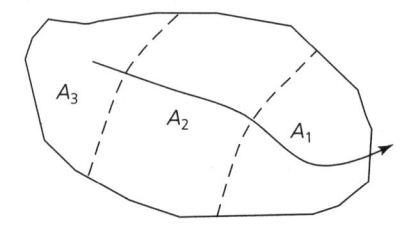

After the first time increment the flow downstream of the catchment is from the first sub-area only and is given by

$$Q_1 = I_0 A_1 \tag{8.19}$$

After the second time increment there will also be a contribution from the second sub-area and the flow now is

$$Q_2 = i_1 A_1 + I_0 A_2 \tag{8.20}$$

The calculations are repeated for the duration of the storm.

The process can become difficult to manage for manual calculation as the number of pipes increases.

8.3.3 Computer modelling of drainage networks

The availability of computer software has enabled limitations of the previous methods to be overcome. An early development was the Wallingford procedure. This consisted of two parts: a surface runoff model and a routing model.

The original surface runoff model used the same equation for percentage runoff as the modified rational method. It is now called the 'constant runoff model' since it assumes runoff does not increase as the catchment gets wetter.

In early versions of Wallingford Software (Wassp) a single percentage runoff value was applied across the whole catchment. The later Wallrus package allowed individual values to be applied to each contributing area.

A 'variable runoff model' was subsequently developed to take account of increasing catchment wetness during long duration storms. The percentage runoff PR is made up of two components: runoff from impermeable surfaces as a fixed percentage decided by the user and a variable element applied to the pervious surfaces updated with time as the catchment surface becomes wetter.

$$PR = IF \times PIMP + \left(100 - IF \times PIMP\right) \times \frac{NAPI}{PF} \tag{8.21}$$

where

$PIMP$ = impermeable area as a percentage of the total catchment area

IF = effective impervious area factor

PF = moisture depth parameter (mm)

$NAPI$ = 30-day antecedent precipitation index

Although theoretically a better model, a practical limitation has been the selection of suitable initial wetness parameters and hence the model has not been as widely used as it might have been. Current software such as InfoWorks allows the choice of a number of different runoff models.

> **Revision points**
>
> - Short-duration high-intensity rainfall events are critical in surface water drainage design.
> - A number of formulae are available relating intensity to return period and maps are available showing regional variations in intensity.
> - The Lloyd-Davies rational method can be used to determine appropriate pipe sizes in simple networks: it is based on an assumption that the peak discharge occurs when the whole catchment contributes to the discharge.
> - The TRRL hydrograph method takes account of variation in rainfall intensity over time.
> - For anything other than simple networks, the TRRL hydrograph method requires the availability of computer facilities.
> - Modern computer packages, such as InfoWorks, allows selection from a range of runoff models to be made.

8.4. Sustainable drainage systems

8.4.1 Background

Traditional piped systems of water management in urban areas, until recently, has worked adequately. Within the past couple of decades however the approach has been questioned from both environmental and flood risk management standpoints.

As part of the European Union's commitment to delivering Sustainable Development, the Water Framework Directive (2000/60/EC) was introduced to raise the ecological status and water quality (chemical status) of all main inland water courses as well as coastal waters across EU member states by 2015. This has implications for discharge of surface water.

Policies designed to reduce the impacts of flooding including planning guidance and building regulations have encouraged the use of non-piped solutions. This was given increased impetus by the Pitt Review (Pitt, 2008) which emphasised the contribution of surface water and traditional drainage systems to major flooding in 2007.

Sustainable Drainage Systems (Suds) have been defined (CIRIA, 2006a) as 'a sequence of management practices and control structures designed to drain surface water in a more sustainable fashion than some conventional techniques'.

Suds techniques include permeable surfaces, filter strips, swales, soakaways (including linear versions called infiltration trenches), infiltration basins and wetlands.

8.4.2 Advantages of Suds

The National Suds Working Group (2004) stated that well designed Suds, implemented and maintained to a high standard can deliver a range of social, economic and environmental benefits by

- reducing runoff rates to watercourse and downstream flooding
- reducing excess runoff volumes and frequency of water directly entering watercourses and sewers in urban areas, reducing the risk of pollution of main water courses and to public health by removing pollutants from diffuse pollution sources generated within urban areas
- encouraging natural groundwater recharge to protect underground aquifers, sources and river-base flows

Figure 8.4 Sustainable drainage at Park and Ride site, Chelmsford

- providing opportunities to enhance biodiversity, amenity and recreation opportunities within urban environments
- reducing the use of potable water for domestic uses, e.g. gardening, toilet flushing, by increasing the use of rain water harvesting.

Creative use of Suds can be integrated into other environmentally desirable objectives such as the provision of wildlife corridors.

Figure 8.4 shows the use of Suds within a Park and Ride scheme at Chelmsford.

8.4.3 Definitions of some Suds elements
The following definitions are based on CIRIA (2007).

- Detention basin: A vegetated depression that normally is dry except following storm events. It is constructed to store water temporarily to attenuate flows and may allow infiltration of water to the ground.
- Extended detention basin: A detention basin where the runoff is stored beyond the time for attenuation. This provides extra time for natural processes to remove some of the pollutants in the water.
- Filter drain: A linear drain consisting of a trench filled with a permeable material, often with a perforated pipe in the base of the trench to assist drainage. Its purpose is to store and conduct water, but may also permit infiltration.
- Filter strip: A vegetated area of gently sloping ground designed to drain water evenly off impermeable areas and filter out silt and other particles.

- Infiltration basin: A dry basin designed to promote infiltration of surface water to the ground.
- Infiltration trench: A trench, usually filled with permeable granular material, designed to promote infiltration of surface water to the ground.
- Permeable surface: A surface that is formed of material that is itself impervious to water but, by virtue of voids formed through the surface, allows infiltration of water to the sub-base – for example, concrete block paving.
- Pervious surface: A surface that allows inflow of rainwater into the underlying construction or soil.
- Retention pond: A pond where runoff is detained for a sufficient time to allow settlement and possibly biological treatment of some pollutants.
- Soakaway: A subsurface structure into which surface water is conveyed to allow infiltration into the ground.
- Swale: A shallow vegetated channel designed to conduct and retain water, but which may also permit infiltration; the vegetation filters particulate matter.
- Wetland: A pond that has a high proportion of emergent vegetation in relation to open water.

Slightly different definitions appear in some earlier CIRIA publications.

8.4.4 The Suds management train

The most successful Suds schemes are those systems designed around the concept of a management train. The management train philosophy (CIRIA, 2001) effectively divides a large development area into small subsections sharing similar local characteristics, that is, soil type, topography and proposed land use, and assesses the most appropriate drainage techniques for each area.

The Suds management train employs four hierarchical techniques for managing excess surface water and the pollutants it carries. These are prevention, source control, site control and regional control. Prevention and source control are the priority, as these enable surface water to be managed close to where it is generated. This however may not always be practical and in such cases the use of site and regional controls will be necessary. The most successful schemes employ a combination of Suds techniques linked via natural conveyance systems, e.g. swales, or through the conventional drainage network. In these circumstances, the different Suds work in series to slow down runoff rates, help reduce surface water flooding, and improve the quality of the water recharging groundwater aquifers or discharging into downstream watercourses. Figure 8.5 illustrates a typical sequence of Suds elements into a train.

CIRIA (2007) provides guidance on the use of Suds techniques. Many local authorities now produce informative guidance on the implementation of Suds in their areas.

8.4.5 Obstacles to implementation of Suds

These have generally centred around responsibility for long-term ownership and responsibility for maintenance and have been a particular problem in England and Wales as compared to Scotland. The principle problem was that the definition of sewer contained in statute did not envisage non-piped systems, leading to reluctance of sewerage undertakers to adopt them.

Pitt (2008) recommended that the government should resolve this issue of ownership and maintenance responsibility, and the issue was finally addressed by the Flood and Water Management Act 2010 (2010).

Figure 8.5 The Suds management train
Source: CIRIA (2001)

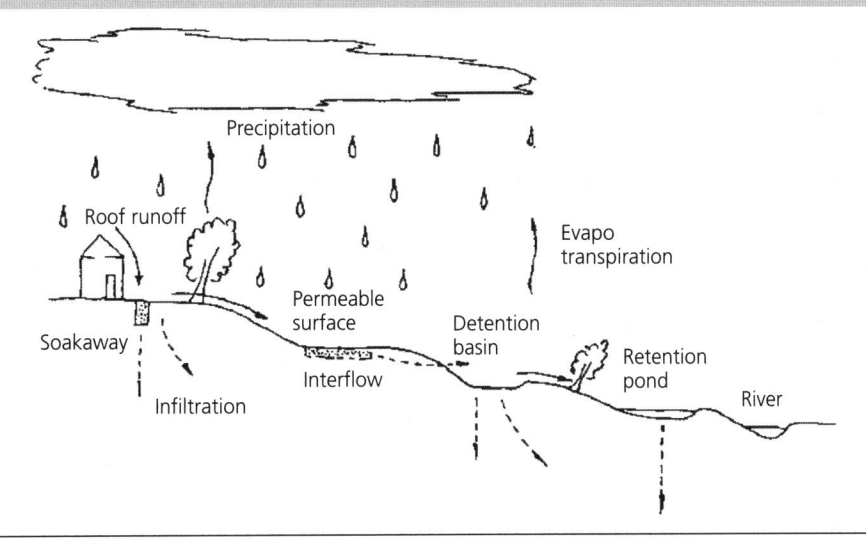

✏ Revision points

- Sustainable drainage systems (Suds) provide a range of environmental and flood risk management benefits.
- Ideally Suds should be designed within a concept of a management train with elements providing retention and source control as the priority.
- Provisions of the Flood and Water Management Act 2010 (2010) seek to overcome past obstacles over ownership and maintenance of Suds.

8.5. Difference between greenfield and development runoff

CIRIA (2006b) provides a method to estimate the difference in runoff volumes before and after development. The approach is based on a 1-100-year 6-hour event and assumes that only 80 per cent runoff occurs from paved areas.

The excess volume Vol_{XS} in m³ is given by the following equation which has been modified from that contained in CIRIA (2006b).

$$Vol_{XS} = 10 \times RD \times A\left[0.8\alpha \times \frac{PIMP}{100} + \beta \times SOIL\left(1 - \frac{PIMP}{100}\right) - SOIL\right] \tag{8.22}$$

where

- RD is the rainfall depth for the 1-in-100-year 6-hour event in mm. This can be obtained from the Flood Estimation Handbook DDF model
- $PIMP$ is the impermeable area as a percentage of the total site area
- A is the area of the site in ha
- $SOIL$ is the index value for the relevant soil type

- α is the proportion of paved area draining to the drainage network or watercourse
- β is the proportion of pervious area draining to the drainage network or watercourse.

Example 8.2

A site of 60 ha is on previously undeveloped land. The one-in-100-year 6-hour rainfall event is 75 mm. The development will contain 15 ha of buildings, 12 ha of car parking and 4 ha of roadway. The soil on the site is an intermediate sandy soil for which *SOIL* may be taken as 0.30.

Using the CIRIA Report C635 (CIRIA, 2006b) approach, calculate the extra runoff due to the development

(a) assuming all the paved area and all of the pervious area drains to the drainage network
(b) assuming all of the paved area drains to the drainage network but that the pervious area is landscaped to prevent drainage from this area to the network.

$$\text{Proportion of impermeable surface} = (15 + 12 + 4)/60 = 0.52 \tag{8.23}$$

On assumption (a)

$$Vol_{XS} = 10 \times RD \times A\left[0.8\alpha \times \frac{PIMP}{100} + \beta \times SOIL\left(1 - \frac{PIMP}{100}\right) - SOIL\right]$$

$$= 10 \times 75 \times 60[0.8 \times 1 \times 0.52 + 1 \times 0.3(1 - 0.52) - 0.3] = 11\,700\,\text{m}^3 \tag{8.24}$$

On assumption (b)

$$Vol_{XS} = 10 \times RD \times A\left[0.8\alpha \times \frac{PIMP}{100} + \beta \times SOIL\left(1 - \frac{PIMP}{100}\right) - SOIL\right]$$

$$= 10 \times 75 \times 60[0.8 \times 1 \times 0.52 + 0 \times 0.3(1 - 0.52) - 0.3] = 5220\,\text{m}^3 \tag{8.25}$$

The difference shows the value of trying to ensure that the runoff, even from the generally permeable surfaces, is contained within the site by, for example Suds elements.

✓ Chapter summary

- Short-duration high-intensity rainfall events are critical in surface water drainage design.
- Simple drainage networks can be analysed using the Lloyd-Davies rational method that assumes that peak discharge occurs when the whole catchment is contributing.
- The TRRL hydrograph method can take account of variation in rainfall intensity over time but requires computer facilities except for simple networks.
- Sustainable drainage systems (Suds) provide a range of environmental and flood risk management benefits, and past obstacles to their implementation are being removed by the provisions of the Flood and Water Management Act 2010 (2010).
- Suds should be designed within the concept of a management train.

Question for practice
- Check whether the pipe diameters calculated in Example 8.1 are adequate for a 1-in-5-year event.

REFERENCES

Bilham EG (1935) Classification of heavy falls in short periods. *British Rainfall* **76**: 262–280.

BSI (British Standards Institution) (2008) BS EN 752:2008 Drain and sewer systems outside buildings. BSI, London, UK

CIRIA (2001) *Sustainable Urban Drainage Systems – Best Practice Manual for England, Scotland, Wales and Northern Ireland* (Report C523). CIRIA, London, UK.

CIRIA (2006a) *Sustainable Water Management in Land-Use Planning* (Report C630). CIRIA, London, UK.

CIRIA (2006b) *Designing for Exceedance in Urban Drainage – Good Practice.* (Report C635). See http://www.ciria.org/service/AM/ContentManagerNet/Search/SearchRedirect.aspx?Section=Search1&content=product_excerpts&template=/contentmanagernet/contentdisplay.aspx&contentfileid=1426 (accessed 10/02/2014). CIRIA, London, UK.

CIRIA (2007) *The Suds Manual* (Report C697). CIRIA, London, UK.

Council Directive 2000/60/EC of the European Parliament and of the Council of 23rd October 2000 (2000) Establishing a framework for Community action in the field of water policy. Official Journal of the European Communities L327 22nd December 2000 pp 1–72.

Flood and Water Management Act 2010 (2010) *Elizabeth II*. Chapter 29. Her Majesty's Stationery Office, London, UK.

Holland DJ (1964) *Rain Intensity Frequency Relations in Britain.* (Hydrological Memorandum No. 33) Meteorological Office, Bracknell, UK.

Houghton-Carr H (1999) *Restatement and Application of the Flood Studies Report Rainfall–Runoff Method.* (Vol. 4 of the *Flood Estimation Handbook*). Institute of Hydrology, Wallingford, UK.

Lloyd-Davies DE (1906) The elimination of storm water from sewerage systems. *Minutes of Proceedings of the Institution of Civil Engineers* **164**: 41–67, http://dx.doi.org/10.1680/imotp.1906.16637.

Ministry of Health (1930) Rainfall and runoff. *Journal of the Institution of Municipal Engineers* **56**: 1172–1176.

National Suds Working Group (2004) *Interim Code of Practice for Sustainable Drainage Systems.* See http://www.susdrain.org/files/resources/other-guidance/nswg_icop_for_suds_0704.pdf (accessed 10/02/2014). Department for Environment, Food and Rural Affairs (Defra), London, UK.

Natural Environment Research Council (NERC) (1975) *Flood Studies Report.* (5 vols). NERC, London, UK.

Norris WH (1948) Sewer Design and the Frequency of Heavy Rain. *Proceedings of the Institution of Municipal Engineers* **75**: 349–364.

Packman JC (1980) *The Effect of Urbanisation on Flood Magnitude and Frequency.* (Report No. 63). Institute of Hydrology, Wallingford, UK.

Pitt M (2008) The Pitt Review: Lessons learned from the 2007 floods. See http://webarchive.nationalarchives.gov.uk/20080906001345/http://cabinetoffice.gov.uk/thepittreview/final_report.aspx (accessed 10/02/2014).

Standing Technical Committee on Sewers and Water Mains (1981) *Design and Analysis of Urban Storm Drainage: The Wallingford Procedure Vol. 1. Principles, Methods and Practice.* NWC, London, UK.

Watkins LH (1962) *The Design of Urban Sewer Systems.* HMSO, London, UK.

FURTHER READING

Cambridge City Council (undated) *Sustainable Drainage Cambridge Design and Adoption Guide*. See https://www.cambridge.gov.uk/sites/www.cambridge.gov.uk/files/docs/SUDS-Design-and-Adoption-Guide.pdf (accessed 30/07/2013). (A number of other local authorities have published similar guides).

Hydraulics for Civil Engineers
ISBN 978-0-7277-5845-3

ICE Publishing: All rights reserved
http://dx.doi.org/10.1680/hce.58453.135

9
Coastal hydraulics

> **Learning aims**
>
> After studying this chapter you should be able to
>
> - appreciate that sea level is made up of a number of components
> - describe changes in mean sea level over time
> - understand the basis of the role of the moon and sun in controlling the tides
> - appreciate the role of meteorological conditions in modifying tides and carry out simple statistical analysis to estimate return periods of surges
> - calculate nearshore wave conditions based on offshore wave data and knowledge of bed topography
> - calculate significant wave height from analysis of wave records
> - describe the process of breaking waves.

9.1. Introduction

Sea level is of primary importance in the design of coastal flood defences. The sea level at any time can be considered as comprising of the superposition of a number of elements

- mean sea level: this varies from place to place and is subject to secular variation over time
- astronomical tidal effects: these are complex, but predictable, changes in level which are tabulated in the Admiralty Tide Tables
- surges: these are changes in sea level caused primarily by meteorological conditions. Their magnitude can be of the same order as the tidal changes and are thus very significant in the design of flood defences. Statistical analysis can be used to establish return periods of surges of a particular height
- waves: these are wind generated changes in water level. Generally speaking waves are most significant in terms of the forces they impose on coastal structures, rather than their contribution to overtopping considerations.

9.2. Sea level records

Sea level data is recognised as important information both nationally and internationally. The Global Sea Level Observing System (Gloss) is an international programme for the establishment of global and regional sea level networks. The Global Core Network has 287 stations.

The European Sea-level Observing System (Eoss) is an EU-supported programme for the enhancement of measurements and analysis across Europe.

The UK network has about 50 gauges, three of which (Lerwick, Newlyn and Stornoway) are part of the Gloss network. Data from the UK network is processed and stored by the British Oceanographic Data Centre (BODC). The Centre is also linked with the international Permanent Service for Mean Sea Level (PSMSL).

9.3. Mean sea level

Historic changes in sea level have resulted from eustasy (changes in the total amount of water in the oceans), tectonic and isostasy (adjustment of the earth's crust to changes in loading). During the ice ages glaciation removed enough water to lower the oceans some 100 m below the present level. The sea level is still rising from the last ice age which finished about 20 000 years ago. The rise since then largely represents water returning to the oceans from glaciers, and warming of the oceans. It is complicated by factors including the isostatic depression of the sea floor as the weight of water on top of it has increased.

Sea level rise over the past century has been estimated to be about 1–1.5 mm per year, with a rise of about 2 mm/year over the past 50 years. Views vary as to the recent effects of temperature change.

9.4. Astronomical tides

Tides are a consequence of the gravitational pull of various bodies on the earth. The most important of these influencing bodies is the moon. The operation of the sun–earth–moon system is outlined in Figure 9.1.

The earth spins on its own axis in 24 hours, while the moon revolves around the combined centre of gravity of the earth and moon once every 29.5 days (the synodic month). It is the combination of the earth and moon motions which produce the approximately 12-and-a-half-hour tidal cycle. This can be derived to a first approximation by considering the time interval between successive occurrences of the

Figure 9.1 Relative positions of sun, moon and earth over a lunar cycle (not to scale)

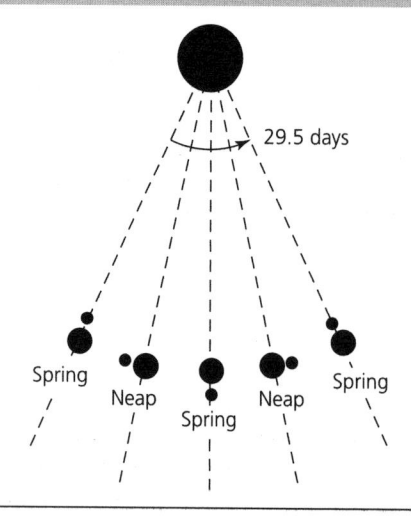

same point on the equator being opposite the moon. The angular speed of the earth is 15°/hour and that of the moon is 0.508°/hour. Consider a time t slightly greater than 24 hours, during which two tides may be expected.

$$(15t - 360) = 0.508t \tag{9.1}$$

$$\therefore 15t - 0.508t = 360 \tag{9.2}$$

$$\therefore t = 24.841 \text{ h (24 h 50.47 min)} \tag{9.3}$$

But it not quite so straightforward. The moon is inclined at an angle of 28°. Thus a line joining the centre of the earth to the moon will cycle between +28° and −28° as the earth–moon system rotates. Another significant effect on tides is that the moon's orbit is slightly elliptical. The effect of this on the tides is such that, when the moon is closest to the earth, the tide-producing force is increased to about 20 per cent above the average, while it is reduced to about 20 per cent below average when the moon is farthest away.

Although the sun is much farther away than the moon, it is much larger. The overall effect is that its tide producing force is slightly less than half of that of the moon. In all other respects the effect is similar, with two tidal bulges being produced. Thus the sun and the moon both produce significant tidal forces.

The combination of the gravitational effects of the sun and moon leads to 'Spring' and 'Neap' tides. Spring tides are the most extreme (highest high tide and lowest low tide), and these occur when the sun and the moon are working together. This happens both when the moon is between the sun and the earth, and when the moon is at its farthest distance from the sun.

Neap tides are the least extreme. These occur when the sun and the moon are acting at right angles to each other, so the tidal bulges from the moon are at the place where the sun's tidal bulge is smallest, and vice versa.

Tidal prediction takes account of the previously mentioned effects and many other smaller scale effects.

The timing of tides does not correspond with 'simple' astronomical theory. There is a lag due to the inability of the oceans to respond instantly to the changes in tractive forces. At latitudes below about 26°, the lag is over 6 hours, and so it never really catches up with itself. By this time the influence of the moon will be pushing the other way, so the tide will end up about 6 hours 12 minutes after the moon has passed overhead. At latitudes in excess of 65° there is zero lag, so the high tide is in line with the moon. At intermediate latitudes the lag is between 6 hours and zero; constant lag for each location, but it is a lag which varies with latitude.

The theory considered so far has assumed the earth to be covered with water. However with the exception of the Southern Ocean, we are dealing with essentially closed basins and have to modify our 'simple' model to take account of the combination of reflection and the Coriolis force to produce a system of rotating tides. The centres of rotation are called amphidromic points and at these locations there is no tidal movement. In the northern hemisphere the tidal wave rotates around this point in an anti-clockwise fashion. Co-tidal lines joining points having high tide at the same time. These lines

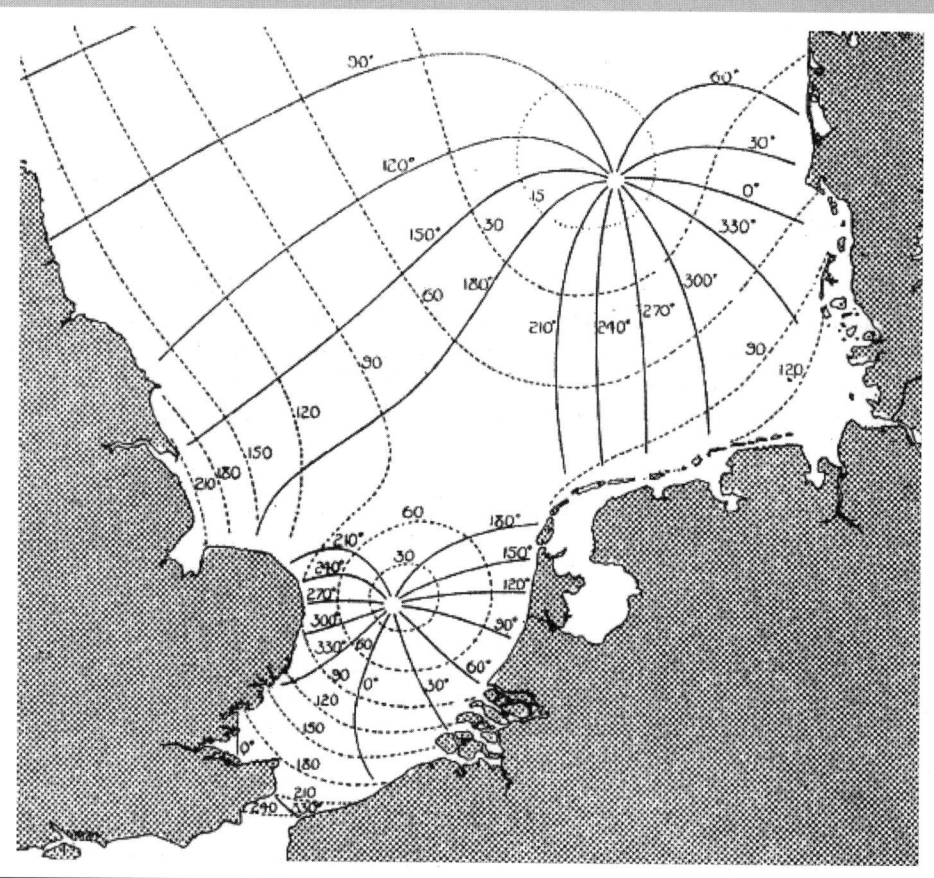

Figure 9.2 Co-tidal lines and amphidromic points in southern North Sea (from Proudman and Doodson (1924))

radiate out from the amphidromic points. From the amphidromic points outwards the range of tides increases and a second set of lines, co-range lines, can be constructed. Figure 9.2 shows an example of these for part of the North Sea.

Tides do not just influence the coast, they also influence rivers. Most rivers are tidal for some part of their length; the tidal part depending on the topography of the river, and sometimes finishing at a fixed point such as a weir. One particular feature is a tidal bore, for which the Severn is famous. This essentially happens because the tide is pushing water in faster than a 'normal' (shallow water) wave can carry it, sending a tidal bore upstream. The Severn Bore is 1 to 2 m high. The Amazon Bore can reach 5 m in height.

9.5. Meteorological effects, including surges

Atmospheric pressure also affects the tides. Sea levels are raised when atmospheric pressure is low, and depressed when atmospheric pressure is high. The effect of the wind can combine with low atmospheric pressure to produce storm surges, and these may be worsened by the geography of the sea. This is the case in the North Sea, where the narrowing of the channel between England and mainland Europe can lead to water 'piling up'. Storm surges in the North Sea can add 4 m to the

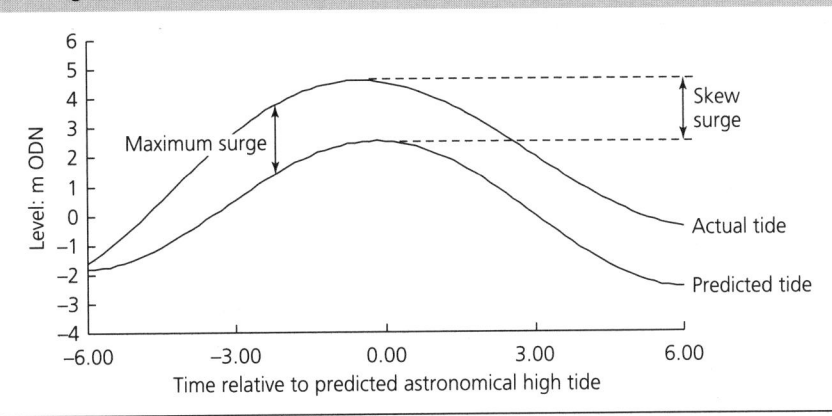

Figure 9.3 Tidal surge recorded at Southend on Sea 31/1/1953 to 1/2/1953 (based on data in Rossiter (1954))

normal tidal height, but are more commonly limited to about 1 m. As indicated in Figure 9.3, the 1953 storm surge added over 2 m to tide levels at Southend on Sea. It resulted in 1800 deaths in Holland and 300 in England. It can be seen that the maximum value of surge did not coincide with predicted high water.

9.5.1 Basic analysis of return periods

Part of the process of design of coastal defence schemes is the prediction of future surge levels. This is based on extrapolation of previous records in a similar way to that used in Chapter 7 for establishing values of river flows having particular return periods. The 1-in-T-year surge is the one that on average will only be equalled or exceeded once in T years.

Example 9.1

Records of the maximum surge tide recorded each year at a particular location are as follows.

1.80   3.10   1.58   3.31   1.66   2.55   1.15   3.07   4.53   2.52

Construct a Gumbel plot of the data based on the Gringorten formula for probability and from this estimate the 50-year-return-period surge.

(Note that in practice a longer series of records would be used: at least 25 as a minimum for reliance to be placed on the analysis.)

The calculations to establish the values of $-\ln(-\ln(1 - P))$ are summarised in Table 9.1.

Figure 9.4 shows the plot of surge level against $-\ln(-\ln(1 - P))$. The trend line is found by spreadsheet calculations to be

$$\text{Surge level} = 0.8447(-\ln(-\ln(1 - P))) + 2.07 \tag{9.4}$$

Table 9.1

Year	Surge: m	Rank	P	$-\ln(-\ln(1-P))$
1	1.80	7	0.648	−0.044
2	3.10	3	0.253	1.232
3	1.58	9	0.846	−0.626
4	3.31	2	0.154	1.787
5	1.66	8	0.747	−0.318
6	2.55	5	0.451	0.513
7	1.15	10	0.945	−1.063
8	3.07	4	0.352	0.836
9	4.53	1	0.055	2.866
10	2.52	6	0.549	0.227

Figure 9.4 Tidal surge return period example

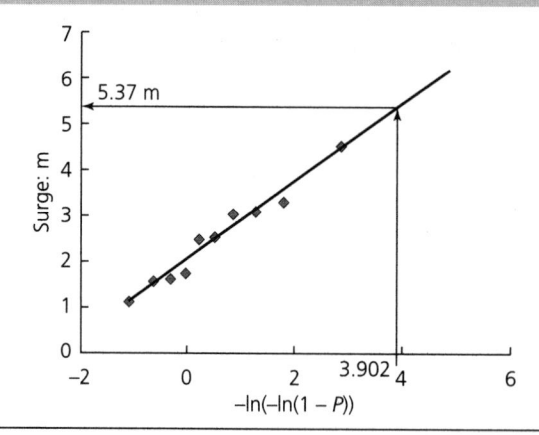

The probability of occurrence of the 1-in-50-year event

$$P = 1/50 = 0.02 \tag{9.5}$$

For this value of P the corresponding value of $-\ln(-\ln(1-P))$ is 3.902. Placing this in the trend line equation, a surge level of 5.37 m is obtained.

9.5.2 Development of work on return periods

Early work by Suthons (1963), following the more general study of Jenkinson (1955), examined the overall tide height, without separating the astronomical and surge elements.

The method assumes data are stochastically stationary (i.e. the underlying process producing the data does not change over time) but has been successfully adapted to deal with the analysis of tidal data having a suspected linear secular trend. This was done for example by Blackman and Graff (1978).

The traditional approach uses the maximum tide level achieved each year of the record and means that no use is made of the remaining 704 tides each year.

In the joint probability method described by Pugh and Vassie (1980) the astronomical and surge effects are separated and all tides during the record period are used. They listed the following advantages of the method over previous approaches.

- Stable values are obtained from very short periods of data. Even a single year can yield useful results.
- There is no waste of data.
- The probabilities are not based on extrapolation.
- Estimates of low-water-level probabilities can also be produced.
- Separate changes in physical factors which affect levels may be identified and incorporated.
- Trends in weather patterns may be identified and incorporated by using variable surge probability statistics.
- Changes in mean sea level can be incorporated by simple addition.
- In some circumstances tide and surge statistics from different places may be combined.

They also cautioned that the joint probability method requires higher quality records with timing to better than two minutes and that there may be some lack of independence between surge level and tide level, the latter point addressed in subsequent refinement of the method described in Tawn and Vassie (1989).

As Figure 9.3 shows, at Southend on Sea the maximum surge during the 1953 flood event occurred about 2 hours before the predicted astronomical high tide. The surge element also increased towards the following astronomical low tide. Recent consideration of such timing differences has led to the concept of the 'skew surge'. This is the difference between the maximum observed tide and the predicted astronomical high tide as indicated in Figure 9.3. Its application to studies in the southern North Sea have been described by Howard *et al.* (2010).

> **Revision points**
>
> - Meteorological conditions may produce significant modifications to predicted astronomical tides.
> - The return period of surges is an important part of the design of coastal defences.
> - Techniques of prediction have developed from extrapolation of records of annual maximum tide to the development of the 'skew surge' approach.

9.6. Waves
9.6.1 Wave generation
Most waves at sea are generated by the transfer of energy from the wind to the water by complex processes of resonance and shear. Factors influencing the wave height that results are

- the fetch over which the wind blows
- the wind velocity
- the duration of the wind.

Figure 9.5 Wave terminology

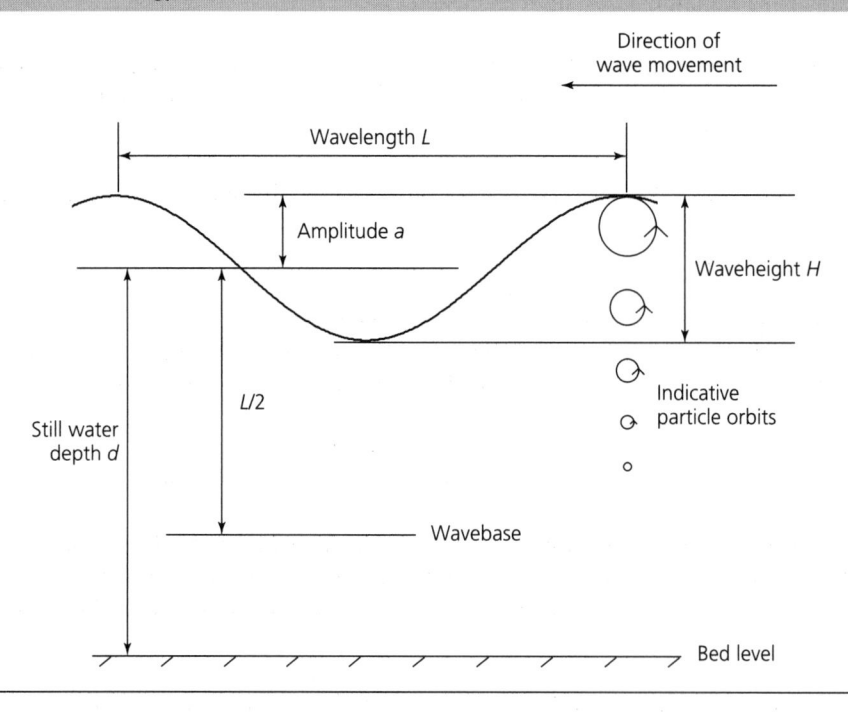

9.6.2 Wave terminology and equations

Figure 9.5 shows an unbroken wave. The highest point on the wave is its crest and the lowest its trough. The distance from crest to crest is the wavelength, L and the difference in elevation between the crest and trough is the wave height, H which is twice the wave amplitude a. The ratio H/L is called the steepness of the wave. The still water depth is denoted by d.

In unbroken waves only the wave shape is transmitted during the process of wave motion. The water particles follow circular orbits which become smaller with depth. Below a depth of $L/2$ the motion has died out. This depth is known as the wave base. The time taken for wave crest to travel one wave length is called the wave period T. The wavelength, period and water depth are related by

$$L = \frac{gT^2}{2\pi} \tanh \frac{2\pi d}{L} \tag{9.6}$$

A complication of using this is that L appears on both sides of the equation. However for deep water, generally taken as $d/L > 0.25$ the following approximation can be used

$$L = \frac{gT^2}{2\pi} \tag{9.7}$$

and for shallow water, with $d/L > 0.05$ we can use

$$L = T\sqrt{gd} \tag{9.8}$$

The celerity (velocity of the wave shape) C of the wave is given by

$$C = L/T \tag{9.9}$$

leading to a general expression

$$C = \sqrt{\frac{gL}{2\pi} \tanh \frac{2\pi d}{L}} \tag{9.10}$$

with approximations

$$C = \sqrt{\frac{gL}{2\pi}} \tag{9.11}$$

for deep water and

$$C = \sqrt{gd} \tag{9.12}$$

for shallow water.

The latter approximation results in the situation that, although celerity can be stated as

$$C = L/T \tag{9.13}$$

in shallow water it is independent of wavelength. An alternative expression for celerity is

$$C = \frac{\sigma}{k} \tag{9.14}$$

where the wave number

$$k = \frac{2\pi}{L} \tag{9.15}$$

represents the number of waves per metre of sea and the angular frequency

$$\sigma = \frac{2\pi}{T} \tag{9.16}$$

represents the number of waves per unit time.

Example 9.2

A wave in water 200 m deep has a period of 15 s and a height of 2.5 m. Determine its wavelength, celerity and wave steepness.

Using the deep water approximation

$$L = \frac{gT^2}{2\pi} = \frac{9.81 \times 15^2}{2\pi} = 351.29 \text{ m } [351 \text{ m to 3 sig. figs}] \tag{9.17}$$

it is sensible to verify that the use of the deep water approximation is valid.

$$d/L = 200/351.29 = 0.57 \tag{9.18}$$

This is greater than 0.25 so the use of the approximation is valid.

$$\text{Celerity} = L/T = 351.29/15 = 23.42 \text{ m/s [23.4 m/s to 3 sig. figs]} \tag{9.19}$$

$$\text{Wave steepness} = H/L = 2.5/351.29 = 0.007 \tag{9.20}$$

9.6.3 Wave energy and power

The energy in a wave is made up of components of kinetic and potential components. It can be expressed in terms of energy per unit crest width

$$E = \frac{\rho g H^2 L}{8} \tag{9.21}$$

Alternatively the energy can be expressed as the average energy per unit surface area, also known as the specific energy or energy density of the wave

$$\overline{E} = \frac{\rho g H^2}{8} \tag{9.22}$$

Wave power P is the rate at which energy is transmitted per unit length of wave. This is given by

$$P = \frac{nE}{T} \tag{9.23}$$

where n, the ratio of the wave group velocity to the individual wave velocity, is given by

$$n = \frac{1}{2}\left(1 + \frac{2kd}{\sinh 2kd}\right) \tag{9.24}$$

Example 9.3

The solitary wave of period 15 s considered in Example 9.2 had a wavelength 351.29 m, celerity 23.42 m/s and height 2.5 m when the still water depth was 200 m. Assuming the seawater has a density of 1025 kg/m^3, what is the wave power per metre of wave crest length?

$$k = \frac{2\pi}{L} = \frac{2\pi}{351.29} = 0.01789 \tag{9.25}$$

$$E = \frac{\rho g H^2 L}{8} = \frac{1025 \times 9.81 \times 2.5^2 \times 351.29}{8} = 2760 \times 10^3 \text{ J/m} \tag{9.26}$$

$$n = \frac{1}{2}\left(1 + \frac{2kd}{\sinh 2kd}\right) = \frac{1}{2}\left(1 + \frac{2 \times 0.01789 \times 200}{\sinh(2 \times 0.01789 \times 200)}\right) = 0.506 \text{ m/s} \quad (9.27)$$

$$P = \frac{nE}{T} = \frac{0.506 \times 2760 \times 10^3}{15} = 93 \times 10^3 \text{ W/m [93 kW/m]} \quad (9.28)$$

9.6.4 Wave transformation

When a wave enters shallow water its period does not change but its wavelength and celerity decrease.

In the process the wave height increases, an effect known as shoaling. By assuming that there is no loss of energy as the wave front advances towards the shore it can be shown that the wave height is related to the deep water wave height H_0 by the relationship

$$H = H_0 K_s \quad (9.29)$$

where the shoaling coefficient K_s can be found using

$$K_s = \sqrt{\frac{C_0}{C\left(1 + \frac{2kd}{\sinh 2kd}\right)}} \quad (9.30)$$

Example 9.4

Determine the wavelength, celerity, wave height and wave steepness of the wave in Examples 9.2 and 9.3 when it has moved inshore to points where the water is (*a*) 10 m deep and (*b*) 2 m deep.

(*a*) When water depth

$$d = 10 \text{ m} \quad (9.31)$$

We can no longer be certain that the deep water approximation for wavelength applies, so use the general form of the equation for wavelength

$$L = \frac{gT^2}{2\pi} \tanh \frac{2\pi d}{L} \quad (9.32)$$

Substituting the numerical values

$$L = \frac{9.81 \times 15^2}{2\pi} \tanh \frac{2\pi \times 10}{L} = 351.29 \tanh \frac{62.83}{L} \quad (9.33)$$

As L appears on both sides of the equation, use successive approximation to obtain a solution

$$L = 144.13 \text{ m [144 m to 3 sig. figs]} \quad (9.34)$$

Celerity $= L/T = 144.13/15 = 9.609$ m/s [9.61 m/s to 3 sig. figs] (9.35)

Wave number $\quad k = \dfrac{2\pi}{L} = \dfrac{2\pi}{144.13} = 0.043\,59$ (9.36)

Wave height $\quad H = H_0 \times \sqrt{\dfrac{C_0}{C\left(1 + \dfrac{2kd}{\sinh 2kd}\right)}} = 2.5 \times \sqrt{\dfrac{23.42}{9.609\left(1 + \dfrac{2 \times 0.043\,59 \times 10}{\sinh(2 \times 0.043\,59 \times 10)}\right)}}$

$= 2.5 \times 1.137 = 2.84$ m (9.37)

Wave steepness $= H/L = 2.84/144.13 = 0.020$ (9.38)

(b)

Where water depth $= 2$ m (9.39)

Using the shallow water approximation for wavelength

$L = T\sqrt{gd} = 15\sqrt{9.81 \times 2} = 66.44$ m [66.4 m to 3 sig. figs] (9.40)

Check that it is appropriate to use the approximation

$d/L = 2/66.44 = 0.03$ (9.41)

This is less than 0.05 so the use is appropriate.

Celerity $= L/T = 66.44/15 = 4.429$ m/s [4.43 m/s to 3 sig. figs] (9.42)

Alternatively using the shallow water approximation for celerity

$C = \sqrt{gd} = \sqrt{9.81 \times 2} = 4.429$ m/s (9.43)

Wave number $\quad k = \dfrac{2\pi}{L} = \dfrac{2\pi}{66.44} = 0.094\,57$ (9.44)

Wave height $\quad H = H_0 \times \sqrt{\dfrac{C_0}{C\left(1 + \dfrac{2kd}{\sinh 2kd}\right)}} = 2.5 \times \sqrt{\dfrac{23.42}{4.429\left(1 + \dfrac{2 \times 0.094\,57 \times 2}{\sinh(2 \times 0.094\,57 \times 2)}\right)}}$

$= 2.5 \times 1.636 = 4.089$ m (9.45)

Wave steepness $= H/L = 4.089/66.44 = 0.062$ (9.46)

Figure 9.6 Refraction of waves

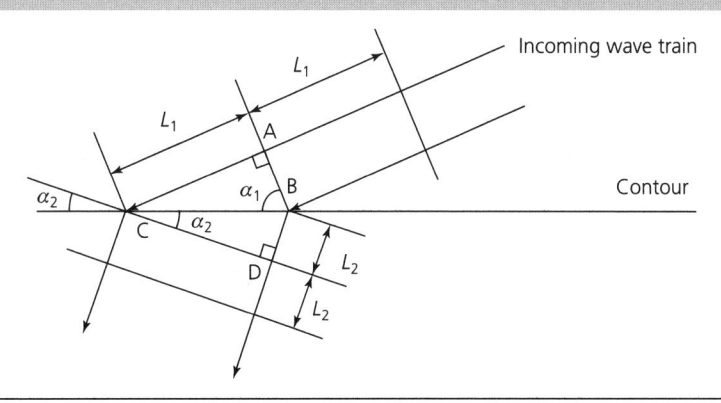

9.6.5 Wave refraction

Waves may not initially approach at right angles to the shore. If this is the case, refraction will tend to bend the waves towards an approach at right angles. The process is analogous to the refraction of light waves. As an approximation consider the bed to be made up of a series of steps defined by each contour line. Figure 9.6 shows successive positions of the wavefront as it approaches and crosses one of these steps. The initial approach of the waves is α_1 and their wavelength is L_1. After passing the step their angle of approach is α_2 and their wavelength is L_2. It can be seen that BC forms the common hypotenuse of the two right angled triangles ABC and BCD. Thus trigonometry lets us relate the angles of approach and wavelengths as

$$\frac{\sin \alpha_1}{\sin \alpha_2} = \frac{L_1}{L_2} \tag{9.47}$$

In practice refraction is a gradual process as the water depth shallows. Nevertheless this equation enables the change in angle of approach to be determined if the wavelengths at different locations are known.

Example 9.5

If the waves in Examples 9.2 to 9.4 were approaching at an angle of 40° to the shoreline, determine the orientation of the waves to the shore when the water depth shallows to 2 m.

We previously found that the deep water wavelength was 351.29 m and that when the water had shallowed to 2 m the wavelength was 66.44 m.

From rearrangement of the refraction equation

$$\alpha_2 = \sin^{-1}\left(\frac{L_1}{L_2} \sin \alpha_1\right) = \sin^{-1}\left(\frac{66.44}{351.29} \sin 40°\right) = 7° \tag{9.48}$$

Figure 9.7 Typical distribution of wave heights

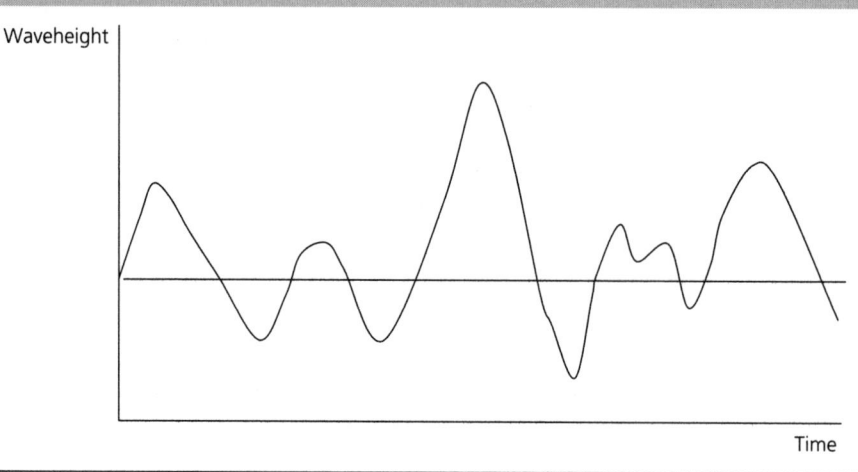

9.6.6 Wave spectrum

So far we have generally concentrated on the characteristics of single waves. However in practice waves are generated with a range of wave heights. The analysis of wave heights is usually based on a simplifying mathematical model. For consistency of approach the zero upcrossing method is generally used. This is illustrated in Figure 9.7. For engineering design purposes for waves generated by a storm, a Rayleigh probability distribution is often assumed as shown in Figure 9.8.

The usual convention is to speak in terms of H_n which is the average of the highest n% of the wave heights. H_{33}, the average height of the highest 1/3 of waves is of special interest and is called the significant wave height and is more specifically denoted as H_s. Other particular values of interest are the average of all the waves H_{100} and the root mean square value H_{rms}.

$$H_{rms} = \sqrt{\frac{\sum H_i^2}{N}} \tag{9.49}$$

where H_i is the height of an individual wave and N is the number of waves in the record.

Figure 9.8 Rayleigh distribution of wave heights

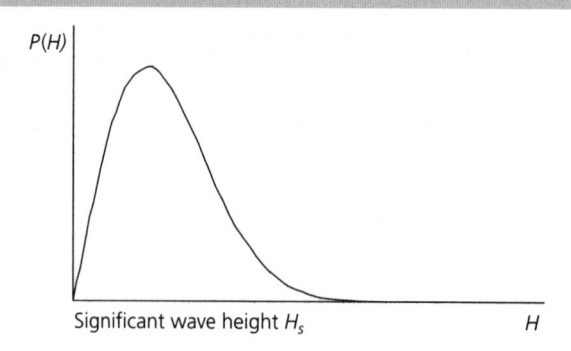

Theoretically for a Rayleigh distribution

$$H_s = 1.414 H_{rms} \tag{9.50}$$

For such a distribution, the percentage of waves in a storm that are higher than a particular height is given by

$$P(>H) = e^{-(H/H_{rms})^2} \tag{9.51}$$

Longuet-Higgins (1952) showed from statistical analysis that the highest wave that may be expected in a storm in deep water is given by

$$H_{max} = 0.707 H_s \sqrt{\ln N} \tag{9.52}$$

where N is the number of waves in the storm.

Example 9.6

The following is an ordered set of 24 observations of wave heights using the zero upcrossing technique:

2.45 2.56 2.96 2.99 3.49 3.71 3.73 3.78 3.79 3.86 3.86 4.02
4.14 4.32 4.53 4.63 4.66 4.85 4.91 5.23 5.33 5.61 5.99 6.31

Estimate the root mean square wave height and from this obtain a value of the significant wave height. Compare the latter value with that obtained from the mean of the highest eight observations.

$$H_{rms} = \sqrt{\frac{\sum H_i^2}{N}} = \sqrt{\frac{454.77}{24}} = 4.35 \text{ m} \tag{9.53}$$

The significant wave height $H_s = 1.41 \times 4.35 = 6.16$ m $\tag{9.54}$

The value of H_s derived from the highest eight observations

$$= (4.66 + 4.85 + 4.91 + 5.23 + 5.33 + 5.61 + 5.99 + 6.31)/8 = 5.36 \text{ m} \tag{9.55}$$

The differences between the two approaches to finding H_s probably represents the small length of the record.

9.6.7 Breaking waves

The example just considered illustrates the increasing wave steepness resulting from both the decrease in wavelength and increase in wave height as shallow water is encountered.

Eventually as a steepening wave encounters even shallower water it will break. Miche (1944) gave the general result for limiting steepness as

$$\left(\frac{H}{L}\right)_{max} = \frac{1}{7} \tanh \frac{2\pi d}{L} \tag{9.56}$$

For d/L less than 0.05, this approximates to

$$\left(\frac{H}{L}\right)_{max} = \frac{1}{7}\left(\frac{2\pi d}{L}\right) \tag{9.57}$$

Galvin (1968) recognised the following breaking wave types

- spilling breakers where the steepened wave crest collapses gently down the front face of the wave
- plunging breakers where the crest curls over as an arch enclosing a cylindrical air space and falls into the base of the wave with a large splash
- collapsing breakers where the lower part of the front face becomes steeper and collapses producing a turbulent water surface
- surging breakers where the crest does not break and the front face advances up the beach with minor breaking.

Attempts have been made by for example Battjes (1974) to correlate the type of breaker produced with the surf similarity parameter χ introduced by Iribarren and Nogales (1949).

$$\zeta = \frac{\tan\beta}{\sqrt{\frac{H}{L_0}}} \tag{9.58}$$

where β is the slope angle of the beach.

This work was further developed by Camenen and Larson (2007) to give the following boundaries between breaker types

- spilling/plunging when ζ lies between 0.2 and 0.6
- plunging/collapsing when ζ lies between 0.8 and 2.9
- collapsing/surging when ζ lies between 3.6 and 6.

To determine the possibility of overtopping of a seawall, it is useful to know the limit of run up of a breaking wave. Early work by Hunt (1959) suggested that the run up could simply be related to the surf similarity parameter by

$$R = H_0 \xi \tag{9.59}$$

where R is the vertical distance above still water reached by the waves. However this area is complicated by factors such as bed roughness and permeability. For rubble mound breakwaters Van der Meer (1993) gave

$$R_{2\%} = 1.5 H_s r_f \xi_p \quad \text{for} \quad \xi < 2 \tag{9.60}$$

and

$$R_{2\%} = 3 H_s r_f \quad \text{for} \quad \xi \geq 2 \tag{9.61}$$

where $R_{2\%}$ is the run up exceeded by 2 per cent of the waves, H_s is the significant wave height, ξ_p is the surf similarity factor based on the peak period of the wave spectrum and r_f is a factor relating to characteristics such as friction and incident wave angle. Further discussion of run up is contained in Eurotop (2007).

Revision points

- The period of a wave remains unchanged as a wave moves towards the shore.
- The speed of propagation of the wave shape is called its celerity.
- The celerity and wavelength decrease as a wave moves towards the shore.
- The assumption of no energy loss can be used to predict wave height as waves progress towards the shore.
- Waves approaching obliquely towards the shore tend to become less oblique as the water shallows as a result of refraction.
- Generated wave heights tend to follow a Rayleigh distribution from which the significant wave height can be estimated.
- The type of breaking wave depends on bed slope.
- The amount of run up can be related to bed slope and significant wave height.

Chapter summary

- Meteorological conditions may produce significant modifications to predicted astronomical tides.
- Techniques of surge prediction for design have developed from extrapolation of records of annual maximum tide to approaches based on analysis of the 'skew surge'.
- The period of a wave remains unchanged as it moves towards the shore.
- The celerity (speed of propagation of the wave shape) and wavelength decrease as a wave moves towards the shore.
- Wave height increases as a wave approaches the shore and can be predicted on the assumption that no energy loss occurs.
- Waves approaching the shore obliquely tend to become less oblique as the result of refraction.
- Significant wave heights can be estimated on the assumption of a Rayleigh distribution.
- Bedslope influences the type of breaking wave and the amount of run up.

Questions for practice

(a) Repeat Example 9.1 using the Weibull formula for probability.
(b) A tsunami wave is caused by an earthquake 1000 km off the coast of a continent where the water depth is 3000 m. The wave height at the point of generation is 1 m and the wavelength is 20 km. How long will the wave take to reach the coastline and what will be its height at a point where the still water depth is 10 m?

REFERENCES

Battjes J (1974) Surf similarity. *Proceedings of the 14th International Conference on Coastal Engineering*. New York, NY, USA. Coastal Engineering Research Council and American Society of Civil Engineers, pp. 466–480.

Blackman DL and Graff J (1978) The analysis of annual extreme sea levels at certain ports in southern England. *Proceedings of the Institution of Civil Engineers* **2(65)**: 339–357, http://dx.doi.org/10.1680/iicep.1978.2950.

Camenen B and Larson M (2007) Predictive formulas for breaker depth index and breaker type. *Journal of Coastal Research* **23**: 1028–1041, http://dx.doi.org/10.2112/05-0566.1.

Eurotop (2007) *Wave Overtopping of Sea Defences and Related Structures: Assessment Manual*. See http://www.overtopping-manual.com/eurotop.pdf (accessed 08/05/2013).

Galvin CJ (1968) Breaker travel and choice of design wave height. *Journal of Geophysical Research* **73**: 3651–3659.

Howard T, Lowe J and Horsburgh (2010) Interpreting century-scale changes in southern North Sea storm surge climate derived from coupled model simulations. *Journal of Climate* **23**: 6234–6247, http://dx.doi.org/10.1175/2010JCLI3520.1.

Hunt A (1959) Design of seawalls and breakwaters. *Journal of Waterway and Harbor Division, ASCE*, **8(WW3)**: 123–152.

Jenkinson AF (1955) Frequency distribution of the annual maximum (or minimum) values of meteorological events. *Quarterly Journal of the Royal Meteorological Society* **81**: 158–177.

Longuet-Higgins MS (1952) On the statistical distribution of the heights of sea waves. *Journal of Marine Research* **11**: 246–266.

Miche R (1944) Mouvements ondulatores de la mer in profondeur constante ou décroissante. *Annals des Ponts et Chaussées* **114**: 369–406 (in French).

Proudman J and Doodson AT (1924) The principal constituent of the tides of the North Sea. *Philosophical Transactions of the Royal Society A* **224**: 185–219, http://dx.doi.org/10.1098/rsta.1924.0005.

Pugh DT and Vassie JM (1980) Applications of the joint probability method for extreme sea level computations. *Proceedings of the Institution of Civil Engineers* **69**: 959–975, http://dx.doi.org/10.1680/iicep.1980.2179.

Rossiter JR (1954) The North Sea storm surge of 31 January and 1 February 1953. *Philosophical Transactions of the Royal Society A* **246**: 371–400.

Tawn JA and Vassie JM (1989) Extreme sea levels: the joint probabilities method revisited and revised. *ICE Proceedings* **2(87)**: 429–442, http://dx.doi.org/10.1680/iicep.1989.2975.

Van der Meer JW (1993) *Conceptual Design of Rubble Mound Breakwaters*. Delft Hydraulics, Emmeloord, The Netherlands, http://dx.doi.org/10.1142/9789812797582_0005.

FURTHER READING

Berkeley Thorn RB and Roberts AG (1981) *Sea Defence and Coast Protection Works*. London: Thomas Telford.

Open University Course Team (1989) *Waves, Tides and Shallow-Water Processes*. Heinemann, Oxford, UK.

Sorensen RM (2006) *Basic Coastal Engineering*, 3rd edn. Springer, New York, NY, USA.

Hydraulics for Civil Engineers
ISBN 978-0-7277-5845-3

ICE Publishing: All rights reserved
http://dx.doi.org/10.1680/hce.58453.153

10

Dimensional analysis

Learning aims

After studying this chapter you should be able to

- recognise that equations need to be dimensionally as well as algebraically correct
- express variables as powers of the fundamental dimensions mass, length and time
- ascertain the dimensions of coefficients when they are not explicitly stated
- use the Buckingham Π method to establish the relationship between variables in terms of functions of dimensionless groups
- appreciate the need to maintain appropriate geometric, kinematic and dynamic similarity between model and prototype in physical modelling.

10.1. Introduction

Hydraulics has developed to a large extent from experimental work. This has resulted in the use of a number of coefficients and constants. Not all of these are dimensionless, and, though hopefully not in this book, some coefficients that do have dimensions may be quoted without them. An appreciation of dimensions is therefore important. This chapter explains the use of dimensions to check the consistency of terms within equations and shows how dimensional analysis can be used in experimental design.

10.2. Dimensions

Irrespective of the system used to measure them, for example SI or Imperial systems, three unique physical components are relevant to the study of mechanics: mass, length and time. They are not defined in terms of each other or any other quantities and they are therefore called fundamental dimensions. It is conventional to use square brackets to indicate when we are talking about the dimensions of the quantities. Thus the dimensions of mass, length and time are shown respectively as [M], [L] and [T].

All other quantities, such as force are made up of a combination of two or more of the fundamental dimensions, for example [velocity] = [L/T] or [LT^{-1}] and [acceleration] = [L/T^2] or LT^{-2}. These are called the dimensional formulae and apply whatever units are used for their measurement.

Force is another derived parameter, given by Newton's second law as force = mass × acceleration. This is called its defining equation. Hence its dimensional formula is [force] = [MLT^{-2}].

Table 10.1 SI units and dimensions of quantities commonly encountered in hydraulics

Quantity	Definition	Dimensions	SI unit
Length, distance		[L]	m
Area	length × length	[L^2]	m^2
Volume	area × length	[L^3]	m^3
Second moment of area	area × length^2	[L^4]	m^4
Time		[T]	s
Velocity	length/time	[LT^{-1}]	ms^{-1}
Acceleration	velocity/time	[LT^{-2}]	ms^{-2}
Flow rate	volume/time	[L^{3}T^{-1}]	m^{3}s^{-1}
Kinematic viscosity	dynamic viscosity/density	[L^{2}T^{-1}]	m^2/s
Mass		[M]	kg
Density	mass/volume	[ML^{-3}]	kg/m^3
Dynamic viscosity	shear stress/velocity gradient	[ML^{-1}T^{-1}]	Pa s
Momentum	mass × velocity	[MLT^{-1}]	kg m s^{-1}
Force	mass × acceleration	[MLT^{-2}]	N
(Intensity of) pressure	force/area	[ML^{-1}T^{-2}]	Pa
Moment of a force	force × distance	[ML^{2}T^{-2}]	N m
Energy, work	force × distance	[ML^{2}T^{-2}]	J
Power	work/time	[ML^{2}T^{-3}]	J s^{-1}

Table 10.1 summarises the dimensions of quantities commonly encountered in hydraulics.

10.3. Dimensional equations

An equation not only has to be algebraically correct, it must also be dimensionally correct or dimensionally homogeneous. Consider for example Bernoulli's equation.

$$\text{Total head} = z + \frac{V^2}{2g} + \frac{P}{\rho g} \tag{10.1}$$

We know that the dimension of both total head and z is length (L), but what about the other terms?

Firstly looking at $V^2/2g$

$$\text{dimensions of } [V^2] = [LT^{-1}]^2 = [L^2T^{-2}] \tag{10.2}$$

g is an acceleration and hence $[g] = [LT^{-2}]$ \hfill (10.3)

2 is a pure number and has no dimensions \hfill (10.4)

Hence

$$[V^2/2g] = [L^2T^{-2}]/[LT^{-2}] = [L] \tag{10.5}$$

which is compatible with the dimension of z.

Checking the $P/\rho g$ term

Pressure P is force per unit area so

$$[P] = [MLT^{-2}]/[L^2] = [ML^{-1}T^{-2}] \tag{10.6}$$

Density ρ is mass per unit volume so

$$[\rho] = [ML^{-3}] \tag{10.7}$$

and we already have

$$[g] = [LT^{-2}] \tag{10.8}$$

Hence

$$[P/\rho g] = [ML^{-1}T^{-2}]/[ML^{-3} \times LT^{-2}] = [M^{1-1}L^{-1+3-1}T^{-2+2}] = [L] \tag{10.9}$$

This is also compatible with the dimension of z so we can say that Bernoulli's equation is dimensionally homogeneous.

It is common in hydraulics for equations to contain coefficients whose units are not always stated. For example an empirical formula sometimes used to determine the discharge Q in m³/s over a rectangular weir is

$$Q = C_d B H^{1.5} \tag{10.10}$$

where C_d is the coefficient of discharge, B is the width of the weir and H is the depth of water over the crest of the weir.

The dimensions of the left hand side of the equation (10.10) are $[L^3 T^{-1}]$ and the dimensions of $BH^{1.5}$ are $[L \times L^{1.5}]$ or $[L^{2.5}]$.

To make the dimensions of equation (10.10) balanced, the dimensions of

$$[C_d] = [L^{0.5}T^{-1}] \tag{10.11}$$

In fact within the coefficient of discharge is a 'hidden' $\sqrt{g}$ and hence its value of C_d will depend on the system of units used. Caution therefore needs to be exercised when using texts that use Imperial units.

Revision points

- Equations must be dimensionally as well as algebraically correct.
- Checks on dimensional consistency may reveal that coefficients in equations have 'hidden' dimensions that mean they are not independent of the system of units being used.

10.4. Dimensional analysis

This is a technique, useful in designing experiments, in which the form of an equation relating a number of variables can be established prior to carrying out the practical work. This enables the experimenter to plan the investigation in a logical way. The approach was first described by Fourier (1822) but has become known as Rayleigh's method after his application of it in Strutt (1877).

Example 10.1

Likely factors influencing the pressure drop ΔP along a pipe conveying a liquid are the pipe diameter D, the pipe length L, the velocity V, the liquid viscosity μ, and the liquid density ρ. Establish a possible relationship between ΔP and these variables.

An initial simplification can be made by considering the problem in terms of the pressure drop per unit length $\Delta P/L$.

Expressing this as an equation where C is an unknown constant and a, b, d and e are unknown exponents, we have

$$\frac{\Delta P}{L} = C D^a V^b \mu^d \rho^e \tag{10.12}$$

Noting that as C is dimensionless it does not appear in the dimensional version of this equation which is

$$[ML^{-2}T^{-2}] = [L]^a \times [LT^{-1}]^b \times [ML^{-1}T^{-1}]^d \times [ML^{-3}]^e \tag{10.13}$$

It is now possible to equate powers of [L], [M], and [T] on each side of the equation

[L]: $-2 = a + b - d - 3e$

[M]: $1 = d + e$

[T]: $-2 = -b - d$

Examination of these relationships shows that it is possible to express each of a, b and e in terms of d.

So from the relationship for powers of [M] we obtain $e = 1 - d$; and the relationship for powers of [T] gives $b = 2 - d$.

These can be substituted in the relationship for powers of L to give

$$-2 = a + (2 - d) - d - 3(1 - d) \tag{10.14}$$

or

$$-2 = a + 2 - d - d - 3 + 3d \tag{10.15}$$

leading to $a = -(1 + d)$.

Substituting all these in the equation for $\Delta P/L$ we get

$$\frac{\Delta P}{L} = CD^{-(1+d)}V^{(2-d)}\mu^d\rho^{(1-d)} = CD^{-1}D^{-d}V^2V^{-d}\mu^d\rho\rho^{-d} = C\frac{V^2\rho}{D}\left(\frac{\mu}{DV\rho}\right)^d \quad (10.16)$$

You may notice that the term in brackets is $1/Re$ where Re is the dimensionless Reynolds number, so we can write

$$\frac{\Delta P}{L}\frac{D}{V^2\rho} = f(Re) \quad (10.17)$$

with $D/V^2\rho$ being another dimensionless group. Dimensional analysis is unable to allow the values of pure numerical constants such as C in the previous equation to be determined.

The application of the method to the analysis of rainfall events is given in Kahlig (1993).

10.4.1 Buckingham Π method

The preceding example resulted in two dimensionless groups (or Π numbers), that is

$$\Pi_1 = \frac{\Delta P}{L}\frac{D}{V^2\rho} \quad (10.18)$$

and

$$\Pi_2 = Re \quad (10.19)$$

The process by which they were obtained could well have seemed obscure. Buckingham's (1915, 1924) theory enables the number of dimensionless groups to be assessed from the start.

Buckingham's theory states that if there are n variables and if there are m fundamentals then there are (n − m) dimensionless groups or Π numbers and a unique relationship exists between the Π numbers, which describes the phenomenon under consideration.

A recurring set is selected using m of the n variables. The m variables in the recurring set must contain all the dimensions needed to define the system. Except in simple cases this will be all of M, L and T. This is so that when combining with the remaining variables, units will cancel to form dimensionless groups. In selecting the recurring set the chosen variables should take account of the reality of the physical situation so for example for modelling they should be capable of being fixed or easily measured.

The recurring set is combined in turn with each of the remaining variables to form the (n − m) dimensionless groups. Each of these groups will therefore contain the recurring set of variables plus one of the remaining variables.

If it is desired that any particular term occurs only once, it should not be included in the recurring set.

Cautionary advice on the use of the Buckingham Π method was contained within Sharp *et al.* (1976). This included the comment that it is 'a relatively mechanical technique and must be combined with some insight of the nature of the problem in order to yield the most useful results'.

Example 10.2

Use the Buckingham Π method to establish dimensionless groups for the pressure drop in a pipe previously considered in Example 10.1.

The variables can be taken as: $\Delta p/L$, D, V, μ and ρ. Hence

$$n = 5 \tag{10.20}$$

The fundamentals are M, L and T. Hence

$$m = 3 \tag{10.21}$$

The number of dimensionless groups is therefore

$$5 - 3 = 2 \tag{10.22}$$

Selecting V, μ and ρ to form the recurring set, we have the following.

$$[V] = [LT^{-1}] \tag{10.23}$$

$$[\mu] = [ML^{-1}T^{-1}] \tag{10.24}$$

and

$$[\rho] = [ML^{-3}]. \tag{10.25}$$

Now we have to combine these in turn with the remaining two variables. Combining with

$$[\Delta P/L] = [ML^{-2}T^{-2}] \tag{10.26}$$

and, remembering that anything raised to the power zero gives an answer of unity, we can write

$$[ML^{-2}T^{-2}] \times [LT^{-1}]^a \times [ML^{-1}T^{-1}]^b \times [ML^{-3}]^c = [M^0L^0T^0] \tag{10.27}$$

By equating the powers of [M], [L] and [T] we obtain $a = -3$, $b = 1$ and $c = 2$. Hence

$$\Pi_1 = \frac{\Delta P}{L} \frac{\mu \rho^2}{V^3} \tag{10.28}$$

In a similar way we can combine the recurring set with D to obtain

$$[L] \times [LT^{-1}]^p \times [ML^{-1}T^{-1}]^q \times [ML^{-3}]^r = M^0L^0T^0 \tag{10.29}$$

from which p = 1, q = −1 and r = 1. Hence

$$\Pi_2 = \frac{\rho D V}{\mu} \tag{10.30}$$

We can therefore say

$$f\left(\frac{\Delta P}{L} \frac{\mu}{\rho V^3}, \frac{\rho D V}{\mu}\right) = 0 \tag{10.31}$$

Revision points

- Dimensional analysis is a technique, based on homogeneity of dimensions, that allows relationships between variables to be expressed in terms of dimensionless groups.
- The Buckingham Π method provides a logical approach to the determination of these groups.

10.5. Similarity

Investigation of hydraulic problems sometimes requires the construction of physical models. The aim is to achieve physical similarity between the model and the real life (prototype) situation. Principal aspects to consider are geometric, kinematic and dynamic similarity. These are not completely independent of each other. Similarity can be illustrated for the hydraulic structure illustrated in Figure 10.1.

10.5.1 Geometric similarity

To maintain similarity of shape, the ratio of lengths L_1 and L_2 in the model and prototype must be the same, that is

$$\frac{(L_1)_m}{(L_2)_m} = \frac{(L_1)_p}{(L_2)_p} \tag{10.32}$$

A number of practical problems arise in trying to achieve this. For example to model a mobile bed of a river the model sediment may have to be so fine that its behaviour no longer matched that of the

Figure 10.1 Illustration of hydraulic similarity

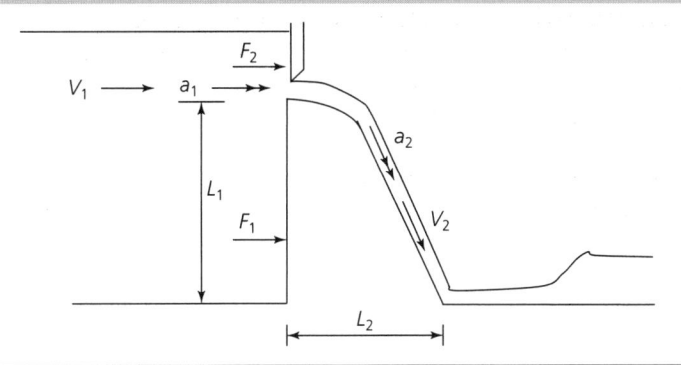

prototype. Some compromise will therefore sometimes be needed but the important consideration is to avoid changing the hydraulic behaviour arising from the boundary conditions.

10.5.2 Kinematic similarity

This requires velocities (V) and accelerations (a) at corresponding locations within the model and prototype to have the same ratios, that is

$$\frac{(V_1)_m}{(V_2)_m} = \frac{(V_1)_p}{(V_2)_p} \quad \text{and} \quad \frac{(a_1)_m}{(a_2)_m} = \frac{(a_1)_p}{(a_2)_p} \tag{10.33}$$

Kinematically similar flows are only possible past geometrically similar boundaries. However geometrically similar boundaries do not always ensure similarity of flow at a distance from the boundaries.

10.5.3 Dynamic similarity

This is similarity of forces, that is

$$\frac{(F_1)_m}{(F_2)_m} = \frac{(F_1)_p}{(F_2)_p} \tag{10.34}$$

In reality the force system is not as simple as shown in Figure 10.1. Dynamic similarity implies geometric similarity of the force polygons of the model and prototype. This will usually be established by finding the ratio of the inertia force to the force resisting motion. The inertia force is proportional to mass × acceleration. Depending on the situation under consideration the resisting forces could arise for example from pressure, gravity, viscosity or surface tension. Dynamic similarity is achieved if the force ratio of the model and prototype are the same.

> **Revision points**
>
> - Geometric similarity refers to the maintenance of consistent shape relationships between the model and the prototype.
> - Kinematic similarity requires the ratios of velocities and accelerations between the model and the prototype to be consistent throughout the model.
> - Dynamic similarity requires the ratio of forces between the model and prototype to be constant throughout the model.

10.6. Use of dimensionless numbers in model scaling

The achievement of dynamic similarity in hydraulic modelling will usually be demonstrated by the consistency of Euler, Froude or Reynolds number between the model and the prototype on the assumption that one of the resisting forces is dominant.

10.6.1 Pressure coefficient and Euler number

If the position head remains constant, it is possible to re-arrange the Bernoulli equation to give the dimensionless equation

$$\frac{(P_1 - P_2)}{0.5\rho V_2^2} = \left(1 - \frac{V_1^2}{V_2^2}\right) \tag{10.35}$$

The term on the left hand side of the equation is called the pressure coefficient C_p and is the ratio of the pressure force to the inertia force.

There is inconsistency over the use of 'Euler number' Eu within hydraulics. It is sometimes taken to be the expression for C_p but without the 0.5 in the denominator. Other usage is to assign it to the square root of the inertia force divided by the pressure force and will usually be written as

$$Eu = \frac{V}{\sqrt{\frac{2\Delta P}{\rho}}} \tag{10.36}$$

These parameters are important in modelling enclosed systems where turbulence is fully developed. Applied pressures are then the controlling force since viscous forces are negligible and surface tension is absent.

In a model based on Euler scaling $(Eu)_m = (Eu)_p$ leading to a velocity ratio

$$\frac{V_m}{V_p} = \sqrt{\frac{\Delta p_m}{\Delta p_p} \frac{\rho_p}{\rho_m}} \tag{10.37}$$

10.6.2 Froude number
In models with a free surface, gravity is the predominant force and hence models must be based on Froude law scaling. We have already encountered the Froude number when examining open channel flow

$$Fr = \frac{V}{\sqrt{gm}} \tag{10.38}$$

where m was the hydraulic mean depth.

More generally for Froude law scaling we require

$$\frac{V_m}{V_p} = \sqrt{\frac{L_p}{L_m}} \tag{10.39}$$

where L is a dominant dimension, usually depth.

Examples of such models are weirs, spillways, open channels, estuaries and gravity waves.

10.6.3 Reynolds number
In cases where viscosity or viscous drag are important, the model must be based on Reynolds law scaling.

In the context of flow in circular pipes

$$Re = \frac{\rho V D}{\mu} = \frac{VD}{\nu} \tag{10.40}$$

If $(Re)_m = (Re)_p$ then more generally the velocity ratio

$$\frac{V_m}{V_p} = \frac{v_m}{v_p}\frac{L_p}{L_m} \qquad (10.41)$$

If the same liquid is used for both model and prototype, then the model velocities will be greater than the prototype velocities. This may provide practical problems which can sometimes be overcome by using a liquid with a different value of viscosity in the model. This is an illustration of the general principle that it is the value of the dimensionless number, in this case Reynolds number, that needs to remain constant between the model and the prototype, not any particular variable that is included within its makeup.

10.6.4 Weber number

It is rare for civil engineering investigations to need this dimensionless number which is appropriate where surface tension is the resisting force. Perhaps the most likely area for it to arise is when investigating low flows over a weir.

As with the Euler number, there are inconsistencies in the definition of the Weber number We with some authors using

$$We = \frac{\text{inertia force}}{\text{surface tension force}} \qquad (10.42)$$

and some using

$$We = \sqrt{\frac{\text{inertia force}}{\text{surface tension force}}} \qquad (10.43)$$

10.6.5 Scale effects

Except in a full-scale model it is impossible to satisfy all conditions of similarity. The deviation of the model is called the scale effect. Effectively scale effects are the distortions brought about by ignoring forces other than the dominant one. Measures of such scale effect can be obtained by building more than one model of the prototype to different scales.

In civil engineering situations rough turbulent flow usually occurs. A laminar flow model of a turbulent flow prototype will give incorrect results. It should also be noted that surface tension effects, that are negligible in the prototype, may become significant in the model if its scale is too small. The latter effect may be significant if a large river system is modelled to an undistorted scale. In such a situation different vertical and horizontal scales are often used.

Example 10.3

The frictional loss h_f in a length L of pipe of diameter D and roughness height k may be expressed in the form

$$h_f = \frac{LV^2}{gD} f\left(\frac{VD}{v}, \frac{k}{D}\right) \qquad (10.44)$$

where V is the mean velocity and v is the kinematic viscosity of the liquid.

A model pipe of diameter 25 mm and relative roughness $k/D = 0.01$ causes a head loss of 1 m per unit length when $V = 4.5$ m/s. Calculate the corresponding velocity and energy gradient h_f/L in the prototype pipe of 250 mm with the same roughness.

We require

$$\left(\frac{VD}{\nu}\right)_m = \left(\frac{VD}{\nu}\right)_p \qquad (10.45)$$

and, since the same liquid is being used in the model as in the prototype,

$$(VD)_m = (VD)_p \qquad (10.46)$$

Substituting the numerical values

$$4.5 \times 25 = V_P \times 250 \qquad (10.47)$$

leading to

$$V_P = 0.45 \text{ m/s} \qquad (10.48)$$

We also require

$$\left(\frac{h_f}{L}\frac{gD}{V^2}\right)_m = \left(\frac{h_f}{L}\frac{gD}{V^2}\right)_p \qquad (10.49)$$

and again substituting the numerical values

$$1 \times \frac{9.81 \times 25}{4.5^2} = \left(\frac{h_f}{L}\right)_p \times \frac{9.81 \times 250}{0.45^2} \qquad (10.50)$$

From this

$$\left(\frac{h_f}{L}\right)_p = 1 \times 10^{-3} \text{ m per unit length} \qquad (10.51)$$

Revision points

- The use of the dimensionless Euler, Froude, Reynolds and Weber numbers provides a logical approach to satisfaction of dynamic similarity in hydraulic modelling.
- For investigations where applied pressure forces are the dominant force, Euler scaling is appropriate.
- Where, for example in open channel flow, gravity is the dominant force, Froude number scaling is appropriate.

- Where viscosity is important, Reynolds number scaling is appropriate.
- Weber scaling is appropriate where surface tension is an important element of the investigation.

✓ Chapter summary

- Equations must be dimensionally as well as algebraically correct.
- Checks on dimensional consistency can be used to identify 'hidden' dimensions that are not independent of the system of units being used.
- Dimensional analysis allows relationships between variables to be expressed in terms of dimensionless groups such as Reynold's number.
- Maintenance of geometric, kinematic and dynamic similarity are important considerations in physical modelling of hydraulic systems.
- The use of dimensionless Euler, Froude, Reynolds and Weber numbers allows a logical approach to maintaining dynamic similarity in modelling.

Questions for practice

During turbulent flow of a liquid in a rough pipe the shear stress τ depends on the liquid's dynamic viscosity μ, density ρ and velocity V as well as the pipe's diameter D and surface roughness k.

Using dimensional analysis show that it is possible to express the relationship between the variables as

$$\frac{\tau}{\rho V^2 D^2} = f\left(\frac{\mu}{\rho V D}, \frac{k}{D}\right) \tag{10.52}$$

REFERENCES

Buckingham E (1915) Model experiments and the form of empirical equations. *Trans. ASCE* **37**: 263–296.

Buckingham E (1924) Dimensional analysis. *Philosophical Magazine Series 6* **48**: 141–145, http://dx.doi.org/10.1080/14786442408634474.

Fourier J (1822) Chapter ii, §9 in *Théorie de la Chaleur*. Firman Didot, Paris, France (In French: English translation in Freeman A (1878) *The Analytical Theory of Heat*. CUP, Cambridge, UK.)

Sharp JJ, Ali KHM, Smith AA, Barr DIH, Thomson A and Shepherd KL (1976) Discussion on 'A Dimensionless Number for the Study of Open Channel Flow'. *ICE Proceedings* **61**: 233–245.

Strutt JW [Lord Rayleigh] (1877) §52 in *The Theory of Sound*, vol. 1. Macmillan, London, UK, http://dx.doi.org/10.1017/CBO9781139058087.

FURTHER READING

Chanson H (1999) Ch. 14 in *The Hydraulics of Open Channel Flow*, pp. 261–283. Arnold, London.

Kahlig (1993) 'On Deterministic Criteria for Heavy Rainfall at a Point'. *Theoretical and Applied Climatology* **46**: 203–208, http://dx.doi.org/10.1007/BF00865707.

Novak P and Cabelka J (1981) *Models in Hydraulic Engineering*. Pitman, London, UK.

Hydraulics for Civil Engineers
ISBN 978-0-7277-5845-3

ICE Publishing: All rights reserved
http://dx.doi.org/10.1680/hce.58453.165

11
Two-dimensional ideal flow

Learning aims
After reading this chapter you should be able to

- appreciate that the assumption of inviscid flow can be a useful modelling tool
- explain the terms 'streamline' and 'stream tube'
- apply the continuity and Bernoulli equations to two-dimensional flow
- derive stream functions and, where defined, velocity potential
- distinguish between rotational and irrotational flow
- describe flow patterns from combinations of basic flow types.

11.1. Introduction
Ideal, or inviscid, flow is a theoretical concept in which the effects of viscosity are ignored and it is assumed that there are no shear stresses between adjoining liquid particles or between those particles and, for example, the side of a pipe. If a liquid has ideal properties, then in a straight pipe it would all be flowing at the same velocity in parallel lines. Although this is an unrealistic situation, the assumption of ideal flow can be a useful simplifying assumption and was used, for example, by Bernoulli in deriving his energy equation.

The analysis involves partial differentiation and you may like to refresh your understanding of the techniques by referring to a textbook such as Stroud and Booth (2007).

11.2. Theoretical basis
11.2.1 Streamlines and stream tubes
Streamlines are continuous imaginary lines in a liquid across which at any particular instant no liquid is flowing. At that instant the velocity of every particle on the streamline is tangential to the line. Flow boundaries, for example the sides of pipes, are themselves streamlines. A bundle of streamlines form a stream tube. No liquid can enter a stream tube except at its ends. An entire flow must at any instant comprise of adjacent stream tubes of some particular pattern. Basic patterns of streamlines are shown in Figure 11.1.

Point P on Figure 11.2 lies on a streamline. At this point the velocity V parallel to the streamline can be resolved into components V_x and V_y parallel to x and y axes respectively. P′ lies a short distance away

Figure 11.1 Basic patterns of flow

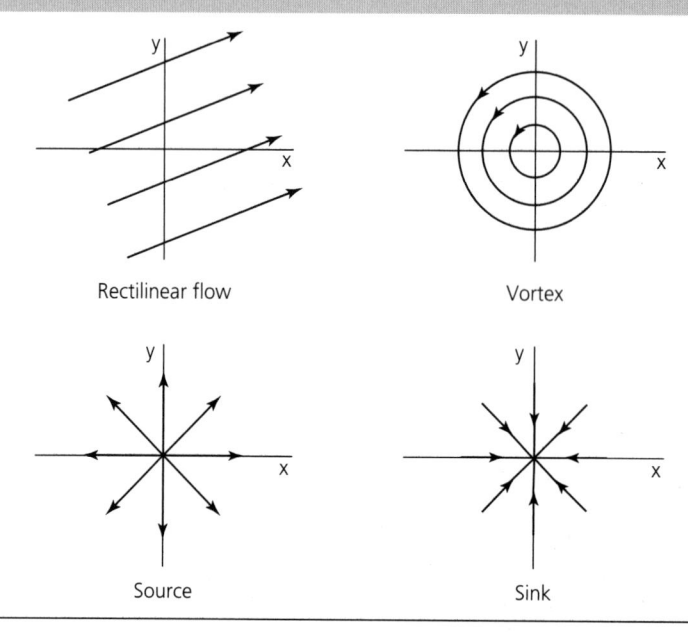

Rectilinear flow

Vortex

Source

Sink

from P but still on the streamline. It can be seen, then, that the triangles of velocity components and incremental distances between P and P′ are similar.

Hence

$$\frac{\delta x}{V_x} = \frac{\delta y}{V_y} \tag{11.1}$$

or

$$0 = V_x \delta y - V_y \delta x \tag{11.2}$$

Figure 11.2 Derivation of streamline equation

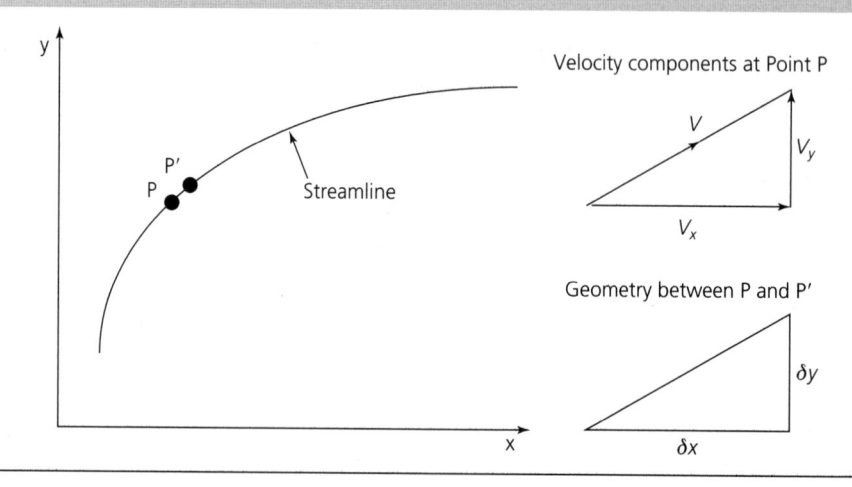

Velocity components at Point P

Geometry between P and P′

Figure 11.3 Flow through an elemental prism

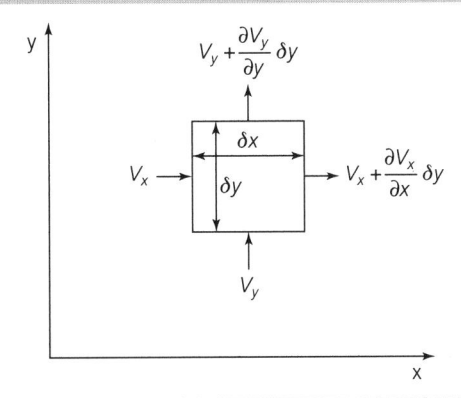

11.2.2 Continuity equation

The principle of continuity of flow has been applied in a simple fashion throughout many of the preceding chapters. We now develop the concept in the context of a two-dimensional continuum. Consider the rate of flow (called the flux) of a liquid of constant density through a prism of unit thickness and dimensions δx and δy as shown in Figure 11.3. Initial velocities are V_x in the x direction and V_y in the y direction.

For continuity

$$V_x \delta y \times 1 + V_y \delta x \times 1 = \left(V_x + \frac{\partial V_x}{\partial x}\delta x\right)\delta y \times 1 + \left(V_y + \frac{\partial V_y}{\partial y}\delta y\right)\delta x \times 1 \tag{11.3}$$

which gives

$$V_x \delta y + V_y \delta x = V_x \delta y + \frac{\partial V_x}{\partial x}\delta x \delta y + V_y \delta x + \frac{\partial V_y}{\partial y}\delta y \delta x \tag{11.4}$$

Simplification gives

$$0 = \delta x \delta y \left(\frac{\partial V_x}{\partial x} + \frac{\partial V_y}{\partial y}\right) \tag{11.5}$$

Since δx and δy are both small but finite quantities, it must be the expression within the brackets that is zero. Hence we can write

$$0 = \frac{\partial V_x}{\partial x} + \frac{\partial V_y}{\partial y} \tag{11.6}$$

11.2.3 Bernoulli's equation

It is now appropriate to have a more formal derivation of Bernoulli's equation. Figure 11.4 shows a section of a stream tube of small but finite length δs whose cross-sectional area increases from A to $A + \delta A$. The average velocity in the direction of motion increases from V to $V + \delta V$ and the pressure

Figure 11.4 Derivation of Bernoulli's equation

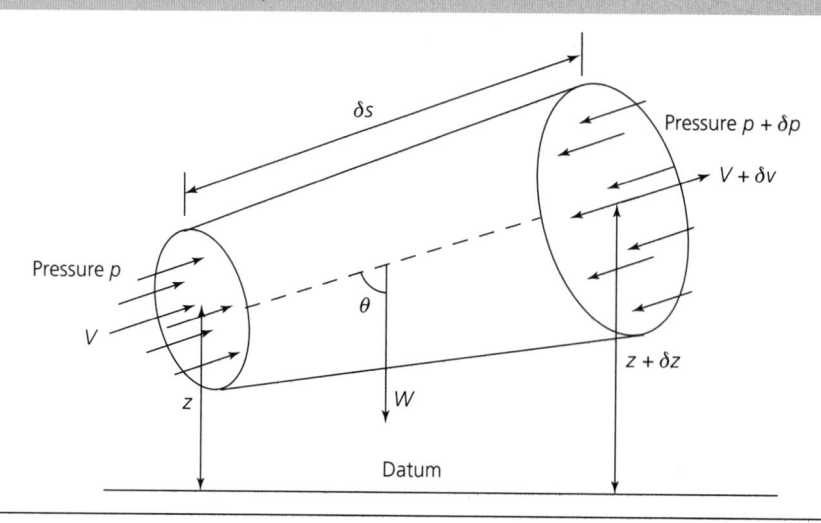

from P to $P + \delta P$. The height from an arbitrary datum level to the midpoints of the two end faces of the section are z and $z + \delta z$. The forces acting in the direction of motion are

- the pressure forces acting on the end areas PA and $(P + \delta P)(A + \delta A)$
- a component of the pressure forces around the side of the tube

$$= \delta A \left(P + \frac{\delta P}{2} \right) \tag{11.7}$$

- the weight of liquid in the stream tube

$$= W \cos \theta = \rho g \left(A + \frac{\delta A}{2} \right) \delta s \cos \theta = \rho g A \delta z \tag{11.8}$$

Taking account of the directions of these, the resultant force F is given by

$$F = PA - (P + \delta P)(A + \delta A) + \delta A \left(P + \frac{\delta P}{2} \right) - \rho g A \delta z \tag{11.9}$$

and, neglecting very small quantities, this becomes

$$F = PA - PA - P\delta A - A\delta P + P\delta A - \rho g A \delta z = -\rho g A \delta z - A \delta P \tag{11.10}$$

By definition the force is also equal to the rate of change of momentum of the liquid. Hence

$$-\rho g A \delta z - A \delta P = \rho \left(A + \frac{\delta A}{2} \right) \delta s \frac{dV}{dt} \tag{11.11}$$

Again neglecting the second-order quantity

$$-\rho g A \delta z - A \delta P = \rho A \delta s \frac{dV}{dt} \tag{11.12}$$

and dividing through by $\rho A \delta s$ and collecting terms on one side

$$g\frac{\delta z}{\delta s} + \frac{dV}{dt} + \frac{1}{\rho}\frac{\delta P}{\delta s} = 0 \tag{11.13}$$

As $\delta s \to 0$,

$$g\frac{dz}{ds} + \frac{dV}{dt} + \frac{1}{\rho}\frac{dP}{ds} = 0 \tag{11.14}$$

For steady flow

$$\frac{\partial V}{\partial t} = 0 \tag{11.15}$$

Hence

$$g\frac{dz}{ds} + V\frac{dV}{ds} + \frac{1}{\rho}\frac{dP}{ds} = 0 \tag{11.16}$$

For a liquid ρ can be considered constant and integration gives

$$gz + \frac{V^2}{2} + \frac{P}{\rho} = \text{constant} \tag{11.17}$$

which is more conveniently expressed as

$$z + \frac{V^2}{2g} + \frac{P}{\rho g} = \text{constant} \tag{11.18}$$

The constant is the total head H.

11.2.4 Stream function

Figure 11.5 shows two sections through a flow ACB and ADB, A being a fixed reference point. Since A and B are common points to both sections, the flux through ADB must equal the flux through ACB and is a function of the position of B relative to A which can be expressed in terms of x and y co-ordinates. This function is called the stream function ψ (Greek letter psi). As a fundamental principle of partial differentiation, if

$$\delta\psi = f(x, y) \tag{11.19}$$

then

$$\delta\psi = \frac{\partial\psi}{\partial y}\delta y + \frac{\partial\psi}{\partial x}\delta x \tag{11.20}$$

Figure 11.5 Two sections through the flow between fixed point A and another point B

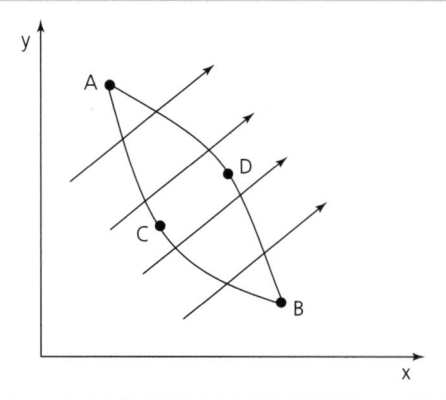

Consider two points B and B' lying on the same streamline as shown in Figure 11.6. As these lie on a streamline there is no flow across BB' and the flux through AB is the same as the flux through AB'. The value of ψ at B and B' must therefore be the same and we can extend this to say that $\delta\psi$ between points B and B' is zero and hence express the equation of a streamline in terms of ψ as

$$0 = \frac{\partial \psi}{\partial y}\delta y + \frac{\partial \psi}{\partial x}\delta x \tag{11.21}$$

But as there can be no flow across a streamline we also derived earlier

$$0 = V_x \delta y - V_y \delta x \tag{11.22}$$

Hence by comparing these two equations we can deduce that

$$V_x = \frac{\partial \psi}{\partial y} \quad \text{and} \quad V_y = -\frac{\partial \psi}{\partial x} \tag{11.23}$$

Figure 11.6 Two points B and B' along the same streamline

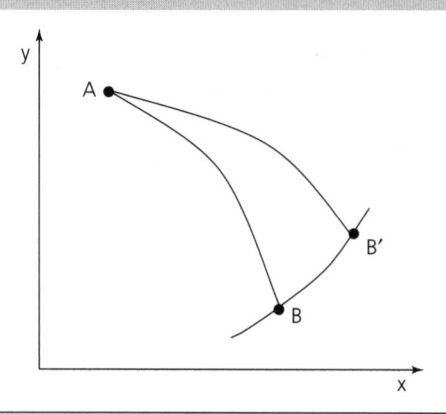

Figure 11.7 Use of polar co-ordinate system

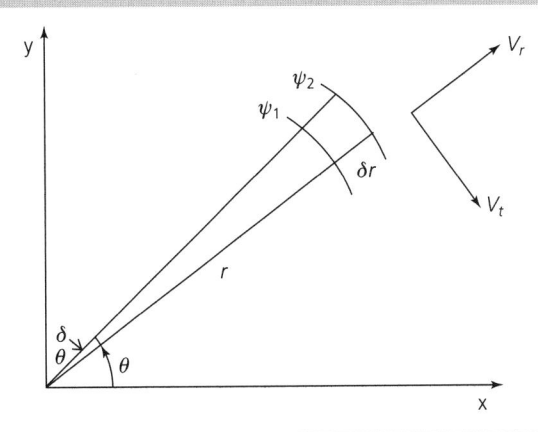

The sign convention used here is for flows from left to right in a conventional x–y co-ordinate system to be considered positive. Other authors reverse this convention.

In some flow patterns, for example sources, sinks and vortices, polar co-ordinates may be more convenient. Velocity is resolved into a tangential component V_r and a radial component V_t as shown in Figure 11.7. The sign convention used here for the polar notation is that tangential velocity is positive anticlockwise and radial velocity is positive in the direction of increasing radius.

The stream function may be expressed as

$$\psi = f(r, \theta) \tag{11.24}$$

which by partial differentiation gives

$$\delta\psi = \frac{1}{r}\frac{\partial \psi}{\partial \theta} r\delta\theta + \frac{\partial \psi}{\partial r} \delta r \tag{11.25}$$

From the continuity equation it can also be expressed as

$$\delta\psi = V_r r\delta\theta - V_t \delta r \tag{11.26}$$

By comparing these two equations for $\delta\psi$ we can write

$$V_t = -\frac{\partial \psi}{\partial r} \tag{11.27}$$

and

$$V_r = \frac{1}{r} \times \frac{\partial \psi}{\partial \theta} \tag{11.28}$$

The stream function ψ has units of flux per unit thickness, that is m³/s/m, which becomes m²/s. It is a scalar quantity.

Figure 11.8 Definition sketch for circulation

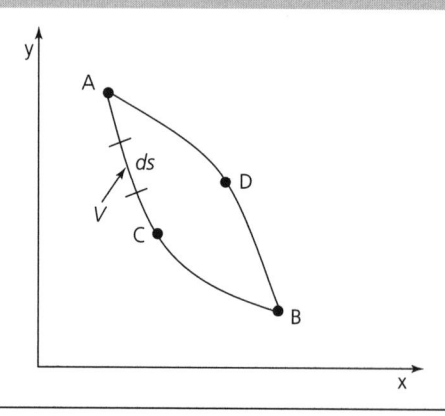

11.2.5 Circulation and vorticity

Flow can only be considered as inviscid if there is no vorticity. To establish this we first need to find the circulation which is defined as the integral round a closed path of the component of the velocity along the path. The vorticity is the circulation per unit area of the circuit.

The concept of circulation was developed by Thomson (Lord Kelvin) (1869). Consider the short length ds of the path ACB shown in Figure 11.8. The velocity V can be resolved into components V_n and V_s normal and tangential to the path at this location. The circulation κ (Greek letter kappa) is the result of integrating the expression V_s ds round the closed circuit ACBDA.

$$\kappa = \oint_A^B V_s \, ds \tag{11.29}$$

By convention the anticlockwise direction is taken to be positive. Figure 11.9 shows this applied to a rectangular circuit of size $\delta x \times \delta y$.

$$\kappa = V_x \delta x + \left(V_y + \frac{\partial V_y}{\partial x}\delta x\right)\delta y - \left(V_x + \frac{\partial V_x}{\partial y}\delta y\right)\delta x - V_y \delta y \tag{11.30}$$

Simplifying this leads to

$$\kappa = \delta x \delta y \left(\frac{\partial V_y}{\partial x} - \frac{\partial V_x}{\partial y}\right) \tag{11.31}$$

This is divided by the area to obtain the vorticity ξ (Greek letter xi)

$$\xi = \frac{\delta x \delta y \left(\dfrac{\partial V_y}{\partial x} - \dfrac{\partial V_x}{\partial y}\right)}{\delta x \delta y} = \frac{\partial V_y}{\partial x} - \frac{\partial V_x}{\partial y} \tag{11.32}$$

If ξ is not equal to zero for all points in the liquid the flow is rotational. A torque and hence shear stresses are required to produce rotation of an element. Hence inviscid flow cannot be rotational.

Figure 11.9 Circulation around an element

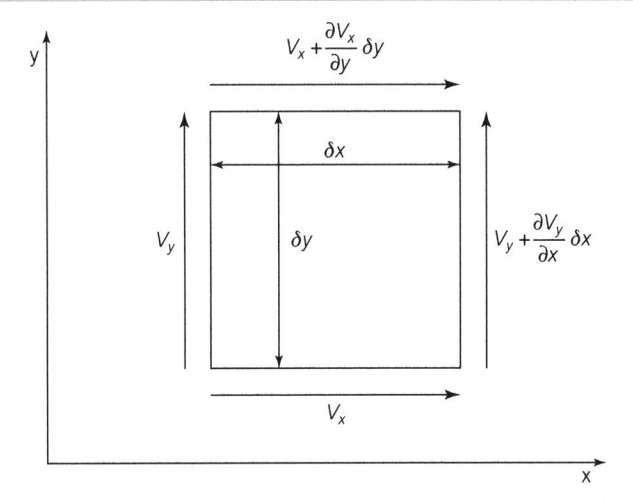

If ξ is zero at all points in a liquid, the flow is irrotational. Every line element in the liquid suffers no net rotation with respect to the axes from one instant to another.

Example 11.1

A flow has the following velocity components: $V_x = x^2 \sin y$ and $V_y = -2x \cos y$. Determine whether the flow is rotational or irrotational.

$$\frac{\partial V_x}{\partial y} = x^2 \cos y \quad \text{and} \quad \frac{\partial V_y}{\partial x} = -2 \cos y \tag{11.33}$$

Hence

$$\frac{\partial V_y}{\partial x} - \frac{\partial V_x}{\partial y} = \cos y (x^2 - 2) \neq 0 \tag{11.34}$$

The flow is therefore rotational.

11.2.6 Velocity potential and Laplace equation

For irrotational flow only it is possible to define velocity potential. Referring once again to Figure 11.8, since $\kappa = 0$, the value of $\int_A^B V_s \, ds$ will be the same whether path ACB or path ADB is followed.

$$\phi = -\int_A^B V_s \, ds \tag{11.35}$$

is known as the velocity potential. The minus sign indicates that velocity potential decreases in the direction of flow.

It follows that

$$V_s \delta_s = -\phi \tag{11.36}$$

and

$$V_s = -\frac{\partial \phi}{\partial s} \tag{11.37}$$

Also

$$V_x = -\frac{\partial \phi}{\partial x} \tag{11.38}$$

and

$$V_y = -\frac{\partial \phi}{\partial y} \tag{11.39}$$

from which

$$\phi = \int V_x \, dx + \int V_y \, dy \tag{11.40}$$

If δs is perpendicular to a streamline

$$V_s = 0 \tag{11.41}$$

and hence

$$\frac{\partial \phi}{\partial s} = 0 \tag{11.42}$$

Hence ϕ is constant along lines perpendicular to streamlines. Such lines are called equipotential lines.

If

$$V_x = -\frac{\partial \phi}{\partial x} \tag{11.43}$$

and

$$V_y = -\frac{\partial \phi}{\partial y} \tag{11.44}$$

are substituted into the continuity equation, then we obtain

$$\frac{\partial^2 \phi}{\partial x^2} + \frac{\partial^2 \phi}{\partial y^2} = 0 \tag{11.45}$$

This is the Laplace equation which is satisfied by all continuous irrotational flows.

Velocity potential can also be expressed in polar co-ordinates

$$\phi = \int V_r \, dr + \int V_t r \, d\theta \tag{11.46}$$

with

$$V_r = \frac{\partial \phi}{\partial r} \tag{11.47}$$

and

$$V_t = \frac{\partial \phi}{r \partial \theta} \tag{11.48}$$

11.2.7 Flow nets

For two-dimensional irrotational flow it is possible to construct a flow net consisting of streamlines along which ψ is constant and equipotential lines along which ϕ is constant. These lines are perpendicular to each other.

Sketched flow nets comprising 'curved squares' provide a convenient approach to solving some problems. A portion of such a flow net is shown in Figure 11.10. It is usual to make $\Delta s = \Delta t$. A check on whether this has been achieved can be made by seeing whether a circle can be constructed touching the adjacent streamlines and equipotential lines. For increasing velocities the 'squares' become smaller.

Figure 11.10 Portion of a flow net

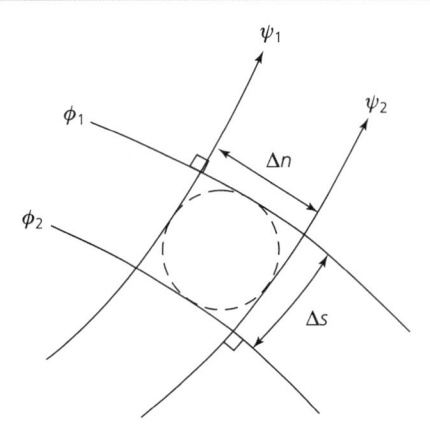

Revision points

- Inviscid flow is an idealised model in which the liquid possesses no viscosity.
- Streamlines represent flow directions at a particular instant in time.
- There is no flow across streamlines.
- Continuity and Bernoulli equations can be derived for two-dimensional flow.
- The stream function is a scalar quantity representing the flux per unit thickness of flow.

> - Irrotational flow has zero vorticity for all points in the liquid.
> - Velocity potential can only be defined for irrotational flow.
> - For irrotational flow it is possible to construct flownets consisting of mutually perpendicular streamlines and equipotential lines.

11.3. Uniform straight line flow
11.3.1 Stream function

Figure 11.11 shows representative flow lines with their ψ values for this case. The velocity can be resolved into components $V_x = V \cos \alpha$ and $V_y = V \sin \alpha$ where α is the angle between the direction of flow and the x axis.

Since

$$V_x = \frac{\partial \psi}{\partial y} \quad \text{then} \quad \psi = yV_x + f(x) \tag{11.49}$$

and since

$$V_y = -\frac{\partial \psi}{\partial x} \tag{11.50}$$

$$\psi = -xV_y + f'(y) \tag{11.51}$$

The solution is therefore

$$\psi = yV_x - xV_y + c \tag{11.52}$$

where c is a constant.

If the value of ψ for a streamline passing through the origin is assigned as 0, then $c = 0$.

Figure 11.11 Uniform straight line flow

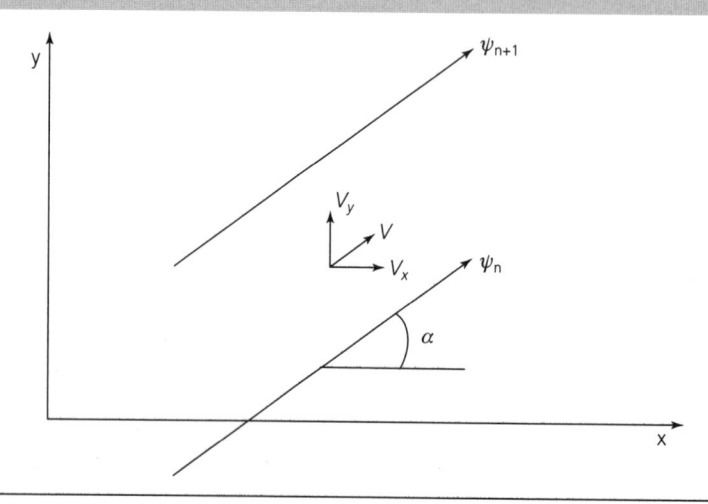

Example 11.2

A flow has component velocities 20 m/s parallel to the positive direction of the x axis and 10 m/s parallel to the negative direction of the y axis. If the value of ψ for the streamline passing through (0, 0) is 0, what is the value of ψ at the point (0.6, 0.4)?

Substituting the values at (0, 0) into

$$\psi = yV_x - xV_y + c \qquad (11.53)$$

gives

$$c = 0 \qquad (11.54)$$

The equation thus becomes

$$\psi = yV_x - xV_y \qquad (11.55)$$

at

$$(0.6, 0.4)\psi = 20 \times 0.4 - (-10) \times 0.6 = 14 \text{ m}^2/\text{s} \; [\text{m}^3/\text{s/m}] \qquad (11.56)$$

11.3.2 Velocity potential

The velocity potential was earlier derived in general terms as

$$\phi = \int V_x \, dx + \int V_y \, dy \qquad (11.57)$$

By substituting for V_x and V_y this becomes

$$\phi = \int V \cos \alpha \, dx + \int V \sin \alpha \, dy \qquad (11.58)$$

leading to

$$\phi = Vx \cos \alpha + Vy \sin \alpha + \text{constant} \qquad (11.59)$$

If ϕ is taken to be zero at the origin, the constant of integration is eliminated, giving

$$\phi = Vx \cos \alpha + Vy \sin \alpha \qquad (11.60)$$

11.4. Sources

A source is a point from which liquid flows out radially. There is no tangential velocity component.

The strength q of a line source of unit depth is the total rate of flow from it. Hence the velocity V_r at radius r from the source is given by

$$V_r = \frac{\text{total rate of flow}}{\text{area}} = \frac{q}{2\pi r} \qquad (11.61)$$

It should be noted that a true source cannot exist because when r approaches zero, v_r approaches infinity.

The streamlines will be radial lines from the line source and the equipotential lines will be concentric circles around it as seen in Figure 11.7.

11.4.1 Stream function
Because there is only a radial component of velocity, the relationship in polar terms

$$\delta\psi = V_r r\delta\theta - V_t \delta r \tag{11.62}$$

simplifies to

$$\delta\psi = V_r r\delta\theta \tag{11.63}$$

and substituting for V_r we obtain

$$\delta\psi = \frac{q}{2\pi r} r\,d\theta = \frac{q}{2\pi}\,d\theta \tag{11.64}$$

Integrating gives

$$\psi = \int \frac{q}{2\pi} r\,d\theta = \frac{q\theta}{2\pi} + c \tag{11.65}$$

where c is a constant of integration. This may be eliminated by taking the stream function to have the value zero at $\theta = 0$.

11.4.2 Rectilinear components of velocity
The components of velocity in the x and y directions are given by

$$V_x = V_r \cos\theta = \frac{q}{2\pi r} \times \frac{x}{r} = \frac{qx}{2\pi(x^2 + y^2)} \tag{11.66}$$

and

$$V_y = V_r \sin\theta = \frac{q}{2\pi r} \times \frac{y}{r} = \frac{qy}{2\pi(x^2 + y^2)} \tag{11.67}$$

11.4.3 Velocity potential
For a line source the velocity potential is

$$\phi = \frac{q}{2\pi}\log_e\left(\frac{r}{c}\right) = \frac{q}{2\pi}\log_e\sqrt{\frac{x^2 + y^2}{(c')^2}} \tag{11.68}$$

with c and c' being constants.

Example 11.3

A two-dimensional line source at position (0, 0) has a strength of $2.5\pi \text{ m}^3/\text{s/m}$. What is the velocity and stream function at the point (2.0, 1.5)?

$$r = \sqrt{2.0^2 + 1.5^2} = 2.5 \text{ m} \tag{11.69}$$

Substituting into

$$V_r = \frac{q}{2\pi r} \tag{11.70}$$

gives

$$q_r = \frac{2.5\pi}{2\pi \times 2.5} = 0.5 \text{ m/s} \tag{11.71}$$

$$\theta = \tan^{-1} \frac{1.5}{2.0} = 0.6435 \text{ radians} \tag{11.72}$$

$$\psi = \frac{q}{2\pi}\theta = \frac{2.5}{2\pi} \times 0.6435 = 0.256 \text{ m}^3/\text{s/m} \, [\text{m}^2/\text{s}] \tag{11.73}$$

11.5. Sinks

A sink is the opposite of a source: the same approaches may be used but with appropriate adjustments of sign.

11.6. Free vortex

Vortices have a flow pattern in which the streamlines are concentric circles.

11.6.1 Vorticity

A free vortex is one in which the elements do not rotate about their own axes. Consider that the circulation around the element contained in the portion of such a flow pattern is shown in Figure 11.12 thus

$$K = 0 \times \delta r - (V_t + \delta V_t)(r + \delta r)\delta\theta + 0 \times \delta r + V_t r \delta\theta \tag{11.74}$$

Ignoring higher order infinitesimal quantities, this becomes

$$K = -\delta\theta(V_t \delta r + r\delta V_t) \tag{11.75}$$

and the vorticity

$$\xi = \frac{K}{\text{area of element}} = \frac{-\delta\theta(V_t \delta r + r\delta V_t)}{\frac{1}{2}(r\delta\theta + (r + \delta r)\delta\theta)\delta r} = \frac{-(V_t \delta r + r\delta V_t)}{r\delta r + \frac{(\delta r)^2}{2}} \tag{11.76}$$

Figure 11.12 Portion of flow net for a free vortex

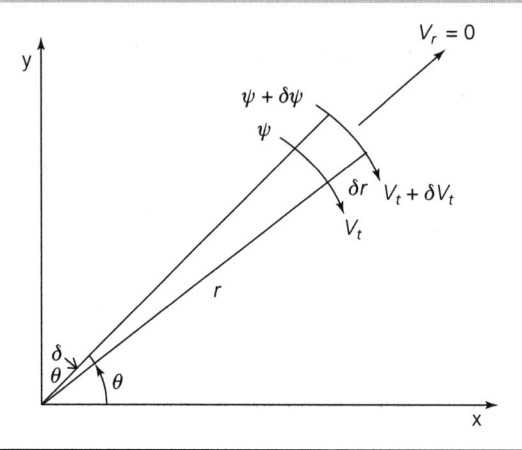

Again neglecting the higher order infinitesimal quantity, we have

$$\xi = -\left(\frac{V_t}{r} + \frac{\delta V_t}{\delta r}\right) \tag{11.77}$$

As a free vortex is irrotational

$$\xi = 0 \tag{11.78}$$

Since any concentric stream filament has constant cross-sectional area, V_t cannot vary along the streamline. Therefore V_t varies only with respect to r so the relationship becomes

$$\frac{dV_t}{dr} + \frac{V_t}{r} = 0 \tag{11.79}$$

or

$$V_t\,dr + r\,dV_t = 0 \tag{11.80}$$

But this can be expressed as

$$d(rV_t) = 0 \tag{11.81}$$

and by integration

$$r\,dV_t = \text{constant} \tag{11.82}$$

Note that as r tends to zero, the tangential velocity must tend to infinity to satisfy this equation. This is not possible in practice. In reality frictional effects cause the core of the vortex to rotate as a solid body and flow is no longer irrotational here.

11.6.2 Stream function

The stream function for a free vortex with its centre at the origin can be obtained starting from the general version in polar co-ordinates

$$\delta\psi = V_r r\delta\theta - V_t \delta r \tag{11.83}$$

which in the absence of a radial velocity component simplifies to

$$\delta\psi = -V\,dr \tag{11.84}$$

Hence

$$\psi = -\int V_t\,dr \tag{11.85}$$

and defining the strength of the vortex as

$$\Gamma = 2\pi r V_t \tag{11.86}$$

$$\psi = -\int \frac{\Gamma}{2\pi r}\,dr = -\frac{\Gamma}{2\pi}\log_e \frac{r}{r_0} \tag{11.87}$$

where r_0 is a constant of integration and is the radius at which $\psi = 0$.

11.6.3 Velocity potential

The general polar co-ordinate form of the velocity potential equation is

$$\phi = \int V_r\,dr + \int V_t r\,d\theta \tag{11.88}$$

Putting $V_r = 0$ and substituting for V_t gives

$$\phi = \int \frac{\Gamma}{2\pi r} r\,d\theta = \frac{\theta \Gamma}{2\pi} + \text{constant} \tag{11.89}$$

If ϕ_0 is assigned to $\theta = 0$, then the value of the constant $= 0$.

11.6.4 Pressure and total head across free vortex

The variation in pressure and total head across a vortex can be determined starting from the principle that the sum of forces towards the centre is equal to the mass times the centripetal acceleration. Figure 11.13 shows the forces acting on the element previously shown in Figure 11.12 and bounded by the equipotential lines ψ and $(\psi + \delta\psi)$.

Using Σ force = mass × centripetal acceleration gives

$$(P + \delta P)(r + \delta r)\delta\theta - Pr\delta\theta - 2\left(P + \frac{\delta\theta}{2}\right)\delta r \sin\frac{\delta\theta}{2} = \rho\left(\frac{2r + \delta r}{2}\right)\delta\theta\,\delta r\,\frac{\left(\dfrac{2V_t + \delta V_t}{2}\right)^2}{r} \tag{11.90}$$

Figure 11.13 Forces on element in a free vortex

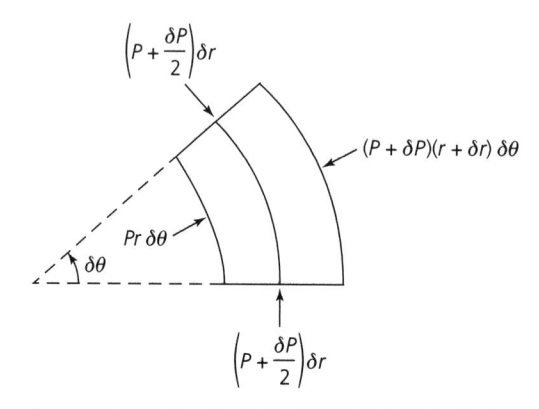

As $\delta\theta \to 0$, $\sin \delta\theta \to \delta\theta$ and neglecting higher order terms we obtain

$$r\delta P\delta\theta = \rho r \delta\theta \delta r \frac{V_t^2}{r} \qquad (11.91)$$

Dividing both sides of the equation by $r\rho g \delta\theta$ gives

$$\frac{\delta P}{\rho g} = \frac{V_t^2}{g} \frac{\delta r}{r} \qquad (11.92)$$

Taking the datum as zero, Bernoulli's equation becomes

$$H = \frac{P}{\rho g} + \frac{V_t^2}{2g} \qquad (11.93)$$

which when differentiated gives

$$\delta H = \frac{\delta P}{\rho g} + \frac{2V_t \delta V_t}{2g} \qquad (11.94)$$

and substituting the value just found for $\delta P/\rho g$ we have

$$\delta H = \frac{V_t^2 \delta r}{rg} + \frac{2V_t \delta V_t}{2g} = \frac{V_t \delta r}{g}\left(\frac{V_t}{r} + \frac{\delta V_t}{\delta r}\right) \qquad (11.95)$$

The expression in brackets here is the vorticity ξ which for a free vortex must equal zero. Hence $\delta H = 0$ meaning that H is constant for all streamlines in a free vortex. As r tends to zero, V_t tends to infinity and the pressure tends to zero, with the result that the upper surface of a free vortex drops towards the centre.

11.7. Forced vortex

This type of vortex is formed when the liquid is caused to rotate as a solid body by for example using an impeller. The effect of such a forced rotation is that all the particles rotate at the same angular velocity ω.

11.7.1 Vorticity

As for the free vortex the vorticity is given by

$$\xi = -\left(\frac{V_t}{r} + \frac{\delta V_t}{\delta r}\right) \tag{11.96}$$

However the tangential velocity $V_t = \omega r$ giving

$$\xi = -\left(\frac{\omega r}{r} + \frac{\omega \delta r}{\delta r}\right) = -2\omega \tag{11.97}$$

As this is non-zero, the flow of a forced vortex is demonstrated to be rotational.

11.7.2 Pressure and total head across forced vortex

As with the free vortex,

$$\frac{\delta P}{\rho g} = \frac{V_t^2}{g}\frac{\delta r}{r} \tag{11.98}$$

Substituting $V_t = \omega r$ gives

$$\frac{\delta P}{\rho g} = \frac{\omega^2 r^2}{g}\frac{\delta r}{r} \tag{11.99}$$

By integration we obtain

$$\frac{P}{\rho g} = \frac{\omega^2 r^2}{2g} + \text{constant} \tag{11.100}$$

Both the velocity and pressure increase with radius and therefore, unlike the free vortex, the total head is not constant for all streamlines.

Example 11.4

A chemical mixing tank consists of a closed hollow cylinder of 750 mm internal diameter with a set of paddle wheels 350 mm diameter mounted concentrically to the axis of the drum. The liquid has a density of 1020 kg/m³. Assuming that within the paddle wheels the liquid is moving as a forced vortex and that outside the paddle wheels it moves as a free vortex, calculate the pressure force exerted on the top of the mixer when the paddles are rotated at 10 revs/s.

The general approach used in the solution of this example is to establish conditions at a radius of 175 mm using the equations for the forced vortex and to then use these to establish 'base' conditions within the free vortex.

For a rotation speed of 10 revs/s, $\omega = 20\pi$ radians/s.

For the forced vortex, the pressure distribution is given by:

$$\frac{P}{\rho g} = \frac{\omega^2 r^2}{2g} + \text{constant} \tag{11.101}$$

If the constant $= 0$ at $r = 0$ this becomes

$$\frac{P}{\rho g} = \frac{\omega^2 r^2}{2g} \tag{11.102}$$

Hence

$$P = \frac{\rho \omega^2 r^2}{2} = \frac{1020 \times (20\pi)^2 \times 0.175^2}{2} = 6247.5\pi^2 \text{ Pa} \tag{11.103}$$

Since force = pressure × area

$$\text{Force } F_{\text{forced}} = \int_0^{0.175} \frac{\rho \omega^2 r^2}{2} 2\pi r \, dr = \rho \omega^2 \pi \int_0^{0.175} r^3 \, dr = \frac{1020 \times (20\pi)^2 \pi}{4} [0.175^4 - 0] \text{N}$$
$$= 95.665\pi^3 \text{ N} \tag{11.104}$$

At a radius of 0.175 m the tangential velocity obtained from the formula for the forced vortex

$$V_t = \omega r = 20\pi \times 0.175 = 3.5\pi \text{ m/s} \tag{11.105}$$

The values $r = 0.175$ m and $V_t = 3.5\pi$ m/s can be used to establish the strength of the free vortex

$$\Gamma = 2\pi r V_t = 2\pi \times 0.175 \times 3.5\pi = 1.225\pi^2 \text{ m}^2/\text{s} \tag{11.106}$$

The total head within the free vortex is given by

$$H = \frac{P}{\rho g} + \frac{V_t^2}{2g} \tag{11.107}$$

and we have established from considering the forced vortex that at $r = 0.175$ m, $P = 6247.5\pi^2$ Pa and $V_t = 3.5\pi$ m/s. Hence

$$H = \frac{6247.5\pi^2}{1020g} + \frac{(3.5\pi)^2}{2g} = \frac{\pi^2(6247.5 + 510 \times 12.25)}{1020g} = \frac{12.25\pi^2}{g} \tag{11.108}$$

As H remains constant in a free vortex, at any other position

$$\frac{P}{\rho g} = \frac{12.25\pi^2}{g} - \frac{V_t^2}{2g} \tag{11.109}$$

leading to

$$P = \rho(12.25\pi^2 - 0.5V_t^2) \tag{11.110}$$

and since

$$V_t = \frac{\Gamma}{2\pi r} = \frac{1.225\pi^2}{2\pi r} = \frac{0.6125\pi}{r} \tag{11.111}$$

$$P = \rho\left(12.25\pi^2 - 0.5 \times \frac{(0.6125\pi)^2}{r^2}\right) = \rho\pi^2\left(12.25 - \frac{0.1876}{r^2}\right) \tag{11.112}$$

Once again the force may be obtained by integration.

$$\text{Force } F_{\text{free}} = \int_{0.175}^{0.375} P \times 2\pi r \, dr = \int_{0.175}^{0.375} \rho\pi^2\left(12.25 - \frac{0.1876}{r^2}\right) \times 2\pi r \, dr$$

$$= \rho\pi^3 \int_{0.175}^{0.375} \left(24.5r - \frac{0.3752}{r}\right) dr$$

$$= 1020\pi^3\left[\left(24.5 \times \frac{0.375^2}{2} - 0.3752\log_e 0.375\right) - \left(24.5 \times \frac{0.175^2}{2} - 0.3752\log_e 0.175\right)\right]$$

$$= 1020\pi^3[2.0907 - 1.0291] = 1082.832\pi^3 \text{ N} \tag{11.113}$$

Total force on top $= F_{\text{forced}} + F_{\text{free}} = (95.665 + 1082.832)\pi^3$

$$= 36\,541 \text{ N } [36.5\,\text{kN to 3 sig. figs}] \tag{11.114}$$

11.8. Combination of flow

As stream functions, and where defined, equipotentials, are scaler quantities it is possible to use simple addition to obtain combined values. This will be examined in some detail for the combination of uniform straight-line flow with a line source. The patterns of streamlines for other combinations will be described without derivation.

11.8.1 Uniform straight line flow and source

The velocity of the combination of flows V_1 and V_2 can be obtained as follows.

- Resolve each of the individual velocities into x and y components V_{1x}, V_{2x}, V_{1y} and V_{2y}.
- Sum x and y components using

$$V_x = V_{1x} + V_{2x} \tag{11.115}$$

and

$$V_y = V_{1y} + V_{2y} \tag{11.116}$$

- Use vector addition to obtain resultant

$$V = \sqrt{V_x^2 + V_y^2} \qquad (11.117)$$

$$\psi_1 = \frac{q\theta}{2\pi} \qquad (11.118)$$

for the source and

$$\psi_1 = V_x r \sin\theta \qquad (11.119)$$

or

$$\psi_1 = yV_x \qquad (11.120)$$

for the straight line flow. The stream function for the combined flow

$$\psi = \psi_1 + \psi_2 = \frac{q\theta}{2\pi} + yV_x \qquad (11.121)$$

Streamlines with the values of the stream function are shown in Figure 11.14.

As the velocity from the source decreases with r, there will be a position S to the left of the origin O, known as the stagnation point, where the velocities of the straight-line flow and from the source are equal and opposite producing zero velocity for the combined flow. The streamline through the stagnation point divides into two and is known as the dividing streamline. In effect the dividing streamline separates the flow originating from the uniform field from that coming from the line source. By substituting $\theta = \pi$ into the general stream function equation for the combined flow, the specific value for the dividing streamline becomes $\psi_s = 0.5q$. As there is no flow across a streamline, the effect of the source is the same as the introduction of a solid body with its outside defined by the shape of the dividing streamline into the flow. This provides a useful way of modelling mathematically the effects of features such as bridge piers. The body is termed a Rankine, or half-body. The shape of the body may be manipulated by changing the strength of the source or introducing additional sources.

Figure 11.14 Line source and uniform linear flow combination

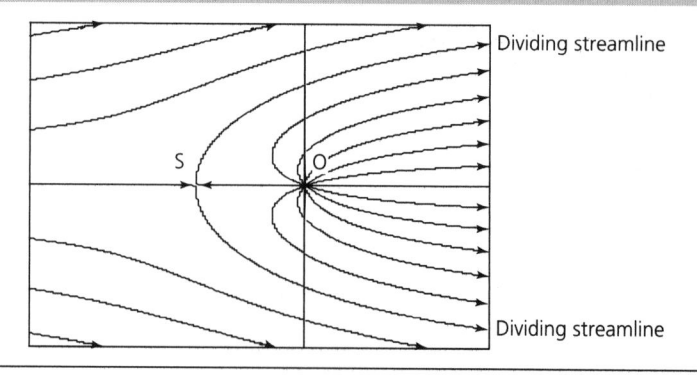

Example 11.5

A half body is to be used to model a long 3-m-wide bridge pier to be placed in a wide watercourse where the flow velocity is 10 m/s. What is the line source strength that should be used in the model?

The distance from the origin to the stagnation point is made equal to half the width of the bridge pier. At the stagnation point the watercourse velocity of 10 m/s will be balanced by the radial velocity from the line source.

Hence

$$10 = \frac{q}{2\pi r} \quad (11.122)$$

where q is the source strength and r is the stagnation point to origin distance leading to

$$q = 20 \times \pi \times 1.5 = 94.25 \text{ m}^3/\text{s} \quad (11.123)$$

11.8.2 Uniform flow with source and sink

If a sink of equal and opposite strength to the source considered in the preceding section is added to the flow, the divided streamline is reunited with two stagnation points as shown in Figure 11.15. The solid body that could fit within the dividing streamline is now called a Rankine oval. The application of the technique to the design of ships' waterline profiles was described in a number of works including Rankine (1863).

11.8.3 Doublet

If a source and an equal-strength sink, centred on A and B along the x axis, are brought close together, the resulting flow pattern, shown in Figure 11.16, is called a doublet or dipole with the streamlines becoming circles tangential to the x axis and centred on the y axis.

If this pairing is then combined with uniform straight-line flow, a limiting case of a Rankine oval is obtained, with the oval becoming a circle. Such a combination can be used to model the effect of a cylindrical obstruction within an otherwise uniform linear flow.

Figure 11.15 Uniform flow with equal strength source and sink

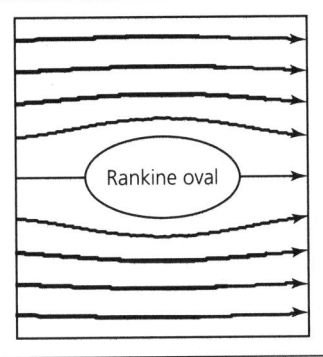

Figure 11.16 Doublet or dipole

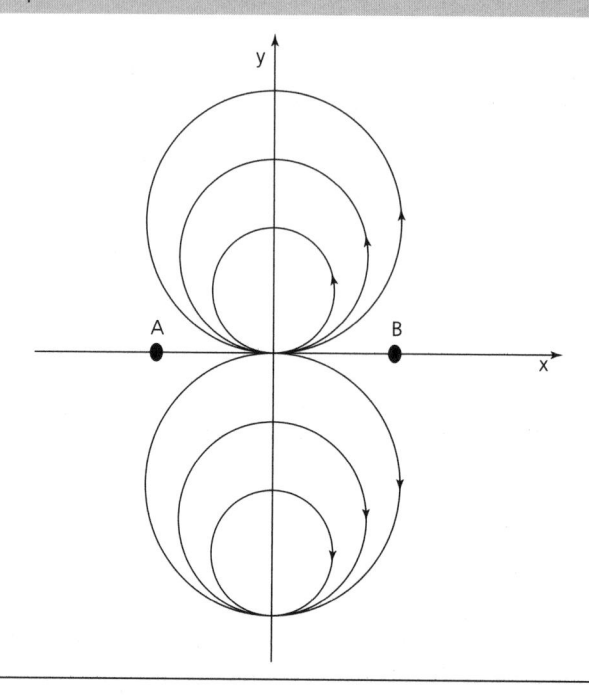

✓ Chapter summary

- Inviscid flow is an idealised model in which the liquid possesses no viscosity.
- There is no flow across streamlines which represent flow directions at a particular time.
- The stream function is a scalar quantity representing the flux per unit thickness of flow.
- Irrotational flow has zero vorticity for all points in the liquid.
- Velocity potential can only be defined for irrotational flow and for such flow it is possible to construct flownets consisting of mutually perpendicular streamlines and equipotential lines.
- Since stream functions and, where defined, equipotentials, are scaler quantities, basic patterns of flow, such as uniform straight-line flow, sources and sinks can be combined by simple addition.

Question for practice

A vertical shaft pump impeller generates a forced vortex in its 0.6-m-dia. casing. It rotates at an angular velocity of 50π radians/s. If the pressure at the centre is atmospheric, what is the pressure adjacent to the casing?

REFERENCES

Rankine WJM (1863) On water-lines in two dimensions. *Philosophical Transactions of the Royal Society* **154**: 369–391, http://dx.doi.org/10.1098/rstl.1864.0010.

Stroud KA and Booth DJ (2007) *Engineering Mathematics*, 6th edn. Palgrave Macmillan, Basingstoke, UK, http://dx.doi.org/10.1007/978-1-4615-9653-0.

Thomson W (Lord Kelvin) (1869) On vortex motion. *Transactions of the Royal Society of Edinburgh* **25**: 217–260, http://dx.doi.org/10.1017/S0080456800028179.

Hydraulics for Civil Engineers
ISBN 978-0-7277-5845-3

ICE Publishing: All rights reserved
http://dx.doi.org/10.1680/hce.58453.189

Index

Page references in italics refer to figures and tables.

Afon Trannon, 66
Amazon Bore, 138
annual maxima records, 105–108, 111
   example, annual maximum flows for a river, 106–108
   extrapolation of flow records to find 1 in 30 year event, *107*
   forms of extreme value distributions, *108*
   table, *106*
   see also FEH method; peak over threshold method
astronomical tides, 136–138, 141, 151
   co-tidal lines and amphidromic points in southern North Sea, *138*
   relative positions of sun, moon and earth over a lunar cycle, *136*
axial pumps, 53, 59, *60*, 63

Bakhmeteff, BA, 76
Barr, DIH, equation, 44, *45*, 49
baseflow, 105, 111, *112*, *113*, 114, 116
baseflow index (BFI), 114, 115
Battjes, J, 150
Bélanger, JB, 84
bends in pipes, 19, 22–25, 34
Bernoulli equation, 19, 26–34, 50, 53, 57, 59, 76, 154, 155, 160, 165, 167–169, 175, 182
   derivation of Bernoulli's equation, *168*
   modification of Bernoulli equation for head loss due to friction, 39–43
   example, head losses at a sudden increase in pipe diameter, 42–43
   example, pipeline between two reservoirs, 40
   example, two pipelines between two large reservoirs, 41
Bilham, EG, 120
Bilham's classification of rainfall for events less than two hours long, *120*

Blackman and Graff, 140–141
Blasius, H, 44
Bourdon gauge, 4
bridge piers, 91–92, 95
British Oceanographic Data Centre (BODC), 136
broad-crested weir, 96–98, *97*, *98*
   example, pressure drop in a pipe, 97–98
Buckingham Π method, 153, 157–159
   example, 158–159
buoyancy, centre of, 1, 12–13, 15, 16
buoyancy and flotation, 12–16, 17
   example of pontoon used for transportation of component by canal to coastal location, 14–16
   illustration of clearance of component under bridge, *15*
   illustration of pontoon in marine situation, *16*
buoyancy force, 12,13, 16, 17
   vertical hydrostatic forces on top and bottom of closed body of constant cross-sectional area, *12*

cavitation, 53, 59, 63
celerity, 68, 69, 143, 144, 145, 146, 151
centre of buoyancy, 1, 12–13, 15, 16
centre of gravity, 1, 7, 12, 13, 14, 15, 16, 17, 136
centrifugal pumps, 53, *59*, *60*, 61, 63
Chadwick and Morfett, 72
charts see depth-duration-frequency (DDF) charts; design charts; Moody chart; Wallingford charts
Chézy's equation, 70–71
China, 58
Chow, VT, 70, 91
circular channel, 76
circulation, 172–173
   circulation around an element, *173*
CIRIA Report C523 2001, 130, *131*
CIRIA Report C635 2006, 119, 128, 131, 132

189

Index

CIRIA Report C697 2009, 129, 130
coastal hydraulics, 135–152
Colebrook, C, 44
Colebrook-White equation, 44, 49, 121
Colebrook and White, 44
combination of flow, 185–188
compound cross-sections, 65
computer modelling, 119, 121, 127, 128
conservation equations, 19–34
    questions, 34
conservation of energy, 19, 26–31, 34, 84
    conservation of energy within a flow system, *27*
    elements of head along pipe, *27*
    example of large tank, 28–29
    example of pipe bend 180°, 29–31
    illustration of pipe bend 180°, *30*
    syphon for withdrawing liquid from a large tank, *28*
    see also renewable energy
conservation of specific energy, 92, 96
constant runoff model (Wallingford procedure), 120, 121, 127
continuity equation, 19, 20–21, 22, 29, 30, 31, 32, 34, 40, 42, 46, 69, 72, 74, 83, 85, 86, 92, 94, 98, 101, 167, 171, 174
    example of domestic hose, 20
control volume, 19, 21, 22, 24
Coriolis force, 137
critical depth, 68, 77–80, 81, 91, 100
    example, 78–79
    specific energy plotted against flow, *79*
    table title, *78*
critical flow, 80, 81
Cross, H, 46
curved immersed surfaces, forces on, 9–11
    components of hydrostatic force, *10*
    cross-section through cylindrical sluice gate, *11*
curved squares, 175

Darcy, H, 39, 44, 46, 61
Darcy-Weisbach equation, 39
density and pressure, 1–3
    example of seawater in a tank, pressure, 2
    example of seawater in a tank, pressure head, 3
Department of the Environment, 120
depth, critical, 68, 77–79, 81, 91, 100
depth, gradient and flow, 83
depth, normal, 70, 80, 81, 86, 89, 97, 100
depth, pressure at, 1, 2, 3, 5, 6, *7–8*, 9, 13, 16, 17
design charts, derivation of λ values, 44–49, 50
    analysis of flow pipe networks using Hardy-Cross method, 35, 46–49

example, concrete pipeline used to convey water to reservoir, 45–46
example, using Hardy-Cross method, 47–49
Hardy-Cross method for flows in a ring main showing initial trial flows, *48*
Hardy-Cross method for flows in a ring main showing final flows, *49*
table, basic properties of pipes, *47*
tables, results of three trials, *48–49*
    values of friction factor λ based on Barr's equation, *45*
Wallingford chart for $k = 0.6$ mm, *46*
see also Moody chart; Wallingford charts
depth-duration-frequency (DDF) charts, rainfall, 113, *114*, 131
design of surface water sewers, hydraulic, 121–128
design storm hydrograph method, 105, 111–116
    outline of method, *113*
    profiles, *115*
    rainfall depth-duration-frequency (DDF) relationship, *114*
    relationship between return periods of rainfall and flooding, *113*
detention basin, 129, *131*
dimensional analysis, 156–159, 164
    example of factors influencing pressure drop along a pipe conveying liquid, 156
    questions, 164
dimensional equations, 154–155, 164
dimensionless numbers in model scaling, 160–164
dimensions, 153
dimensions of quantities, *154*
dipole see doublet
direct step method, 100, 101, *102*
discharge equations, 70–74
discharge rates see head-discharge relationships; Manning's equation
doublet, 187–188
    doublet or dipole, *188*
drainage, hydrology of surface water, 119–133
drainage systems, sustainable, 119, 128–131, 132
duty points of a pump, 53, *62*, 63
dynamic similarity, 160, 163, 164
dynamic viscosity, 35, 37, 50

earthquake, 151
elevation head, 26, *27*
energy, specific see specific energy
energy, wave, 144–145
energy conversion, 53, 58, 63
    see also conservation of energy; kinetic energy; renewable energy

energy equation *see* Bernoulli equation; conservation of energy; specific energy equations
energy loss, 83, 84, 86, *87*, 90, 101
  specific energy loss, 95
Environment Agency, 58, 66
equipotential lines, 174, 175, 176, 178, 181, 188
Euler number, 160–161, 162, 163, 164
European Sea-level Observing System (Eoss), 136
European Union, Sustainable Development, Water Framework Directive, 66, 128
extended detention basin, 129
extreme value (EV), 105, *108*, 109

Fanning, JT, 39
Faulkner, D, 113, 114
filter drain, 129
filter strip, 128, 129
Fischenich, J, 72
fixed percentage runoff model, 121, 127
floating body, immersion depth of, 13, 16
  distribution of hydrostatic pressure on undisplaced floating body, *13*
floating body, stability of, 1, 17
Flood and Water Management Act 2010, 130, 131, 132
Flood Estimation Handbook (*FEH*), 105, 108, 109, 110, 121
  DDF model, 113, *114*, 131
  FEH method, 108–109, 111
  see also design storm hydrograph method
Flood Studies Report, 105, 108. 122
floodplain flow depths, 72
flow, combination of, 185–188
flow, critical, 80
flow, gradually varied, 99–101, *102*
  energy variation along channel in gradually varied flow, *99*
  example, steep spillway discharging into a mild channel, 100–101, *102*
  questions, 101
flow, hydrology of river flow *see* hydrology
flow, ideal, 165–188
  questions, 188
flow, inviscid, 165, 172, 175, 188
flow, irrotational, 165, 173, 174, 175, 176, 188
flow, laminar, 35, 37–39, 43, 50, 162
  characteristics of laminar and turbulent flow, 38
    variation of instantaneous velocity at a point with time, *38*
  distinction between laminar and turbulent flow, 37–38
flow, non-uniform, 19, 101
flow, normal, 80
flow, open channels *see* open channel flow with varying conditions; open channels, steady uniform flow in

flow, real flow in pipes, 35–50
flow, rotational, 165, 172, 173, 183
flow, rough turbulent, 44, 162
flow, smooth turbulent, 44
flow, steady, 19, 34, 65–81
flow, subcritical 68, 69, 80, 81, 83–87, *90*, 91, 92, 93, 94, 95, 100, 101
flow, supercritical 69, 80, 81, 83–87, *90*, 92, 93, 94, 95, 100, 101
flow, transitional turbulent, 44
flow, turbulent, 35, 37–39, 43, 49, 50, 162, 164
  boundary layers in, 43–44
flow, uniform, 19, 34, 65–81, 83
flow, unsteady, 19
flow and gradient, 83, 88, 95
flow below vertical underflow sluice gate, 94–95
flow depth and gradient, 83, 88
flow changes, examples of, 87–95
flow nets, 175, 188
  portion of a flow net, *175*
  portion of flow net for a free vortex, *180*
flow rate measurement, changes in section, 96–98
flow regime, changes to, 83–87
flow type and Froude number, 68–69, 70
flumes, 96, 98, 101
forced vortex, 183–185
  example, 183–185
  pressure and total head across forced vortex, 183
Fourier, J, 156
France, 70
Francis turbine, *56*, *57*, 58, 59, 63
free vortex, 179–182
  example, 183–185
  forces on element in a fee vortex, 182
  portion of flow net for a free vortex, *180*
  pressure and total head across free vortex, 181
friction, head loss due to, 35, 39–43
  see also friction factor λ
friction factor λ, 44–49, 50, 61
Froude number, 77, 78, 79, 80, 81, 85, 86, 89, 91, 93, 96, 160, 161, 163, 164
Froude number and flow type, 68–69, 70
  example, sub and supercritical flow, 69–70

Galvin, CJ, 150
geometric similarity, 159–160, 164
Global Core Network, 135
Global Sea Level Observing System (Gloss), 135
gradient, 83, 88, 95
gradually varied flow, 99–101
gravity, 160, 161, 163
  see also centre of gravity; specific gravity

191

Index

greenfield runoff, difference between development and, 131–132
Gringorten, II, 106, 107, 139
Gumbel, EJ, 105
Gumbel distribution, 106, 108, 111, 116, 139

Hagen, G, 37
Hagen-Poiseuille equation, 39
Hagenbach, E, 39
Hamill, L, 72
Hardy-Cross method, 35, 46–49
head, elevation, 26, *27*
head, pressure 3, 17, *27*, 32, 181, 183
head, total, 181, 183
head, velocity, 26, *27*, 56, 96
head-discharge relationships, 53, 59, 61–62, 63
head loss, open channels, 65
head loss due to friction, 35, 39–43, 49, 50, 163
  see friction factor λ *for more detail*
head loss plotted against discharge, pumps, 53, 61–62
height of a column of liquid, 3, 17
Holland, 139
Holland, DJ, 120
Houghton-Carr, H, 112, *113*, 114, *115*, 121
Howard *et al.*, 141
Hunt, A, 150
hydraulic design of surface water sewers, 121–126
hydraulic jumps, 83–87, 89, 90, 94, 95, 100, 101, *102*
  analysis of the hydraulic jump, *84*
  flow transitions along a spillway, *87*
  specific energy plotted against flow at hydraulic jump, *84*
  types of hydraulic jump based on Peterka, *87*
hydraulic mean depth, 68
hydraulic pressure, 2, 3, 17, 59
hydraulic radius, 66–67, 70
  hydraulic radius for some common channel cross-sections, *66*
hydraulic similarity, *159*
hydraulics, coastal, 135–152
  questions, 151
hydrograph method of flow prediction, 105, 111–116
  relation between hydrograph, baseflow and rainfall event, *112*
hydraulic design of surface water sewers, 121–128
hydro-electric generation, 58
hydrology, river flow, 105–117
  questions, 116
hydrology of surface water drainage, 119–133
  questions, 133

ideal flow, 165–188

immersed surfaces, 5–12
  example of tank holding seawater, 5–7
    determination of depth below water level of centre of pressure of submerged screen, *7–8*
    use of general formula, 8
immersed surfaces, curved, 9–11
  example, determination of magnitude and direction of hydrostatic force on sluice gate, 10–11
immersed surfaces, inclined, 8–9
  example, calculation of force exerted on formwork, 8–9
  calculation of depth below top of concrete can force exerted on formwork be taken to act, 9
immersion depth of floating body, 13, 16
Imperial systems, 153
impulse turbines, 53–55, 58, 59, 63
  Pelton wheel, 53, *54*, 58, 63
  Pelton wheel bucket, *54*, 58
inclined immersed surfaces, force acting on, 8–9
  formwork supporting concrete pour, *9*
inclined immersed surfaces, location of resultant force acting on, 9
index flood, 109
infiltration basin, 128, 130
InfoWorks, 127, 128
Institution of Civil Engineers, 114
intensity of hydraulic pressure, 2, 3, 5, 17
Institute of Hydrology (IOH), 105, 108
inviscid flow, 165, 172, 175, 188
Iribarren and Nogales, 150
irrotational flow, 165, 173, 174, 175, 176, 188
  example, 173

Jenkinson, AF, 140

Kahlig, 157
Kaplan turbine, *56*, *57*, 58, 59, 63
kinematic similarity, 160, 164
kinematic viscosity, 35, 36, 37, 50
kinematics, 36
kinetic energy, 54, 59

laminar flow, 35, 37–39, 43, 50, 162
Laplace equation and velocity, 173–175
law of conservation of mass, 19, 20
Leeks *et al.*, 66
Lewis and Williams, 66
Lloyd-Davis rational method, 119, 121–126, 128, 132
  details of proposed surface water drainage system, *124*
  example of surface water sewage system for a small development, 123–126
  formulae for rainfall intensity, *121*

limitations of rational method, 126
modified rational method, 123
plan of drainage layout to be investigated, *123*

management train, 119, 130, *131*, 132
Manning's equation, 65, 70–71, 74, 81, 88, 89, 97, 98, 101
   use of Manning's equation for steady uniform flow in channel of simple geometry, 71–72
      example, 71–72
      flow in trapezoidal channel, *71*
   use of Manning's equation for steady uniform flow in compound channels, 72–74
      example, 73–74, *73*
      subdivision of a compound section, *72*
Marriott, M, 10
mass density, 1–2, 3
maxima records, annual, *see* annual maxima records
mean annual maximum flood, determining the, 105, 110, 111, 116
mean sea level, 135, 136
median annual maximum flood (QMED), 109
   example, 109–110
   positions and weights for QMED, *110*
mechanical pressure gauges, 4
Met Office, 120
metacentre, 1, 13–14, 16, 17
meteorological effects, 138–141, 151
Miche, R, 149
Ministry of Health, 119–120
Mississippi, 66
mixed flow pumps, 53, *60*, 63
momentum equation, 19, 21–25, 54, 55, 58, 63, 84, 86
Moody, LF, 44
Moody chart, 44, 49
Moore, RJ, 112
Moore and Clark, 112

narrowing of a channel, 90–92
   effect of constriction in bed width on flow depth, *90*
   example of rectangular channel narrowing between bridge piers, 91–92
National Annex to BS EN 752 (BSI 2008), 121
National Suds Working Group, 128
National Water Council, 122
Natural Environment Research Council (NERC), 105, 108, *114*, *115*
Neumann, 39
Newton's second law, 153
Newtonian liquid, 36
non-uniform flow, 19, 101
normal depth, 70, 80, 81, 86, 89, 97, 100

normal flow, 80
North Sea, 138, 141
Norris, WH, 120
numerical integration method, 100, 101

open channel flow with varying conditions, 83–103
   questions, 101
open channels, steady uniform flow in, 65–81
   basic definitions, 67–70
   questions, 81

Packman, JC, 119
peak over threshold method, 105, 108, 111, 116
   example, median annual maximum flood, 109–110
   peak over threshold method, *109*
   positions and weights for *QMED*, *110*
Pelton wheel, 53, *54*, *57*, 58, 63
Permanent Service for Mean Sea Level (PSML), 136
permeable surface, 128, 130
Perspex, 44
pervious surface, 130
Peterka, AJ, 86, *87*
physical modelling, 153, 164
piezometers, 3–4, 32
   illustration of piezometer and manometer, *4*
pipe roughness, 39, 43, 46, 47, 50
   example, 162–163
pipes, analysis of flow pipe networks using Hardy-Cross method, 35, 46–49
pipes, bends in, 19, 22–25, 34
   example, 30° bend, 24–25
      forces and flows, *25*
   example, 90° bend, 22–24
      forces and flows, *23*
pipes, flow of liquid in, conservation equations, 19–34
   questions, 34
pipes, head loss due to friction, 35, 39–43
   head losses at change of pipe section, 35, 41–43
      table, *42*
   pipes in parallel, 40–41
   see also friction factor λ
pipes, real flow in, 35–50
   questions, 50
Pitt, M, Pitt Review, 128, 130
Poiseuille, JLM, 4, 37, 39
polar co-ordinates, *171*, 175, 181
pontoon, example of use of, 14–16
pontoon, question about use of, 17
power input of pumps, 53, 57, 58, 61
power output of turbines, 53, 57, 58
pressure, 1–17
pressure, measurement of, 3–4

Index

pressure coefficient, 160–161
pressure head, 3, 17, *27*, 32, 181
Proudman and Doodson, *138*
Pugh and Vassie, 141
pumps, 53, 59–63
   comparison of pump types, 60–61, *60*
   determination of duty point, *62*
   example, head loss plotted against discharge, 61–62
   example, operation at 5000 rpm, 61
   matching of pump to rising main characteristics, 53, 61–62
   pump characteristics, 53, *61*
   question, 63, 188
   values for system head, *62*
Purseglove, J, 66

QMED see median annual maximum flood

rainfall, hydrograph approach, 111, *112*, *113*, *114*, 116
rainfall, standard average (SAAR), 113
rainfall, surface water drainage systems, 119, 131–132
rainfall analysis (Kahlig), 157
rainfall intensity, short duration, 119–120, 128, 132
   Bilham's classification of rainfall for events less than two hours long, *120*
raised beds, 92–94
   example of rectangular channel through factory site, 93–94
raised hump, 98
Raleigh distribution, *148*, 149, 151, 156
Rankine, WJM, 187
Rankine body, 186
Rankine oval, 187
rational method and derivatives *see* Lloyd-Davies rational method
reaction turbines, 53, 55–57, 58
   Francis turbine, *56*, *57*, 58, 59, 63
   Kaplan turbine, *56*, *57*, 58, 59, 63
real flow in pipes, 35–50
rectangular channel, 75, 77–80, 84, 85, 88–90, 91–92, 93–94, 94–95, 97
rectilinear components of velocity, 178
renewable energy, 59
reservoirs, 40, 41, 45–46, 114
retention pond, 130, *131*
return period approach, 105–111, 139–140
return periods, development of work on, 140–141
Reynolds, O, 37–38
   Reynolds's experiments on laminar and turbulent flow, *37*
Reynolds number, 35, 38, 39, 44, *45*, 48–49, 49, 50, 61, 157, 160, 161–162, 163, 164

rivers, 58, 61, 65, 80, 138
   hydrology of river flow, 105–117
   sustainable design of river channels, 65–66
      concrete-lined channel through urban area, *66*
Robson and Reed, 105
Rossiter, JR, *139*
rotational flow, 165, 172, 173, 183
rough turbulent flow, 44, 162
roughness, Manning's roughness coefficient, 70
roughness, surface, 44, 45
   see also pipe roughness; rough turbulent
Rouse, H, 44
runoff *see* surface runoff

scalar quantity, 171, 175, 188
scale effects, 66, 137, 162
scaling, 160, 161, 163, 164
Schiller and Eisner, 38
sea level, 135, 138
   mean sea level, 135, 136
   sea level records, 135–136
Severn Bore, 138
sewage system for a small development, 123–126
sewer pipes, 50, 65
sewers, hydraulic design of surface water, 121–128
Sharp *et al.*, 157
Shaw *et al.*, 105
shear stress, 35, 36, 70, *154*, 165, 172
Sherman, LK, 111
short duration rainfall intensity, 119–120, 128, 132
SI system, 1, 2, 5, 35, 36, 70, 153, *154*
similarity, 159–160, 163, 164
simple cross-sections, 65, 67–68, *67*
simple drainage networks, 119, 132
sinks, 179, 187
skew surge, *139*, 141, 151
sluice gates, 10–11, 94–95
smooth turbulent flow, 44
soakaway, 128, 130
sources, 177–178
Southend on Sea, *139*, 141
Southern Ocean, 137
specific energy, 76–80, 81, 83–84, 90, 92, 101
   specific energy plotted against flow at hydraulic jump, *84*
   specific energy profile along an open channel, *77*
   specific energy equations, 83, 86, 92, 93–94, 95, 96, 101
specific gravity, 37
specific speed, pumps, 53, 60, 61
specific speed, turbines, 53, 57, *58*, 59
spillway, 87–90, 95, 100–101
   example, steep spillway of rectangular cross-section, 88–90

flow transitions along a spillway, *87*
table of parameters for two channels, *88*
tables of calculations of depth of flow, *102*
stability of a floating body, 1, 17
stagnation point, 186, 187
standard average rainfall (SAAR), 113
standard step method, 100, 101, *102*
standing wave flume, 96, 98
steady flow, 19, 34, 65–81
step method, direct, 100, 101, *102*
step method, standard, 100, 101, *102*
Stokes, GG, 37
stream function, 165, 169–171, 175, 176–177, 178, 181, 185, 186, 188
   example, 179
   two points along the same streamline, *170*
   two sections through the flow between two fixed points, *170*
   use of polar co-ordinate system, *171*
stream tube, definition, 165
streamline, 27, 65–166, 170, 174, 175, 176, 178, 179, 183, 185, 186, 188
   basic patterns of flow, *166*
   derivation of streamline equation, *166*
   example, 177
   two points along the same streamline, *170*
Stroud and Booth, 165
Strutt, JW, 156
subcritical flow, 68, 69, 80, 81, 83, *90*, 90, 91, 92, 93, 94, 95, 100, 101
   subcritical to supercritical transition, 83, 91, 95
Suds, 119, 128–131
   advantages of, 128–129
   definitions, 129–130
   management train, 130, *131*, 132
   obstacles to implementation, 130
   sustainable drainage at Park and Ride site, Chelmsford, *129*
supercritical flow, 69, 80, 81, 83, *90*, 91, 92, 93, 94, 95, 100, 101
   supercritical to subcritical transition and hydraulic jump, 83–87
surface roughness *see* roughness, surface
surface runoff, 105, 111, *112*, *113*, 115, 116, 119
   difference between greenfield and development runoff, 131–132
      example of previously undeveloped land, 132
   see also constant runoff model (Wallingford procedure); fixed percentage runoff model; variable runoff model
surface water drainage, 119–133
surges, 135, 138–139, 151

example of maximum surge tide, 139–140
table, *140*
tidal surge recorded at Southend on Sea, 1953, *139*
tidal surge return period example, *140*
Sustainable Development, Water Framework Directive, 66, 128
sustainable drainage systems (Suds), 119, 128–131, 132
swale, 128, 130
system head, *62*, 63

tides, 135
   astronomical tides, 136–138
   meteorological effects, 138–141
total head, 181, 183
transducers, 4
transitional turbulent flow, 44
trapezoidal channel, *71*, 75–76, 81
TRRL hydrology method, 121, 126–127, 128, 132
   sub-division of catchment area, *126*
tsunami, 151
tuberculation, 44
turbines, 53–59, 63
   comparison of types, 57
   example of use in hydro-electric scheme, 58
   use of turbines, 58
turbulent flow, 35, 37–39, 43, 43–44, 49, 50, 162, 164

U-tube manometer, *4*
UK, 39, 58, 66, 105, 108, 114, 116, 136, 120, 121, 129, 136, 138–139
uniform flow, 19, 34, 65–81, 83, 176–177
   uniform straight line flow, *176*
   uniform straight line flow and source, 185–187
      line source and uniform linear flow combination, *186*
   uniform flow with source and sink, 187
      uniform flow with equal strength source and sink, *187*
unit hydrograph, 105, 111, 112, *113*
unsteady flow, 19
USA, 39, 58, 66, 70
   Bureau of Reclamation, 86

Van der Meer, JW, 150
variable runoff model, 121, 127
vector quantity, 21, 22
velocity, 19, 21, 40, 42–43, 45, 74, 101, 162–163
   absolute and relative velocities, 55, 58
   variation of instantaneous velocity at a point with time, *38*
   see also celerity; Manning's equation; momentum equation
velocity, ideal flow, 165, 166, 167, 171, 172, 173, 175, 180, 183, 184, 184, 186, 187

Index

velocity, ideal flow
   rectilinear components of velocity, 178
   velocity potential, 165, 176, 177, 178, 181, 188
   velocity potential and Laplace equation, 173–175
   see also stagnation point
velocity, most economically efficient section, 74–76
   principle, 74–75
velocity, narrowing of channel, 91–92
velocity distribution coefficient, 76, 78
velocity head, 26, *27*, 57, 96
velocity variation over channel cross-section, 74, *75*
Venturi flume, 96, 98
Venturi meter, 19, 31–33, 34, 96
   actual and theoretical flow rates, *33*
   example, 33
   long section through Venturi meter, *31*
   table of data, *33*
vertical immersed surfaces, force acting on, 5–7
   pressure distribution on submerged vertical surface, *6*
   question, 17
vertical immersed surfaces, location of resultant force acting on, 7–8
   force elements and overall force on submerged vertical surface, *7*
   second moment of area of selected shapes about an axis through their centroid, *8*
vertical immersed surfaces of any shape, location of resultant force acting on, 8
vertical underflow sluice gate, flow below, 94–95, *94*
   example of sluice gate occupying full width of rectangular channel, 94–95
viscosity, dynamic, 35, 37, 50
viscosity, ignoring effects of (inviscid flow), 165, 175, 188
viscosity, kinematic, 35, 36, 37, 50
   example, 36
viscosity of fluids, 35–37, 162–163, 164
   velocity profile for a liquid between a fixed and a moving plate, *36*

von Kármán, T, 44
vortex, forced, 183–185, 188
vortex, free, 179–182
vorticity, 176, 179–180, 182, 183, 188

Wales, 66
Wallingford charts, 35, 44, *46*, 49, 123
Wallingford procedure *see* constant runoff model
Wallingford Software (Wassp), 127
Wallrus package, 127
Water Framework Directive, 66, 128
water surface profiles, 83
waves, 135, 141–151
   breaking waves, 135, 149–151
   celerity, 68, 69, 143, 144, 145, 146, 151
   equations, 142–144
      example, 143–144
   terminology, *142*
   wave energy and power, 144–145
   wave generation, 141
   wave refraction, 147
   wave spectrum, 148–149
      example, 149
      Rayleigh distribution of wave heights, *148*, 149
      typical distribution of wave heights, *148*
   wave transformation, 145–146
Weber number, 162, 163, 164
Weibull, W, 107, 151
weight, 1, 17
   unit weight/specific weight, 2
weight density, 2, 3
Weisbach, J, 39
wetland, 128, 130
wetted perimeter, 67–68, *67*, 70, 71, 72, 74, 75
wind, 135, 138, 141
Wormleaton and Merrett, 72